KU-773-059

The Demand
for Travel:
Theory and
Measurement

The Demand for Travel: Theory and Measurement

EDINBURGH UNIV. EDINBURGH UNIVERSITY LIBRARY BIBL UNIV. EDINBURGEN EX WITHDRAWN

Edited by

Richard E. Quandt
Princeton University

Heath Lexington Books
D.C. Heath and Company
Lexington, Massachusetts

Copyright © 1970 by D. C. Heath and
Company

All rights reserved. No part of this publication may be reproduced or transmitted in
any form or by any means, electronic or
mechanical, including photocopy, recording,
or any information storage or retrieval system, without permission in writing from
the publisher.

Printed in the United States of America

Library of Congress Number: 72-133220

**To my son
Stephen**

Table of Contents

Preface

Recent contributions to the analysis of travel demand have their origins in economics, operations research, physics, transport and regional studies and perhaps several other fields. The decision to collect in a single volume a number of essays on the demand for passenger transportation was motivated chiefly by the nearly simultaneous appearance in the past few years of several fruitful and related avenues of quantitative research. The decision was strengthened by the realization that, upon careful reading, a marked family resemblance can be noted among the various contributions, despite the different backgrounds of their authors and the different settings in which they were prepared. There is, of course, always an element of arbitrariness in making selections for a volume written by numerous contributors and the actual content clearly betrays the editor's sympathies or prejudices; if not with respect to the content of particular studies that have been omitted, at least with respect to how the whole fits together.

I am indebted to all the contributors as well as to the numerous scholarly journals in which some of these contributions have previously appeared for making them available for this volume. I am particularly indebted to two of the contributors, Anthony J. Blackburn and John P. Mayberry, for responding to my request that they write brand new essays for this volume in their special areas of research and competence. Finally, no acknowledgement would be complete without listing those friends and colleagues whose interest and encouragement over the years have stimulated my own research into questions of travel demand, namely Roger Alcaly, William J. Baumol, Tibor Fabian, Stephen M. Goldfeld, Alan Goldman, Alvin Klevorick, Michel Pinton, Francis Sand and many others.

Richard E. Quandt

**The Demand
for Travel:
Theory and
Measurement**

1

Introduction to the Analysis of Travel Demand

Richard E. Quandt

1. Preliminaries

As indicated in the Preface, the past few years have witnessed considerable amounts of innovative activity in transportation research and several new avenues of quantitative research have opened up.* The most important ideas in these new approaches and the relationships among them are discussed in Section 2. The statistical and computational complexities emerging from the newer quantitative approaches are highlighted in Section 3. Finally, in Section 4 we point out some of the important problems requiring additional study. The remainder of the present section is devoted to a discussion of certain broad similarities and differences among the essays.

Common Traits. The first major characteristic held in common by most, if not all these essays is the extent to which travel is viewed as the result of individuals' rational decision-making in an economic context. Early and naive attempts to predict the volume of passenger traffic between two population centers by gravity models would argue in justification that traffic is proportional to the number of potential pairwise interactions between the members of the two populations; hence, if P_i and P_j denote the population size at nodes i and j, traffic will be proportional to the product $P_i P_j$. This is not to argue that population terms such as P_i and P_j or their product or some other function of them are not properly part of any model attempting to explain the demand for travel; nor that it is unnecessary to provide an adequate theoretical justification for the use of some particular function of P_i and P_j. Indeed, an important illustration of such a justification by sophisticated techniques is provided by Chapter 3 (Wilson). But the contrast to be highlighted

---

*I am grateful to S. M. Goldfeld for a critical reading of this chapter. Of course, I alone am responsible for errors or omissions.

here is with many of the approaches rooted in economics which stress the alternative opportunities available to the consumer and his rates of substitution among them. Although the various chapters differ from each other in terms of the specific manner in which these notions manifest themselves, they share the characteristic that the various modes or destinations of travel are regarded as commodities, each with its own price and among which the consumer chooses so as to maximize, either implicitly or explicitly, some index of satisfaction.

A second common bond among the papers in this volume is the fact that they are oriented toward the use of cross-sectional rather than time-series data. Time series models have certain distinct advantages such as their ability to predict the effect of short-run changes in the independent variables. On some occasions they have been employed in transportation research with distinguished success.[1] They do encounter, however, some difficulties in comparison with cross-sectional models.

The first difficulty is the conceptually trivial but nevertheless bothersome fact that time series data on travel do not, and for the foreseeable future, will not exist in sufficient abundance to permit large-scale estimation of models of the type employed by Fisher. If demand analysis is used to forecast what changes of capacity are to be undertaken in an entire network it is not sufficient to have data on isolated links and for single modes as was the case in the Fisher study of rail travel between Boston and New York. A second, and conceptually more serious, difficulty is the fact that it is very difficult in time-series models explaining traffic along a single link to account for the consumer's entire opportunity set. Clearly, in a time series model explaining travel by some particular mode the prices (trip costs) of the competing modes must appear in some form in order to account for the possibility of substitution. But substitution of one mode for another is not the only form of substitution, though it may be the most plausible type in the short run. In the long run the potential traveler at node i may decide not to travel to node j at all if opportunities or incentives to travel to some other node k have improved markedly. Thus the possibility of substitution of one link in a network for another ought to be included in a model explicitly. Cross-sectional models are well suited for this purpose.

---

[1] Fisher, F. M., *A Priori Information and Time Series Analysis: Essays in Economic Theory and Measurement* (North-Holland Publishing Co., 1962), Ch. 6.

This is the characteristic of cross-sectional models that is responsible for two problems associated with them. The first is that they require us to formulate long-run theories of economic behavior — a chronically difficult thing to do. In order to provide a complete model of this type it is usually not sufficient to explain only the long-run consequences of changes in relative modal attractiveness. Thus, although we clearly are interested in conclusions concerning the effect of a drop in the cost of travel between i and j relative to the cost of travel between i and k on the diversion of some traffic from the latter to the former link in the network, we must also do more and explain the long-run factors that have made the traffic volume between i and j what it is. Whereas long-run factors influencing the level of some activity may properly be removed from a time series model expressed in terms of first differences, the crux of the cross-sectional approach is that levels must be explained.[2]

In order to estimate such long-run relationships we must assume that the observations, representing contemporaneous travel but referring to different links in a network, are sample points drawn from the same underlying structure. Violations of this assumption may occur because the long-run theory is not sufficiently all-encompassing. If one assumed that the level of traffic depends only on the product of the population masses, the model might predict badly because, in reality, traffic depends on the occupational composition of the labor force as well. But the assumption that there are no omitted variables or other specification errors not only begs the question but fails to help in cases in which apparent violations of the assumption are caused by disequilibrium along one or more links in the cross-section. Unfortunately there does not seem to be any obvious or direct way at present to test the hypothesis that a cross-sectional sample of travel and travel-related exogenous variables represents a uniform structure. This must then perforce be the maintained hypothesis of such models.

Differences and Classifications. With the exception of Chapter 5 by Mayberry and Chapters 8 and 9 by Blackburn, the papers in this

---

[2]There are good arguments in favor of the position that the most powerful theories will be based on pooled time-series and cross-sectional data. See Balestra, P. and M. Nerlove, "Pooling Cross Section and Time Series Data in the Estimation of a Dynamic Model," *Econometrica*, 34 (1966), 585-612 and Wallace, T. D. and A. Hussain, "The Use of Error Components Models in Combining Cross Section with Time Series Data," *Econometrica*, 39 (1969), 55-72.

volume have been published previously in a variety of journals. An important but not unequivocal basis for differentiating among them is the extent to which their orientation is theoretical or empirical. Three chapters are unambiguously theoretical, namely Chapter 2 (Lancaster), Chapter 3 (Wilson) and Chapter 5 (Mayberry). The others are mixtures of theory and econometric implementation and tend to follow a pattern consisting of (a) the construction of a model and (b) its estimation by sundry statistical and econometric techniques. Chapters 4 through 9 (Quandt and Baumol, Mayberry, Quandt and Young, Quandt, and Blackburn) had their intellectual origins in work arising from contracts between Mathematica, Inc. and the U.S. Department of Commerce and subsequently the U.S. Department of Transportation. These papers essentially employ three samples involving (a) aggregate traffic flows for 20 city-pairs in California, (b) aggregate traffic flows for 32 city-pairs in the Northeast Corridor and (c) a disaggregated household survey. The remaining papers with an empirical orientation employ several other sources of data, e.g., a sample of commuters in the Chicago area in Chapter 10 (Moses and Williamson), a sample of London commuters in Chapter 11 (Beesley), and finally, a sample of commuters in Leeds is used in Chapter 12 (Quarmby).

2. Theoretical Contributions

Since rational decision-making by individuals is assumed to underly the generation of travel, it seems reasonable to approach the problem of estimating the demand for travel through a consideration of the individual's utility function. Nearly all the subsequent chapters have something to say on this subject, either implicitly or explicitly. Perhaps one of the major contributions of these chapters is to draw special attention to the reformulations of traditional utility theory that become necessary when we attempt travel-oriented applications.

Attributes and Abstract Modes. In orthodox utility theory utility is usually expressed as a function, unique up to a monotonic transformation, the arguments of which are the quantities of the various commodities that can be consumed. Utility is then maximized subject to a budget constraint; and it is often assumed, at least implicitly, that the solution to this problem occurs at an interior point. Approaching the analysis of the travel demand decision in this manner seems to create at least three difficulties: (a) Since the hypothetical consumer located at node i may potentially travel to any one of a very large number of alternative destinations by several possible modes, the list of travel-oriented "commodities" to be entered into the utility function is intractably large. (b) The implicit assumption that the maximum of the utility function occurs at an interior point of the budget plane has the unrealistic implication that the consumer consumes some of every commodity; i.e., undertakes a little bit of travel by every mode on every link in a network. (c) Traditional utility theory has very little, if anything, to contribute to estimating the demand for new products, i.e., for as yet nonexistent commodities (links in the network or modes of transporation). The importance of forecasting the demand for new products is perhaps particularly great in the case of travel, where technological change may cause radical alterations in the characteristics of new modes, where the initial investment is very large and where the transport services consumed may essentially represent a public good.[3]

The unsatisfactory state of utility theory has led to numerous attempts to reformulate it. Many of these attempts arise in the course of estimating the demand for travel and are not expressed explicitly in terms of the usual constructs of utility theory. The clearest example of an explicit reformulation is contained in Chapter 2 (Lancaster) and has nothing to do with travel as such. In spite of the fact that some of the newer approaches are on a high level of generality, such as that in Chapter 2, whereas others represent a direct attempt to cope with problems of estimating the demand for travel, such as Chapter 4 (Quandt and Baumol), all bear a certain family resemblance to one another. The crucial modification is that the consumer is now regarded as deriving utility from characteristics or attributes while commodities are regarded as producing attributes in varying amounts and proportions. In most general terms the utility maximization problem can be formulated as a nonlinear programming problem as follows. Let z be a vector the elements of which are the quantities of various attributes, x be a vector the elements of which are quantities of various commodities,

---

[3]Manufacturers of, say, packaged consumer goods also face the problem of forecasting the demand for new products. Various techniques are employed for gaining insight into potential appeal of new products such as test marketing, consumer clinics, surveys, and so forth. None of these seems entirely feasible or desirable when the demand for travel is under consideration.

p the vector of corresponding prices and Y the level of income. Then the consumer desires to maximize

$$U = U(z)$$
$$\text{subject to} \quad z = g(x)$$
$$p'x \leqslant Y$$
$$x \geqslant 0$$
$$z \geqslant 0$$

The vector valued function $g(x)$ describes the "production" of attributes by commodities. An immediate simplification is provided by replacing it by the linear approximation Bx, where B is a matrix with as many rows as there are attributes and as many columns as there are commodities. The matrix B may be called the consumption technology and the introduction of new commodities may be viewed as adjoining additional columns to the matrix B. In this formulation, as is not the case in orthodox utility theory, the introduction of new commodities does not require a redefinition of the utility function. The suitability of this approach to travel demand arises from the observation that trips on the one hand and all remaining goods on the other hand represent what Lancaster calls intrinsically unrelated commodity groups; i.e., only the taking of trips provides travel-oriented attributes and trips provide no attributes other than travel-oriented attributes.[4] A consequence of this is that changes in the prices of goods other than travel do not affect the efficient combination of trips.

Lancaster's theory is rich in insights but does not provide a direct avenue to the mathematical form of the demand function. Chapter 4 (Quandt and Baumol) contains a direct attempt to formulate the demand function for travel. The underlying ideas are very similar to those of Lancaster. The consumer is assumed to care only about the attributes of the various modes but not about the name ("railroad," "bus," etc.) by which the modes are known. It is in this sense that travel modes have been called "abstract."

The demand functions employed in Chapter 4 are in a general form suitable for estimation by least-squares regression analysis, but their precise mathematical form is somewhat *ad hoc* and is not derived in detail from attribute-oriented utility theory, except for the simple observation that the demand for travel from i to j by mode k (T_{ijk}) must depend in some sense on both the attribute content of

---

[4] The matrix B is then decomposable.

the kth mode relative to the other modes and on the attribute contents of all modes relative to the consumer's income. In this this initial formulation T_{ijk} is a power function in both the demographic-economic variables (chiefly population and income at nodes i and j) and in the variables measuring modal attributes (chiefly the travel cost, travel time and departure frequency).[5]

The Form of the Demand Function. It is fortunate that some of the most important travel attributes are easily enumerated and may be measured without excessive difficulty. Travel cost, travel time and departure frequency occur regularly in the work of many investigators. This obviously distinguishes travel from other commodities such as apparel which may be characterized by a large number of considerations of style that are difficult to define. But the relative ease of judging relevant attributes for travel does not solve all problems. Among these problems are at least two: (a) In what form should the various variables be included in the demand function, and (b) What invariance properties should the demand function possess with respect to erroneous and irrelevant enumeration of attributes?

The relevance of the first of these problems is underscored by the absence of a natural functional form. This observation was the original impetus for Chapter 6 (Quandt and Young) which experiments with numerous alternatives to the basic attribute-oriented model outlined in Chapter 4. It may be somewhat gratifying that independent investigators have occasionally employed very similar formulations; thus the relevance of the cost/income ratio is recognized in Chapter 6 as well as in Chapter 12 (Quarmby). Even though some solace may be derived from consensus, it is still true that the various variables and functional forms employed are not deeply rooted in theory.[6]

A related problem emerges from the very concept of attribute orientation and from the notion of abstract modes. What does the

---

[5] Departure frequency (or its reciprocal, measuring mean waiting time till the next departure) seems to be the most easily obtained measure of convenience. Many other attributes of travel may be relevant (safety, vibration, cleanliness, punctuality, services provided en route, etc.) but are much harder to measure.

[6] An important recent attempt to improve the theoretical underpinning of the particular form of the demand function employed is based on a reconsideration of the manner in which the attributes of competing modes enter the demand function for any one mode. See Young, K. H., "An Abstract Mode Approach to the Demand for Travel," *Transportation Research*, 3 (1969), 443-461.

demand function predict if the attributes are incorrectly enumerated? Such incorrect enumeration may be of two kinds: Some important attributes may be neglected or irrelevant attributes may be employed for classifying modes. In the former case one would mistakenly predict that one mode dominates another. For example, if air travel is faster but more expensive and bus travel slower but cheaper, we would expect some people (who value time over money) to travel predominantly by air and some others (who value money over time) to travel mostly by bus. If, in the analysis, one inadvertently omitted the travel-time attribute, bus travel would appear preferable from everyone's point of view; and we would erroneously predict zero amount of travel by air.

The use of irrelevant attributes for mode classification potentially has even more serious consequences. If the demand for travel by some mode on a given link in a network is a function only of demographic-economic variables and of modal attribute variables, then the introduction of a new mode will generate a predicted demand that can be calculated from the demand function by substituting in it the attribute content of the new mode. The new mode will affect the demand for the already existing modes only to the extent that the demand for any mode is expressed as a function of attributes describing other modes. For example, the rudimentary formulation in Chapter 2 assumes that the demand for the kth mode (T_{ijk}) is a function of the relative cost of that mode (e.g., the cost of the kth mode divided by the least cost of any mode serving the ij^{th} link) and is also a function of the least cost of any mode on that link. Such a formulation has the immediate consequence that the predicted demand for an existing mode will not change as a result of introducing a new mode unless that new mode becomes the best (cheapest, fastest, or otherwise most convenient) in terms of some attribute. It also follows that the classification of modes by irrelevant attributes has peculiar effects: if, for example, half the buses were painted blue and the other half red, and if red and blue buses were considered different modes, the total demand for travel would increase. Early attempts to cope with this type of problem, as exemplified in Chapter 6, consisted mostly of devising artificial variables measuring the range and density of attribute configurations and thereby permitting the existence of "diminishing returns" to the number of modes serving a given link. A much more elegant and satisfactory approach is the axiomatic approach of Chapter 5 (Mayberry) which starts out with axioms that rule out nonsensical behavior on the part of the demand function and ends up with the implied restrictions that the form of the demand function must satisfy.[7]

Utility and Generalized Cost. In contrast to a direct specification of the demand function several approaches attempt to specify the consumers (dis-)utility function of travel or, what is quite similar, attempt to define the cost of travel in a sufficiently generalized manner to account not only for out-of-pocket money costs but for the time cost of travel and perhaps other attributes as well.

There are considerable individual differences among the chapters employing this type of approach. They differ with respect to some of the basic assumptions and the theoretical and econometric techniques employed. They are, however, all variations on the same theme to the extent that they attempt to devise and estimate an index of the generalized cost of travel.

Among the relevant chapters three are most closely related: Chapter 10 (Moses and Williamson), Chapter 11 (Beesley) and Chapter 12 (Quarmby). Consider the choice between two modes with costs c_1 and c_2 and travel times t_1 and t_2 and assume that mode one is slower but cheaper. The generalized differential cost of mode 2 is then given by

$$z = c_2 - c_1 + \alpha(t_2 - t_1).$$

A given consumer is assumed to choose the mode which makes him incur a smaller generalized cost. In such a formulation α is the rate of substitution between money and time: an increase of money cost by one dollar will leave the consumer indifferent if it is accompanied by a reduction in time by $1/\alpha$ hours. In Chapter 10, α is chosen as the wage rate (which may differ from individual to individual) and the generalized cost of traveling by the second most preferred mode is then computed for a group of individuals for whom automobile is the most preferred mode. This procedure provides an estimate of the elasticity of demand: one can determine what fractions of automobile users would be attracted to alternative modes by various changes in the generalized cost.[8]

[7] Also see Young, *op. cit.*

[8] The computation is subject to qualification because institutional reasons usually prevent individuals from finely adjusting their optimal mix between work and leisure.

Just as the choice of a discrete mode in Chapter 10 is assumed to be made in such a manner that generalized cost is minimized, so in Chapter 11 (Beesley) the choice is assumed to minimize the disutility of travel. This latter again depends on money cost and travel time, but the relevant rate of substitution is estimated from survey data as that rate which simultaneously best explains the choices made by those who prefer money savings at a time cost and the choices of others who prefer the converse. Finally, in Chapter 12 (Quarmby) the approach is further refined by introducing other variables into the disutility function and by estimating the relevant rates of substitution by discriminant analysis.

The rate of substitution between money cost and time, i.e., the "value of time," is characteristically found to increase with the level of income. It is, however, assumed to be the same for all individuals in the same income class. In other words, and more generally, given a sufficiently precise identification of a group of individuals in terms of exogenous variables describing them, their utility functions are assumed to be identical. Specific departures from this assumption are discussed in Chapter 7 (Quandt) and Chapters 8 and 9 (Blackburn). In varying ways both posit utility or generalized cost functions which are identical over individuals only in their mathematical form but the parameters of which are functions of random variables. The parameters of the joint distribution of rates of substitution are then the target of estimation. From these estimates one may then compute the probability that a randomly selected person will choose a particular mode. To the extent that these models are capable of predicting the probability of choice among an arbitrary number of modes, they represent useful extensions of the binary choice model.[9] They contain the important generalization that rates of substitution are allowed to vary from individual to individual, even within otherwise homogeneous classes, or at least vary systematically with the level of income.

Levels of Disaggregation. The models of Chapters 4 and 6 are based on aggregate data and have aggregative assumptions built into them that are somewhat questionable. As soon as the geographic definition of a node is decided upon, all individuals at that node are assumed to act as one, in the sense that they are all subject to the same values of

---

[9]Warner, S. L., *Stochastic Choice of Mode in Urban Travel: A Study in Binary Choice* (Northwestern University Press, 1962). There seem to be no examples in the analysis of travel demand of employing discriminant analysis for *multiple* classification.

the causal variables and all react to them in the same manner. In fact, different individuals in a given node have different incomes, face different journey times and so forth. Nor do they necessarily have the same rates of substitution, even if all exogenous variables are held constant.

Both types of aggregation are likely to introduce significant biases. The data aggregation problem can best be coped with by employing survey data as in Chapters 9 (Blackburn) and in Chapters 10, 11 and 12. The aggregation, of preferences is best avoided by explicitly not incorporating it in the model, as in Chapters 7, 8 and 9. Models which avoid both types of aggregation are likely to be the most successful ones.

Demographic and Socio-economic Theorizing. All models contain at least a rudimentary demographic and socio-economic theory since travel propensities depend not only on modal attributes (although the attribute-oriented approach is perhaps the most significant contribution of several of the chapters) but also on the environment in which travel takes place. The environment exerts a predominantly long-run influence on travel. On the whole, long-run theories explaining travel propensities leave a great deal to be desired.

The most obvious demographic factor influencing the volume of travel between nodes i and j is the populations at those nodes Population variables have traditionally entered travel models in a form similar to the gravity model, without any particular attempt at justifying the presence of terms such as $(P_i P_j)^\alpha$ or $P_i^{\alpha_1} P_j^{\alpha_2}$. An exception, being a theoretical justification of the gravity approach in terms of the constructs of statistical mechanics, is contained in Chapter 3 (Wilson). Even so, there is a fair variety of ways in which population terms enter the various models; for example, the influence of P_i and P_j on travel between i and j is expressed as $P_i P_j (P_i^\beta + P_j^\beta)$ in Chapters 5 and 8. Even greater variety can be found with respect to other variables pertaining to the environment.

Household disposable income is often suggested for inclusion in models for at least two reasons: (a) it provides an indirect way of including the budget constraint of the consumer, expressing the belief that travel is not an inferior good and that higher incomes will lead to more travel and (b) it can be used to account for the frequent observation that the value of time increases with income (Chapters 8, 9, 11, 12). Other variables may measure the occupational mix of the population, which may be a relevant variable on the grounds that cities with high concentrations of financial intermediaries, educational and governmental institutions and other service industries give rise to more travel per capita than cities with predominantly manufacturing industries (Chapter 4). Since the class of travelers defined by the purpose of the trip (pleasure, business, commuting) is more homogeneous than the class of all travelers, improved explanations can be obtained by stratifying samples by trip purpose (Chapters 9, 10, 11, 12).[10] If only aggregate data are available and stratification is not possible, proxy variables may be used to capture the effects arising from the fact that the fraction of, say, business travel varies from city to city. Since theorizing about long-run socio-economic factors is still in a rudimentary stage, proxies rather than genuine causal variables are generally in abundance. The difficulty of formulating long-run theories with good predictive power is recognized in Chapter 6 which contains an attempt to estimate unspecified characteristics which are intrinsic to city-pairs. Although the attempt is moderately successful, it falls short of being a long-run theory itself, since it provides no mechanism by which changes over time in intrinsic characteristics can be forecast. It seems plausible to suggest that this area is one in which the marginal product of future research is likely to be quite high.

3. Econometric and Computational Methods

The purpose of the present section is not to give a detailed account of all the methodological aspects of estimating the demand for travel but merely to review some more difficult problems upon which a fair amount of general attention has been focused in recent years. Among the standard techniques about which nothing needs to be said here are regression analysis (Chapters 4 and 6) and discriminant analysis (Chapter 12). [11]

Nonlinear Estimation. Many travel demand models are highly nonlinear in the parameters to be estimated. The nonlinearities are characteristically intrinsic to the models and arise either from the specification of the systematic part of the model or from the

---

[10] See also Pinton, M., "Socio-Economic Determinants of the Demand for Travel," *Studies in Travel Demand,* Vol. IV, Mathematica, 1968, pp. 89-118.

[11] For a good discussion of the particular suitability of regression and discriminant analysis to binary choice problems, see Warner, *op. cit.*

specification of the stochastic part of the model. Nonlinearities in the systematic part of the model can arise in relatively simple gravity models (Chapter 3) or from the more complex axiomatic restrictions discussed in Chapter 5. Other intrinsic nonlinearities occur in Chapters 7, 8 and 9. The specification of the error term in a regression model may be nonspherical and thus require the use of generalized least squares (Chapter 6). In regression models in which the systematic part of the model is a power function the error term may be specified either in a multiplicative manner, in which case a logarithmic transformation turns the model into standard linear form, or additively, in which case nonlinear estimation of the parameters is involved in minimizing the sum of squares.[12]

For minimizing sums of squares of errors (Chapters 7 and 8) or for maximizing likelihood functions (Chapter 9) several more or less standard numerical techniques may be employed.[13] The various algorithms are iterative procedures that successively improve the minimand. They have varying degrees of robustness with respect to various topographical features such as narrow valleys, flat regions, initial starting points that are far from the minimum, and similar problems. As a result and in spite of the relative efficacy of many of these and other techniques, the finding of stationary points on the sum of squares of nonlinear functions still remains somewhat of an art, although it is becoming increasingly routinized. An additional and special problem in some of the newer models is the fact that numerical integration may be necessary for the evaluation of the function that is required to be minimized or maximized (Chapters 7 and 8). This clearly adds a new dimension to the problem of finding acceptable estimates.

---

[12]For similar concerns see Bodkin, R. C. and L. R. Klein, "Nonlinear Estimation of Aggregate Production Functions," *Review of Economics and Statistics*, XLIX (1967), 28-44; Goldfeld, S. M. and R. E. Quandt, "The Estimation of Cobb-Douglas Type Functions with Multiplicative and Additive Errors," *International Economic Review* (1970), forthcoming.

[13]Powell, M.J.D., "An Efficient Method for Finding the Minimum of a Function of Several Variables Without Calculating Derivatives," *Computer Journal* 7 (1964), 155-162; Goldfeld, S. M., H. F. Trotter and R. E. Quandt, "Maximization by Quadratic Hill-Climbing," *Econometrica*, 34 (1966), 541-551; Hooke, R. and T. A. Jeeves, "Direct Search Solution of Numerical and Statistical Problems," *Journal of the ACM*, 8 (1961), 212-221; Davidon, W. C., "Variable Metric Method for Minimization," AEC Research and Development Report, ANL-5990, 1959; Marquardt, D. W., "An Algorithm for Least-Squares Estimation of Non-linear Parameters," *SIAM Journal*, 11 (1963), 431-441.

A special problem of nonlinear estimation that is not tackled adequately by any of the chapters is the problem of interval estimation. This is due to the fact that there is no general and exact theory of confidence intervals and hypothesis testing in the nonlinear case although approximations to a confidence region are obtainable by suitably adapting the confidence theory of the linear model.[14]

The Choice Among Competing Theories. Within limits, economic theory is often quite effective for discriminating among alternative formulations. In general, however, a residue of uncertainty almost always remains. It is then desirable to let the data reveal which formulation of a theory is relatively the best. Although it seems hardly feasible to pit each of the formulations discussed in this volume against each of the others, limited testing of alternative specifications against one another occurs in Chapters 4, 6, 7 and 12. The basis for distinguishing alternatives is threefold and involves (1) the behavior of standard statistical measures such as t-statistics, and the like, (2) the predictive success of the various formulations relative to each other and (3) the extent to which estimated elasticities or slopes agree in sign or in magnitude with strongly held prior notions. Rigorous testing of different families of hypotheses against one another by likelihood ratio criteria appears to be difficult and has not been attempted by any of the present contributions.[15]

In spite of some difficulties and deficiencies, recent work in estimating transportation demand has tackled nonlinearities and the associated computational and statistical problems in a reasonably effective manner. The existence of these problems is not an insurmountable obstacle, as is demonstrated repeatedly in this volume.

4. *Concluding Remarks*

Perhaps the major contribution of the subsequent chapters is to have opened up certain avenues of attack on the problems of estimating

---

[14]See Draper, N. R. and H. Smith, *Applied Regression Analysis,* Wiley, 1966, Ch. 10.

[15]See Hoel, P. G., "On the Choice of Forecasting Formulas," *Journal of the American Statistical Association* 24 (1947), 605-611; Cox, D. R., "Tests of Separate Families of Hypotheses," *Proceedings of the Fourth Berkeley Symposium on Probability and Statistics,* 1 (1961), 105-123; Cox, D. R., "Further Results on Tests of Separate Families of Hypotheses," *Journal of the Royal Statistical Society,* Series B, 24 (1962), 406-423.

the demand for passenger transportation. What the precise nature of these contributions is has been argued briefly in the preceding pages. It remains for us to indicate what some of the continuing problems are and where future research might make significant contributions. Among the numerous problems we shall single out four.

(1) Much further work remains to be done on the form of the demand function. Areas where further improvements or refinements are needed are (a) the specification of the manner in which attribute variables enter the models, (b) the specification of the socio-economic theory that underlies the generation of travel, and (c) the specification of the stochastic part of the model.

(2) More attention has to be paid to the possibility of simultaneous equation bias in long-run cross-sectional models than has been in the past. This bias may arise from the possibility that in the long run travel intensities and modal attributes may be jointly determined; that is to say, in the long-run travel volumes depend on modal attributes but modal attributes, in turn, depend on capacity and capacity on travel volumes.

(3) The increasing proliferation of models heightens the importance of systematic testing of models against one another. It is important that we attack more systematically than before the problem of choosing among competing formulations on statistical grounds since it seems impossible to settle the problem of the choice of model on a purely *a priori* basis.

(4) Finally, and not surprisingly, considerable advances may be achieved by improving the data used for estimating travel demand functions. It seems reasonably clear that the most important achievement in this respect would be the creation of a reliable and highly disaggregated data base, preferably with information on a household level. Although some household surveys have been available in the past, they frequently cover different periods and geographic areas. The yield from disaggregated data of uniformly high quality covering wide regions is likely to be great.

It is hoped that the theoretical contributions contained in this volume, the relative ease of coping with many difficult problems of estimation, and the existence of many unsolved problems will inspire numerous further studies.

2

A New Approach to Consumer Theory

Kelvin J. Lancaster

1. The Current Status of Consumer Theory

The theory of consumer behavior in deterministic situations as set out by, say, Debreu (1959, 1960) or Uzawa (1960) is a thing of great aesthetic beauty, a jewel set in a glass case.* The product of a long process of refinement from the nineteenth-century utility theorists through Slutsky and Hicks-Allen to the economists of the last twenty-five years,[1] it has been shorn of all irrelevant postulates so that it now stands as an example of how to extract the minimum of results from the minimum of assumptions.

To the process of slicing away with Occam's razor, the author made a small contribution (1957). This brought forth a reply by Johnson (1958) which suggested, somewhat tongue-in-cheek, that the determinateness of the sign of the substitution effect (the only substantive result of the theory of consumer behavior) could be derived from the proposition that goods are goods.

Johnson's comment, on reflection, would seem to be almost the best summary that can be given of the current state of the theory of consumer behavior. All *intrinsic* properties of particular goods, those properties that make a diamond quite obviously something different from a loaf of bread, have been omitted from the theory, so that a consumer who consumes diamonds alone is as rational as a consumer who consumes bread alone, but one who sometimes consumes bread,

Reprinted from the *Journal of Political Economy*, Vol. LXXXIV (1966), pp. 132-157. Copyright © by the University of Chicago Press. Used with permission.

*The author wishes to acknowledge helpful comments from various sources, including Gary Becker, Harry Johnson, and colleagues and students at Johns Hopkins University, especially Carl Christ, F. T. Sparrow, William Poole, C. Blackorby, T. Amemiya, and T. Tsushima.

[1] The American Economic Association *Index of Economic Journals* lists 151 entries under category 2.111 (utility, demand, theory of the household) over the period 1940-63.

sometimes diamonds (*ceteris paribus,* of course), is irrational. Thus, the only property which the theory can build on is the property shared by all goods, which is simply that they are goods.

Indeed, we can continue the argument further, since goods are simply what consumers would like more of; and we must be neutral with respect to differences in consumer tastes (some consumers might like more of something that other consumers do not want), that the ultimate proposition is that *goods are what are thought of as goods.*

In spite of the denial of the relevance of intrinsic properties to the pure theory, there has always been a subversive undercurrent suggesting that economists continue to take account of these properties. Elementary textbooks bristle with substitution examples about butter and margarine, rather than about shoes and ships, as though the authors believed that there was something intrinsic to butter and margarine that made them good substitutes and about automobiles and gasoline that made them somehow intrinsically complementary. Market researchers, advertisers, and manufacturers also act as though they believe that knowledge of (or belief in) the intrinsic properties of goods is relevant to the way consumers will react toward them.

The clearest case of conflict between a belief that goods do have intrinsic properties relevant to consumer theory but that they are not taken into account has been the long search for a definition of "intrinsic complementarity." The search was successful only where Morishima (1959) turned from traditional theory to an approach somewhat similar to that of the present paper.

Perhaps the most important aspects of consumer behavior relevant to an economy as complex as that of the United States are those of consumer reactions to new commodities and to quality variations. Traditional theory has nothing to say on these. In the case of new commodities, the theory is particularly helpless. We have to expand from a commodity space of dimension n to one of dimension $n + 1$, replacing the old utility function by a completely new one, and even a complete map of the consumer's preferences among the n goods provides absolutely no information about the new preference map. A theory which can make no use of so much information is a remarkably empty one. Even the technique of supposing the existence of a utility function for all possible goods, including those not yet invented, and regarding the prices of nonexistent goods as infinite — an incredible stretching of the consumers' powers of imagination — has no predictive value.

Finally we can note the unsuitability of traditional theory for dealing with many of the manifestly important aspects of actual relationships between goods and consumers in I. F. Pearce's (1964) recent heroic but rather unsuccessful attempts to deal with complementarity, substitution, independence, and neutral want associations within the conventional framework.

2. A New Approach

Like many new approaches, the one set out in this paper draws upon several elements that have been utilized elsewhere. The chief technical novelty lies in breaking away from the traditional approach that goods are the direct objects of utility and, instead, supposing that it is the properties or characteristics of the goods from which utility is derived.

We assume that consumption is an activity in which goods, singly or in combination, are inputs and in which the output is a collection of characteristics. Utility or preference orderings are assumed to rank collections of characteristics and only to rank collections of goods indirectly through the characteristics that they possess. A meal (treated as a single good) possesses nutritional characteristics but it also possesses aesthetic characteristics, and different meals will possess these characteristics in different relative proportions. Furthermore, a dinner party, a combination of two goods, a meal and a social setting, may possess nutritional, aesthetic, and perhaps intellectual characteristics different from the combination obtainable from a meal and a social gathering consumed separately.

In general — and the richness of the approach springs more from this than from anything else — even a single good will posses more than one characteristic, so that the simplest consumption activity will be characterized by joint outputs. Furthermore, the same characteristic (for example, aesthetic properties) may be included among the joint outputs of many consumption activities so that goods which are apparently unrelated in certain of their characteristics may be related in others.

We shall assume that the structure we have interposed between the goods themselves and the consumer's preferences is, in principle, at least, of an objective kind. That is, the characteristics possessed by a good or a combination of goods are the same for all consumers and, given units of measurement, are in the same quantities,[2] so that the personal element in consumer choice arises in the choice between collections of characteristics only, not in the allocation of characteristics to the goods. The objective nature of the goods — characteristics relationship plays a crucial role in the analysis and enables us to distinguish between objective and private reactions to such things as changes in relative prices.

The essence of the new approach can be summarized as follows, each assumption representing a break with tradition:

1. The good, per se, does not give utility to the consumer; it possesses characteristics, and these characteristics give rise to utility.
2. In general, a good will possess more than one characteristic, and many characteristics will be shared by more than one good.
3. Goods in combination may possess characteristics different from those pertaining to the goods separately.

A move in the direction of the first assumption has already been made by various workers including Strotz (1957, 1959) and Gorman (1959), with the "utility tree" and other ideas associating a particular good with a particular type of utility. The theory set out here goes much further than these ideas. Multiple characteristics, structurally similar to those of the present paper but confined to a particular problem and a point utility function, are implicit in the classical "diet problem" of Stigler (1945), and multidimensioned utilities have been used by workers in other fields, for example, Thrall (1954). The third assumption, of activities involving complementary collections of goods, has been made by Morishima (1959) but in the context of single-dimensioned utility.

A variety of other approaches with similarities to that of the present paper occur scattered through the literature, for example, in Quandt (1956), or in Becker (1965), or in various discussions of investment-portfolio problems. These are typically set out as ad hoc approaches to particular problems. Perhaps the most important aspect of this paper is that the model is set out as a general

---

[2] Since the units in which the characteristics are measured are arbitrary, the objectivity criterion relating goods and characteristics reduces to the requirement that the *relative* quantities of a particular characteristic between unit quantities of any pair of goods should be the same for all consumers.

replacement of the traditional analysis (which remains as a special case), rather than as a special solution to a special problem.

It is clear that only by moving to multiple characteristics can we incorporate many of the intrinsic qualities of individual goods. Consider the choice between a gray Chevrolet and a red Chevrolet. On ordinary theory these are either the same commodity (ignoring what may be a relevant aspect of the choice situation) or different commodities (in which case there is no a priori presumption that they are close substitutes). Here we regard them as goods associated with satisfaction vectors which differ in only one component, and we can proceed to look at the situation in much the same way as the consumer – or even the economist, in private life – would look at it.

Traditional theory is forever being forced to interpret quite common real-life happenings, such as the effects of advertising in terms of "change of taste," an entirely non-operational concept since there is no way of predicting the relationship between preference before and after the change. The theory outlined here, although extremely rich in useful ways of thinking about consumer behavior, may also be thought to run the danger of adding to the economist's extensive collection of non-operational concepts. If this were true, it need not, of course, inhibit the heuristic application of the theory. Even better, however, the theory implies predictions that differ from those of traditional theory, and the predictions of the new approach seem to fit better the realities of consumer behavior.

3. A Model of Consumer Behavior

To obtain a working model from the ideas outlined above, we shall make some assumptions which are, on balance, neither more nor less heroic than those made elsewhere in our present economic theorizing and which are intended to be no more and no less permanent parts of the theory.

1. We shall regard an individual good or a collection of goods as a consumption activity and associate a scalar (the level of the activity) with it. We shall assume that the relationship between the level of activity k, y_k, and the goods consumed in that activity to be both linear and objective, so that, if x_j is the jth commodity we have

$$x_j = \sum_k a_{jk} y_k , \qquad (1)$$

and the vector of total goods required for a given activity vector is given by

$$x = Ay. \tag{2}$$

Since the relationships are assumed objective, the equations are assumed to hold for all individuals, the coefficients a_{jk} being determined by the intrinsic properties of the goods themselves and possibly the context of technological knowledge in the society.

2. More heroically, we shall assume that each consumption activity produces a fixed vector of characteristics[3] and that the relationship is again linear, so that, if z_i is the amount of the ith characteristic

$$z_i = \sum_k b_{ik} y_k , \tag{3}$$

or

$$z = By. \tag{4}$$

Again, we shall assume that the coefficients b_{ik} are objectively determined — in principle, at least — for some arbitrary choice of the units of z_i.

3. We shall assume that the individual possesses an ordinal utility function on characteristics $U(z)$ and that he will choose a situation which maximizes $U(z)$. $U(z)$ is provisionally assumed to possess the ordinary convexity properties of a standard utility function.

The chief purpose of making the assumption of linearity is to simplify the problem. A viable model could certainly be produced under the more general set of relationships

$$F_k(z, x) = 0, \quad k = 1 \ldots m. \tag{5}$$

The model could be analyzed in a similar way to that used by Samuelson (1953b), and others in analyzing production, although

---

[3] The assumption that the consumption technology A, B is fixed is a convenience for discussing those aspects of the model (primarily static) that are the chief concern of this paper. The consequences of relaxing this particular assumption is only one of many possible extensions and expansions of the ideas presented and are discussed by the author elsewhere (Lancaster, 1966).

the existence of much jointness among outputs in the present model presents difficulties.

In this model, the relationship between the collections of characteristics available to the consumer — the vectors z — which are the direct ingredients of his preferences and his welfare, and the collections of goods available to him — the vectors x — which represent his relationship with the rest of the economy, is not direct and one-to-one, as in the traditional model, but indirect, through the activity vector y.

Consider the relationships which link z and x. These are the equation systems: $x = Ay$ (2) and $z = By$ (4). Suppose that there are r characteristics, m activities, and n goods. Only if $r = m = n$ will there be a one-to-one relationship between z and x. In this case both the B and A matrixes are square (the number of variables equals the number of equations in both sets of equations) and we can solve for y in terms of x, $y = A^{-1}x$ giving $z = BA^{-1}x$. $U(z)$ can be written directly and unambiguously as a function $u(x)$. Otherwise the relations are between vectors in spaces of different dimensions. Consider some x^* in the case in which $m > n$: equation (2) places only n restrictions on the m-vector y, so that y can still be chosen with $m-n$ degrees of freedom. If $r < m$, then there are $m-r$ degrees of freedom in choosing y, given some z, but whether the ultimate relationship gives several choices of z for a given x, or several x for a given z, and whether all vectors z are attainable, depends on the relationships between r, m, and n and the structures of the matrixes A, B. In general, we will expect that the consumer may face a choice among many paths linking goods collections with characteristics collections. The simple question asked (in principle) in the traditional analysis — does a particular consumer prefer collection x_1 or collection x_2 — no longer has a direct answer, although the question, does he prefer characteristics collection z_1 or z_2, does have such an answer.

If we take this standard choice situation facing the consumer in a free market, with a linear budget constraint, this situation, in our model, becomes:

$$
\begin{aligned}
\text{Maximize } & U(z) \\
\text{subject to } \quad px & \leqslant k \\
\text{with} \qquad\quad z & = By \\
x & = Ay \\
x,\, y,\, z & \geqslant 0.
\end{aligned}
$$

This is a non-linear program of an intractable kind. The problem of solution need not worry us here, since we are interested only in the properties of the solution.

4. The Simplified Model

We shall simplify the model in the initial stages by supposing that there is a one-to-one correspondence between goods and activities so that we can write the consumer-choice program in the simpler form

$$
\begin{aligned}
\text{Maximize } & U(z) \\
\text{subject to } \quad px & \leqslant k \\
\text{with} \qquad\quad z & = Bx \\
z, x & \geqslant 0.
\end{aligned}
$$

This is still, of course, a non-linear program, but we now have a single step between goods and characteristics.

The model consists of four parts. There is a maximand $U(z)$ operating on characteristics, that is, U is defined on characteristics-space (C-space). The budget constraint $px \leqslant k$ is defined on goods-space (G-space). The equation system $z = Bx$ represents a transformation between G-space and C-space. Finally, there are non-negativity constraints $z, x \geqslant 0$ which we shall assume to hold initially, although in some applications and with some sign conventions they may not always form part of the model.

In traditional consumer analysis, both the budget constraint and the utility function are defined on G-space, and we can immediately relate the two as in the ordinary textbook indifference-curve diagram. Here we can only relate the utility function to the budget constraint after both have been defined on the same space. We have two choices: (1) We can transform the utility function into G-space and relate it directly to the budget constraint; (2) we can transform the budget constraint into C-space and relate it directly to the utility function $U(z)$.

Each of these techniques is useful in different circumstances. In the case of the first, we can immediately write $U(z) = U(Bx) = u(x)$, so we have a new utility function directly in terms of goods, but the properties of the function $u(x)$ depend crucially on the structure of the matrix B and this, together with the constraints $x \geqslant 0$ and $z = Bx \geqslant 0$ give a situation much more complex than that of conventional utility maximization. The second technique again depends crucially on the structure of B and again will generally lead to a constraint of a more complex kind than in conventional analysis.

The central role in the model is, of course, played by the transformation equation $z = Bx$ and the structure and qualitative[4] properties of the matrix B. Most of the remainder of the paper will be concerned with the relationship between the properties of B, which we can call the *consumption technology*[5] of the economy, and the behavior of consumers.

Certain properties of the transformations between G- and C-space follow immediately from the fact that B is a matrix of constants, and the transformation $z = Bx$ is linear. These can be stated as follows, proof being obvious.

a) A convex set in G-space will transform into a convex set in C-space, so that the budget constraint $px \leqslant k$, $x \geqslant 0$ will become a convex constraint on the z's.

b) An inverse transformation will not necessarily exist, so that an arbitrary vector z in C-space may have no vector x in G-space corresponding to it.

c) Where an inverse transformation does exist from C-space into G-space, it will transform convex sets into convex sets so that, for any set of z's which do have images in G-space, the convexity of the U function on the z's will be preserved in relation to the x's.

The properties are sufficient to imply that utility maximization subject to constraint will lead to determinate solutions for consumer behavior.

5. The Structure of Consumption Technology

The consumption technology, which is as important a determinant of consumer behavior as the particular shape of the utility function, is described fully only by the A and B matrixes together, but certain types of behavior can be related to more generalized descriptions of

---

[4]"Qualitative" is used here in a somewhat more general sense than in the author's work on the properties of qualitatively defined systems for which see Lancaster (1962, 1965).

[5]If the relationship between goods and activities is not one-to-one, the consumption technology consists of the two matrixes B, A, as in the technology of the Von Neumann growth model.

the technology. We shall distinguish broadly between structural properties of the technology, such as the relationship between the number of rows and columns of B and/or A and whether A, B are decomposable, and qualitative properties, such as the signs of the elements of A and B.

The leading structural property of the consumption technology is the relationship between the number of characteristics (r) and the number of activities (m), that is, between the number of rows and columns of B. It will be assumed that B contains no linear dependence, so that its rank is the number of rows or columns, whichever is less. We shall assume, unless otherwise stated, a one-to-one relationship between goods and activities.

1. The number of characteristics is equal to the number of goods. In this case, there is a one-to-one relationship between activities vectors and characteristics vectors. We have $z = Bx$, $x = B^{-1}z$. If B is a permutation of a diagonal matrix then there is a one-to-one relationship between each component of z and each component of y, and the model becomes, by suitable choice of units, exactly the same as the traditional model. If B is not a diagonal permutation, the objects of utility are composite goods rather than individual goods, and the model has some important differences from the conventional analysis. Note how specialized is the traditional case in relation to our general model.

If B is a diagonal permutation but there is not a one-to-one relationship between activities and goods so that A is not a diagonal permutation, we have a model similar to that of Morishima (1959).

2. The number of characteristics is greater than the number of goods. In this case, the relationships $Bx = z$ contain more equations than variables x_i so that we cannot, in general, find a goods vector x which gives rise to an arbitrarily specified characteristics vector z. We can take a basis of any arbitrarily chosen n characteristics and consider the reduced $n \times n$ system $\overline{B}x = \overline{z}$, which gives a one-to-one relationship between n characteristics and the n goods, with the remaining $r - n$ characteristics being determined from the remaining $r - n$ equations and the goods vector x corresponding to $\overline{z}$. In this case, it is generally most useful to analyze consumer behavior by transforming the utility function into G-space, rather than the budget constraint into C-space. What does the transformed utility function look like?

As shown in the Appendix, the utility function transformed into G-space retains its essential convexity. An intuitive way of looking at the situation is to note that all characteristics collections which are actually available are contained in an n-dimensional slice through the r-dimensional utility function, and that all slices through a convex function are themselves convex. The transformation of this n-dimensional slice into G-space preserves this convexity.

For investigation of most aspects of consumer behavior, the case in which the number of characteristics exceeds the number of goods — a case we may often wish to associate with simple societies — can be treated along with the very special case (of which conventional analysis is a special subcase) in which the number of characteristics and goods is equal. In other words, given the consumption technology, we concern ourselves only with the particular n-dimensional slice of the r-dimensional utility function implied by that technology[6] and, since the slice of the utility function has the same general properties as any n-dimensional utility function, we can proceed as if the utility function was defined on only n characteristics.

3. In the third case, in which the number of goods exceeds the number of characteristics, a situation probably descriptive of a complex economy such as that of the United States, there are properties of the situation that are different from those of the two previous cases and from the conventional analysis.

Here the consumption technology, $z = Bx$, has fewer equations than variables so that, for every characteristics vector there is more than one goods vector. For every point in his characteristics-space, the consumer has a choice between different goods vectors. Given a price vector, this choice is a pure efficiency choice, so that for every characteristics vector the consumer will choose the most efficient combination of goods to achieve that collection of characteristics, and the efficiency criterion will be minimum cost.

The efficiency choice for a characteristics vector z^* will be the solution of the canonical linear program

$$\begin{aligned} \text{Minimize} \quad & px \\ \text{subject to } Bx \ & = \ z^* \\ x \ & \geqslant \ 0. \end{aligned}$$

---

[6]Assuming no decomposability or singularities in the consumption technology matrix B, then, if z_n is the vector of any n components of z and B_n, the corresponding square submatrix of B, the subspace of C-space to which the consumer is confined, is that defined by $z_{r-n} = B_{r-n}B_n^{-1} z_n$, where z_{r-n}, B_{r-n} are the vector and corresponding submatrix of B consisting of the components not included in z_n, B_n.

Since this is a linear program, once we have the solution x^* for some z^*, with value k^*, we can apply a scalar multiple to fit the solution to any budget value k and characteristics vector $(k/k^*)z^*$. By varying z^*, the consumer, given a budget constraint $px = k$, can determine a characteristics frontier consisting of all z such that the value of the above program is just equal to k. There will be a determinate goods vector associated with each point of the characteristics frontier.

As in the previous case, it is easy to show that the set of characteristics vectors in C-space that are preferred or indifferent to z transforms into a convex set in G-space if it is a convex set in C-space; it is also easy to show that the set of z's that can be obtained from the set of x's satisfying the convex constraint $px \leqslant k$ is also a convex set. The characteristics frontier is, therefore, concave to the origin, like a transformation curve. For a consumption technology with four goods and two characteristics, the frontier could have any of the three shapes shown in Figure 2-1. Note that, in general, if B is a positive matrix, the positive orthant in G-space transforms into a cone which lies in the interior of the positive orthant in C-space, a point illustrated in the diagrams.

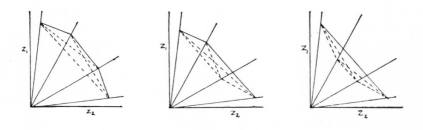

Figure 2-1

A consumer's complete choice subject to a budget constraint $px \leqslant k$ can be considered as consisting of two parts:

a) An efficiency choice, determining the characteristics frontier and the associated efficient goods collections.

b) A private choice, determining which point on the characteristics frontier is preferred by him.

The efficiency choice is an objective not a subjective choice. On the assumption that the consumption technology is objective, the characteristics frontier is also objective, and it is the same for all consumers facing the same budget constraint. Furthermore the characteristics frontier is expanded or contracted linearly and proportionally to an increase or decrease in income, so that the frontier has the same *shape* for all consumers facing the same prices, income differences simply being reflected in homogeneous expansion or contraction.

We should note that, if the consumption technology matrix has certain special structural properties, we may obtain a mixture of the above cases. For example, a matrix with the structure

$$B \equiv \begin{bmatrix} B_1 & 0 \\ 0 & B_2 \end{bmatrix},$$

where B_1 is an $(s \times k)$ matrix and B_2 is an $(r - s) \times (n - k)$ matrix, partitions the technology into two disconnected parts, one relating s of the characteristics to k of the goods, the other separately relating $r - s$ of the characteristics to $n - k$ of the goods. We can have $s \geqslant k$ and $r - s < n - k$ giving a mixed case.

Dropping the assumption of a one-to-one relationship between goods and activities does not add greatly to the difficulties of the analysis. We have, as part of the technology, $x = Ay$, so that the budget constraint $px \leqslant k$ can be written immediately as $pAy \leqslant k$. The goods prices transform directly into implicit activity prices $q = pA$. Interesting cases arise, of course. If the number of goods is less than the number of activities, then not all q's are attainable from the set of p's; and if the number of goods exceeds the number of activities, different p vectors will correspond to the same q vector. This implies that certain changes in relative goods prices may leave activity prices, and the consumer's choice situation, unchanged.

In most of the succeeding analysis, we will be concerned with the B matrix and the relationship between activities and characteristics, since this represents the most distinctive part of the theory.

6. The Efficiency Substitution Effect and Revealed Preference

At this stage, it is desirable to examine the nature of the efficiency choice so that we can appreciate the role it plays in the consumer behavior implied by our model. Consider a case in which there are two characteristics, a case that can be illustrated diagrammatically, and, say, four activities.

The activities-characteristics portion of the consumption technology is defined by the two equations

$$z_1 = b_{11}y_1 + b_{12}y_2 + b_{13}y_3 + b_{14}y_4;$$
$$z_2 = b_{21}y_1 + b_{22}y_2 + b_{23}y_3 + b_{24}y_4. \qquad (6.1)$$

With activity 1 only, the characteristics will be obtained in proportion, b_{11}/b_{21} (the ray labeled 1 in Figure 2-2). Similarly with activities 2, 3, 4, one at a time, characteristics will be obtained in proportions b_{12}/b_{22}, b_{13}/b_{23}, b_{14}/b_{24}, respectively, corresponding to the rays 2, 3, 4 in the diagram.

We are given a budget constraint in goods space of the form $\Sigma_i p_i x_i \leqslant k$. If there is a one-to-one correspondence between goods and activities, the prices of the activities are given by p_i. If there is not a one-to-one relationship, but a goods-activities portion of the consumption technology

$$x_i = a_{i1}y_1 + a_{i2}y_2 + a_{i3}y_3 + a_{i4}y_4$$

$$i = 1 \ldots n, \qquad (6.2)$$

then the budget constraint can be transformed immediately into characteristics space

$$\left(\sum_i p_i a_{i1} \right) y_1 + \left(\sum_i p_i a_{i2} \right) y_2 + \left(\sum_i p_i a_{i3} \right) y_3$$

$$+ \left(\sum_i p_i a_{i4} \right) y_4 \leqslant k \qquad (6.3)$$

where the composite prices $q_j = \Sigma_i p_i a_{ij}, j = 1 \ldots 4$ represent the prices of each activity. The number of goods in relation to the number of activities is irrelevant at this stage, since each activity has a unique and completely determined price q_j, given the prices of the goods.

Given q_1, q_2, q_3, q_4, and k, the maximum attainable level of each activity in isolation can be written down (corresponding to the points E_1, E_2, E_3, E_4 in Figure 2,) and the lines joining these points represent combinations attainable subject to the budget constraint. In the diagram it has been assumed that prices are such that

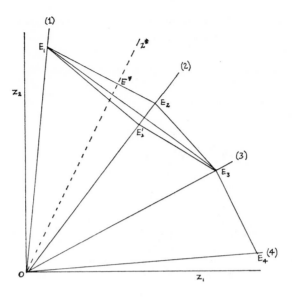

Figure 2-2

combinations of 1 and 2, 2 and 3, 3 and 4 are efficient, giving the characteristics frontier, while combinations 1 and 3, 2 and 4, or 1 and 4 are inefficient.

Suppose that the consumer chooses characteristics in the combination represented by the ray z^*, giving a point E^* on the frontier. Now suppose that relative prices change: in particular, that the price of activity 2 rises so that, with income still at k, the point E_2 moves inward on ray 2. If the movement is small enough, the characteristics frontier continues to have a corner at E_2, and the consumer will continue to obtain characteristics in proportion z^* by a combination of activities 1 and 2. If income is adjusted so that the new frontier goes through E^*, the consumer will use the same activities in the same proportions as before.

If the price of activity 2 rises sufficiently, however, the point E_2 will move inward past the line joining E_1 and E_3 to E_2'. Combinations of 1 and 2 and of 2 and 3 are now inefficient combinations of activities, their place on the efficiency frontier being taken by a combination of 1 and 3. The consumer will switch from a combination of activities 1 and 2 to a combination of 1 and 3.

Thus there is an efficiency substitution effect which is essentially a switching effect. If price changes are too small to cause a switch, there is no efficiency substitution effect: If they are large enough, the effect comes from a complete switch from one activitiy to another.

The manifestation of the efficiency substitution effect in goods space depends on the structure of the A (goods-activities) matrix. There are two polar cases:

a) If there is a one-to-one relationship between goods and activities, the efficiency substitution effect will result in a complete switch from consumption of one good to consumption of another. This might be regarded as typical of situations involving similar but differentiated products, where a sufficiently large price change in one of the products will result in widespread switching to, or away from, the product.

b) If there is not a one-to-one relationship between goods and activities and, in particular, if all goods are used in all activities, the efficiency substitution effect will simply result in less consumption of a good whose price rises, not a complete disappearance of that good from consumption. If all cakes require eggs but in different proportions, a rise in the price of eggs will cause a switch from egg-intensive cakes to others, with a decline in the consumption of eggs, but not to zero.

The existence of an efficiency substitution effect depends, of course, on the number of activities exceeding the number of characteristics (otherwise switching of activities will not, in general, occur[7]) but does not require that the number of goods exceed the number of characteristics. In fact, with two goods, two characteristics, and three activities, the effect may occur. With two goods, two characteristics and one hundred activities (well spread over the spectrum), an almost smooth efficiency substitution effect would occur.

Since the efficiency substitution effect implies that consumers may change goods collections as a result of compensated relative price changes, simply in order to obtain the same characteristics collection in the most efficient manner, it is obvious that the existence of substitution does not of itself either require or imply convexity of the preference function on characteristics. In other words, the axiom of revealed preference may be satisfied even if the consumer always consumes characteristics in fixed proportions (and possibly

---

[7]This is a somewhat imprecise statement in that, if the B matrix is partitionable into disconnected subtechnologies, for some of which the number of activities exceeds the number of characteristics and for others the reverse, an efficiency-substitution effect may exist over certain groups of activities, although the number of activities is less than the number of characteristics over-all.

even if the consumers have *concave* preferences), so that the "revelation" may be simply of efficient choice rather than convexity. A formal proof is given in the Appendix.

7. Objective and Subjective Choice and Demand Theory

In an economy or subeconomy with a complex consumption technology (many goods relative to characteristics), we have seen that there are two types of substitution effect:

1. Changes in relative prices may result in goods bundle I becoming an *inefficient* method of attaining a given bundle of characteristics and being replaced by goods bundle II even when the characteristics bundle is unchanged.

2. Changes in relative prices, with or without causing efficiency substitutions as in type 1, may alter the slope of the characteristics frontier in a segment relevant to a consumer's characteristics choice. The change in the slope of the frontier is analogous to the change in the budget line slope in the traditional case and, with a convex preference function, will result in a substitution of one characteristics bundle for another and, hence, of one goods bundle for another. Note that, even with smoothly convex preferences, this effect may not occur, since the consumer may be on a corner of the polyhedral characteristics frontier, and thus his characteristics choice could be insensitive to a certain range of slope changes on the facets.

The first effect, the efficiency substitution effect, is universal and objective. Subject to consumer ignorance or inefficiency,[8] this substitution effect is independent of the shapes of individual consumers' preference functions and hence of the effects of income distribution.

The second effect, the private substitution effect, has the same properties, in general, as the substitution effect in traditional theory. In particular, an aggregately compensated relative price change combined with a redistribution of income may result in no substitution effect in the aggregate, or a perverse one.

These two substitution effects are independent — either may occur

---

[8] One of the properties of this model is that it gives scope for the consumer to be more or less efficient in achieving his desired characteristics bundle, although we will usually assume he is completely efficient. This adds a realistic dimension to consumer behavior (traditional theory never permits him to be out of equilibrium) and gives a rationale for the Consumers' Union and similar institutions.

without the other in certain circumstances — but in general we will expect them both to take place and hence that their effects will be reinforcing, if we are concerned with a complex economy. Thus, the consumer model presented here, in the context of an advanced economy, has, in a sense, more substitution than the traditional model. Furthermore, since part of the total substitution effect arises from objective, predictable, and income-distribution-free efficiency considerations, our confidence in the downward slope of demand curves is increased even when income redistribution takes place.

Since it is well known that satisfaction of the revealed preference axioms *in the aggregate* (never guaranteed by traditional theory) leads to global stability in multimarket models (see, for example, Karlin, 1959), the efficiency substitution effect increases confidence in this stability.

In a simple economy, with few goods or activities relative to characteristics, the efficiency substitution effect will be generally absent. Without this reinforcement of the private substitution effect, we would have some presumption that perverse consumer effects ("Giffen goods," backward-bending supply curves) and lower elasticities of demand would characterize simple economies as compared with complex economies. This seems to be in accord with at least the mythology of the subject, but it is certainly empirically verifiable. On this model, consumption technology as well as income levels differentiate consumers in different societies, and we would not necessarily expect a poor urban American to behave in his consumption like a person at the same real-income level in a simple economy.

8. Commodity Groups, Substitutes, Complements

In a complex economy, with a large number of activities and goods as well as characteristics, and with a two-matrix (A, B) consumption technology, it is obvious that taxonomy could be carried out almost without limit, an expression of the richness of the present approach. Although an elaborate taxonomy is not very useful, discussion of a few selected types of relationships between goods can be of use. One of the important features of this model is that we can discuss relationships between goods, as revealed in the structure of the technology. In the conventional approach, there are, of course, no relationships between goods as such, only properties of individual's preferences.

The simplest taxonomy is that based on the zero entries in the technology matrixes. It may be that both matrixes A, B are almost "solid," in which case there is little to be gained from a taxonomic approach. If, however, the B matrix contains sufficient zeros to be decomposable as follows,

$$B \equiv \begin{bmatrix} B_1 & 0 \\ 0 & B_2 \end{bmatrix}, \qquad (7.1)$$

so that there is some set of characteristics and some set of activities such that these characteristics are derived only from these activities and these activities give rise to no other characteristics, then we can separate that set of characteristics and activities from the remainder of the technology. If, further, the activities in question require a particular set of goods which are used in no other activities (implying a decomposition of the A matrix), then we can regard the goods as forming an *intrinsic commodity group*. Goods within the group have the property that efficiency substitution effects will occur only for relative price changes within the group and will be unaffected by changes in the prices of other goods. If the utility function on characteristics has the conventional properties, there may, of course, be *private* substitution effects for goods within the group when the prices of other goods change. For an intrinsic commodity group, the whole of the objective analysis can be carried out without reference to goods outside the group.

Goods from different intrinsic commodity groups can be regarded as *intrinsically unrelated*, goods from the same group as *intrinsically related*.

If, within a group, there are two activities, each in a one-to-one relationship with a different good, and if the bundles of characteristics derived from the two goods differ only in a scalar (that is, have identical proportions), we can regard the two goods in question as *intrinsic perfect substitutes*. If the associated characteristics bundles are similar, the goods are *close substitutes*. We can give formal respectability to that traditional butter-margarine example of our texts by considering them as two goods giving very similar combinations of characteristics.

On the other hand, if a certain activity requires more than one good and if these goods are used in no other activity we can consider them as *intrinsic total complements* and they will always be consumed in fixed proportions, if at all.

Many goods within a commodity group will have relationships to each other which are partly complementary and partly substitution. This will be true if two goods, for example, are used in different combinations in each of several activities, each activity giving rise to a similar combination of characteristics. The goods are complements within each activity, but the activities are substitutes.

9. Labor, Leisure, and Occupational Choice

Within the structure of the present theory, we can regard labor as a reversed activity, using characteristics as inputs and producing commodities or a commodity as output. This is similar to the standard approach of generalized conventional theory, as in Debreu (1959).

We can add to this approach in an important way within the context of the present model by noting that a work activity may produce characteristics, as well as the commodity labor, as outputs. This is structurally equivalent to permitting some of the columns of the B matrix to have both negative and positive elements, corresponding to activities that "use up" some characteristics (or produce them in negative quantities) and produce others. In a work activity, the corresponding column of the A matrix will contain a single negative coefficient for the commodity labor, or, more differentiated, for one or more types of labor. If a work activity corresponds to a column of mixed signs in the B matrix, it is a recognition of the obvious truth that some work activities give rise to valued characteristics directly from the work itself.

Consider a very simple model of two characteristics with two commodities, labor and consumption goods. Both labor and consumption goods correspond to separate activities giving rise to the two characteristics in different proportions — perhaps negative in the case of labor. With no income other than labor, and only one good available to exchange for labor, we can collapse work and consumption into a single work-consumption activity. Given the wage rate in terms of the consumption good, the characteristics resulting from the work-consumption activity are given by a linear combination of the characteristics from work and consumption separately, the weights in the combination being given by the wage rate.

Add another activity, leisure, which gives rise to the two

characteristics, and the constraint that the weighted sum of the levels of activity labor and activity leisure is a constant.

The model is illustrated in Figure 2-3. W represents a work-consumption activity giving positive levels of both characteristics, l represents a leisure activity, also giving positive levels of both characteristics. The constraint on total time (so that a linear combination of w and l is a constant) is represented by some line joining w, l.

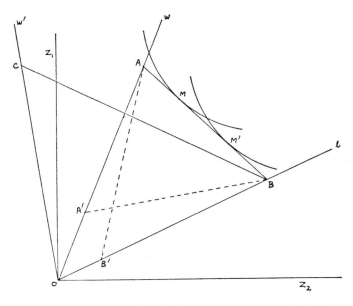

Figure 2-3

If the constraint line has, like AB in the diagram, a negative slope, then individual consumers' utility functions will be tangent to the constraint at different points (like m, m') and we will have a neoclassical type of labor-leisure choice in which the proportions depend on individual preferences. Some consumers' preferences may be such that they will choose A (maximum work) or B (maximum leisure), but it is a private choice.

In this model, however, for a certain level of the wage, given the coefficients of the technology, the constraint may have a positive slope as in $A'B$, or AB'. If the constraint is $A'B$ (corresponding, *ceteris paribus,* to a sufficiently low real wage), *all* individuals will choose B, the only efficient point on the constraint set $OA'B$. At a sufficiently high wage, giving constraint set OAB', A, the maximum labor choice, is the only efficient choice and will be chosen by *all* individuals.

The above effect, in which for some wage range there is a private labor-leisure choice between efficient points while outside the range all individuals will take maximum work or maximum leisure, can only occur if both the work-consumption and leisure activities give both characteristics in positive amounts. If the using up of characteristic 2 in labor exceeded the amount of that characteristic gained by consumption, then the work-consumption activity might lie outside the positive quadrant, like w'. In this case, a constraint like $A'B$ can exist, but not one like AB'. Furthermore, if the consumer will choose only positive characteristics vectors, no consumer will choose maximum work.

This model of the labor-leisure choice, which provides for objective and universal efficiency choices as well as private choices, may be the basis for a useful working model for an underdeveloped area. If the "leisure" be defined as "working one's own field," the work-consumption activity as entering the market economy, we see that there will be wages below which no peasant will offer himself as paid labor and that this is an *efficiency* choice and not a private choice.

We can use the same type of model also to analyze occupational choice. Suppose that we have two types of work (occupations) but otherwise the conditions are as above. If and only if the characteristics arising from the work itself are different in the two occupations, the two work-consumption activities will give rise to activities in different combinations. If the work characteristics are in the same proportion, the characteristics of the work-consumption activity will be in the same proportions and one or the other occupation will be the only efficient way to achieve this characteristics bundle.

Figure 2-4 illustrates one possible set of relationships for such a model. In the diagram, w_1, w_2 represent the characteristics combinations from work-consumption activities in occupations 1 and 2, l the characteristics combinations from leisure. The frontier consists of the lines AC (combinations of w_1 and leisure) and AB (combinations of w_2 and leisure). We shall impose the realistic restriction that an individual can have only a single occupation so that AB is not a possible combination of activities.

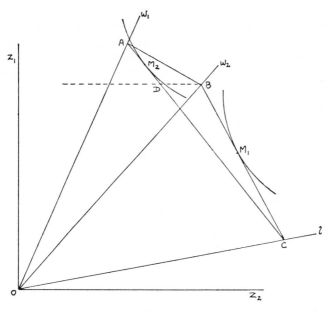

Figure 2-4

The choice of occupation, given the relationships in the figure, depends on personal preferences, being M_1 (combination of w_2 and leisure) for an individual with preferences skewed towards z_2 and M_2 for an individual with preferences skewed towards z_1. But note a special effect. For some individuals whose indifference curves cannot touch BC but can touch AC, the efficient choice will be the corner solution M_3 (=B). There is, in fact, a segment of AC to the left of w_2 (the part of AC to the right of w_2 is dominated by BC), lying below the horizontal through B which is inefficient relative to B and will never be chosen.

In a configuration like the above we have the very interesting effect, where those who choose occupation 1 will work very hard at it; leisure-lovers will choose private combinations of occupation 2 and leisure — surely a good description of effects actually observed.

The loss to certain individuals from confinement to a single occupation is obvious. Could he choose a combination of occupations 1 and 2, the individual at M_2 would do so and be better off than with a combination of occupation 1 and leisure. In a two-characteristic, three-activity model, of course, two activities will be chosen at most; so that leisure plus both occupations will not appear.

The configuration in the diagram (Fig. 2-4) represents the situation for some set of technical coefficients and specific wages in the two occupations. A large number of other configurations is possible. In particular, if the wage rate in occupation 2 fell sufficiently, BC would lie inside AC and occupation 2 would cease to be chosen by any individual. All individuals, in this case, would choose their various personal combinations of occupation 1 and leisure.

Confinement to a single occupation need not result in a welfare loss, even when neither occupation dominates the other in an efficiency sense. If the technical coefficients were different, so that the characteristics vectors representing occupation 2 and leisure changed places, then the work-leisure combinations would be given by AB and BC, both efficient relative to any combination of occupations 1 and 2. In this case, all individuals would optimize by some combination of leisure and any one of the occupations.

Approaches similar to those outlined above seem to provide a better basis for analysis of occupational choice than the traditional, non-operational, catch-all "non-monetary advantages."

10. Consumer Durables, Assets, and Money

Within the framework of the model, we have a scheme for dealing with durable goods and assets. A durable good can be regarded simply as giving rise to an activity in which the output consists of dated characteristics, the characteristics of different dates being regarded as different characteristics.

Given characteristics as joint outputs and two types of dimension in characteristics space — cross-section and time — any asset or durable good can be regarded as producing a combination of several characteristics at any one time, and that combination need not be regarded as continuing unchanged through time. In the decision to buy a new automobile, for example, the characteristic related to "fashion" or "style" may be present in relative strength in the first season, relatively less in later seasons, although the characteristics related to "transportation" may remain with constant coefficients over several seasons.

Elementary textbooks stress the multidimensional characteristics of money and other assets. The present model enables this multidimensionality to be appropriatedly incorporated. "Safety," "liquidity," and so forth become workable concepts that can be related to characteristics. We can use analysis similar to that of the preceding sections to show why efficiency effects will cause the universal disappearance of some assets (as in Gresham's Law) while other assets will be held in combinations determined by personal preferences. It would seem that development along these lines, coupled with development of some of the recent approaches to consumer preferences over time as in Koopmans (1960), Lancaster (1963), or Koopmans, Diamond, and Williamson (1964) might eventually lead to a full-blooded theory of consumer behavior with respect to assets — saving and money — which we do not have at present.

In situations involving risk, we can use multiple characteristics better to analyze individual behavior. For example, we might consider a gamble to be an activity giving rise to three characteristics — a mathematical expectation, a maximum gain, and a maximum loss. One consumer's utility function may be such that he gives more weight to the maximum gain than to the maximum loss or the expected value, another's utility function may be biased in the opposite direction. All kinds of models can be developed along these lines, and they are surely more realistic than the models (Von Neumann and Morgenstern, 1944; Friedman and Savage, 1952) in which the expected value, alone, appears in the utility-maximizing decisions.

11. New Commodities, Differentiated Goods, and Advertising

Perhaps the most difficult thing to do with traditional consumer theory is to introduce a new commodity — an event that occurs thousands of times in the U.S. economy, even over a generation, without any real consumers being unduly disturbed. In the theory of production, where activity-analysis methods have become widely used, a new process or product can be fitted in well enough; but in consumer theory we have traditionally had to throw away our n-dimensional preference functions and replace them by totally new $(n + 1)$ dimensional functions, with no predictable consequences.

In this model, the whole process is extraordinarily simple. A new product simply means addition of one or more activities to the consumption technology. Given the technology (or the relevant portion of it) and given the intrinsic characteristic of the activity associated with the new good, we simply insert it in the appropriate place in the technology, *and we can predict the consequences.*

If a new good possesses characteristics in the same proportions as some existing good, it will simply fail to sell to anyone if its price is too high, or will completely replace the old good if its price is sufficiently low.

More usually, we can expect a new good to possess characteristics in somewhat different proportions to an existing good. If its price is too high, it may be dominated by some *combination* of existing goods and will fail to sell. If its price is sufficiently low, it will result in adding a new point to the efficiency frontier. In Figure 2-5, ABC represents the old efficiency frontier, on which some individuals will consume combinations of goods g_1 and g_2 in various proportions, some combinations of g_2 and g_3. If the price of the new good, g_4, is such that it represents a point, D, on the old efficiency frontier, some persons (those using combinations of g_1 and g_2) will be indifferent between their old combinations and combinations of either g_1 and g_4 or g_2 and g_4. If the price of g_4 is a little lower, it will push the efficiency frontier out to D'. Individuals will now replace combinations of g_1 and g_2 with combinations of g_1 and g_4 or g_2 and g_4, depending on their preferences. The new good will have taken away some of the sales from both g_1 and g_2, but completely replaced neither.

If the price of g_4 were lower, giving point D'', then combinations of g_4 and g_3 would dominate g_2, and g_2 would be replaced. At an even lower price, like D''', combinations of g_4 and g_3 would dominate g_2, and the corner solution g_4 only would dominate all combinations of g_1 and g_4 (since AD''' has a positive slope), so that g_4 would now replace both g_1 and g_2.

Differentiation of goods has presented almost as much of a problem to traditional theory as new commodities. In the present analysis, the difference is really one of degree only. We can regard a differentiated good typically as a new good within an existing intrinsic commodity group, and within that group analyze it as a new commodity. Sometimes there appear new commodities of a more fundamental kind whose characteristics cut across those of existing groups.

We may note that differentiation of goods, if successful (that is, if the differentiated goods are actually sold) represents a welfare improvement since it pushes the efficiency frontier outward and enables the consumer more efficiently to reach his preferred combination of characteristics.

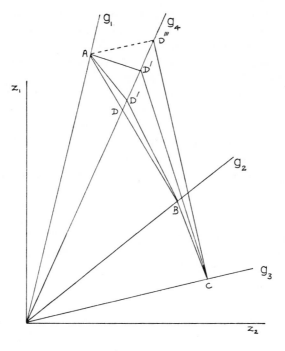

Figure 2-5

Many economists take a puritanical view of commodity differentiation since their theory has induced them to believe that it is some single characteristic of a commodity that is relevant to consumer decisions (that is, automobiles are only for transportation), so that commodity variants are regarded as wicked tricks to trap the uninitiated into buying unwanted trimmings. This is not, of course, a correct deduction even from the conventional analysis, properly used, but is manifestly incorrect when account is taken of multiple characteristics.

A rather similar puritanism has also been apparent in the economist's approach to advertising. In the neoclassical analysis, advertising, if it does not represent simple information (and little information is called for in an analysis in which a good is simply a good), is an attempt to "change tastes" in the consumer. Since "tastes" are the ultimate datum in welfare judgments, the idea of changing them makes economists uncomfortable.

On the analysis presented here, there is much wider scope for informational advertising, especially as new goods appear constantly. Since the consumption technology of a modern economy is clearly very complex, consumers require a great deal of information concerning that technology. When a new version of a dishwashing detergent is produced which contains hand lotion, we have a product with characteristics different from those of the old. The consumption technology is changed, and consumers are willing to pay to be told of the change. Whether the new product pushes out the efficiency frontier (compared, say, with a combination of dishwasher and hand lotion consumed separately) is, of course, another matter.

In any case, advertising, product design, and marketing specialists, who have a heavy commitment to understanding how consumers actually do behave, themselves act as though consumers regard a commodity as having multiple characteristics and as though consumers weigh the various combinations of characteristics contained in different commodities in reaching their decisions. At this preliminary stage of presenting the model set out here, this is strong evidence in its favor.

12. General Equilibrium, Welfare, and Other Matters

Since the demand for goods depends on objective and universal efficiency effects as well as on private choices, we can draw some inferences relative to equilibrium in the economy.

A commodity, especially a commodity within an intrinsic commodity group, must have a price low enough relative to the prices of other commodities to be represented on the efficiency frontier, otherwise it will be purchased by no one and will not appear in the economy. This implies that if there are n viable commodities in a group, each in a one-to-one relation to an activity, the equilibrium prices will be such that the efficiency frontier has $n - 1$ facets in the two-characteristic case. In Figure 2-6, for example, where the price of commodity 3 brings it to point A on the efficiency frontier, that price could not be allowed to rise to a level bringing it inside point B, or it would disappear from the market; and if its price fell below a level corresponding to C, commodities 2 and 4 would disappear from the market. Thus the limits on prices necessary for the existence of all commodities within a group can be established (in principle) from objective data. Only the demand within that price range depends on consumer preferences.

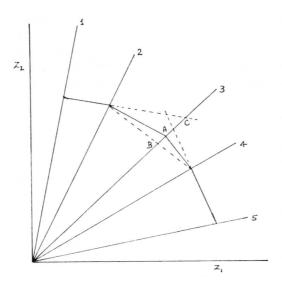

Figure 2-6

With a large number of activities relative to characteristics, equilibrium prices would give a many-faceted efficiency frontier that would be approximated by a smooth curve having the general shape of a production possibility curve. For many purposes it may be mathematically simple to analyze the situation in terms of a smooth efficiency frontier. We can then draw on some of the analysis that exists, relating factor inputs to outputs of goods, as in Samuelson (1953b). Goods in our model correspond to factors in the production model, and characteristics in our model to commodities in the production model.

The welfare implications of the model set out here are quite complex and deserve a separate treatment. We might note several important aspects of the welfare problem, however, which arise directly from a many-faceted, many-cornered efficiency frontier:

1. Consumers whose choices represent a corner on the efficiency frontier are not, in general, *equating* marginal rates of substitution between characteristics to the ratio of any parameters of the situation or to marginal rates of substitution of other consumers.

2. Consumers whose choices represent points on different facets of the efficiency frontier are equating their marginal rates of substitution between characteristics to different implicit price ratios

between characteristics. If there is a one-to-one relationship between goods and activities, the consumers are reacting to relative prices between different sets of goods. The traditional marginal conditions for Paretian exchange optimum do not hold because the price ratio relevant to one consumer's decisions differs from the price ratio relevant to another's. In common-sense terms, the price ratio between a Cadillac and a Continental is irrelevant to my decisions, but the price ratio between two compact cars is relevant, while there are other individuals for whom the Cadillac/Continental ratio is the relevant datum. If the A matrix is strongly connected, however, the implicit price ratios between different activities can correspond to price ratios between the same sets of goods, and the Paretian conditions may be relevant.

Finally, we may note that the shape of the equilibrium efficiency frontier and the existence of the efficiency substitution effect can result in demand conditions with the traditionally assumed properties, even if the traditional, smooth, convex utility function does not exist. In particular, a simple utility function in which characteristics are consumed in constant proportions — the proportions perhaps changing with income — can be substituted for the conventional utility function.

13. Operational and Predictive Characteristics of the Model

In principle, the model set out here can be made operational (that is, empirical coefficients can be assigned to the technology). In practice, the task will be more difficult than the equivalent task of determining the actual production technology of an economy.

To emphasize that the model is not simply heuristic, we can examine a simple scheme for sketching out the efficiency frontier for some commodity group. We shall assume that there is a one-to-one relationship between activities and goods, that at least one characteristic shared by the commodities is capable of independent determination, and that a great quantity of suitable market data is available.

In practice, we will attempt to operate with the minimum number of characteristics that give sufficient explanatory power. These may be combinations of fundamental characteristics (a factor-analysis situation) or fundamental characteristics themselves.

Consider some commodity group such as household detergents. We have a primary objective characteristic, cleaning power, measured in some chosen way. We wish to test whether one or more other characteristics are necessary to describe the consumer-choice situation.

We take a two-dimensional diagram with characteristic "cleaning power" along one axis. Along the axis we mark the cleaning power per dollar outlay of all detergents observed to be sold at the same time. If this is the same for all detergents, this single characteristic describes the situation, and we do not seek further. However, we shall assume this is not so. From our observed market data, we obtain cross-price elasticities between all detergents, taken two at a time. From the model, we know that cross-price elasticities will be highest between detergents with adjacent characteristics vectors, so that the order of the characteristics vectors as we rotate from one axis to the other in the positive quadrant can be established.

The ordering of "cleaning power per dollar" along one axis can be compared with the ordering of the characteristics vectors. If the orderings are the same, an equilibrium efficiency frontier can be built up with two characteristics as in Figure 2-7a. The slopes of the facets can be determined within limits by the limiting prices at which the various detergents go off the market. If the ordering in terms of cleaning power does not agree with the ordering in terms of cross-elasticity, as in Figure 2-7b, two characteristics do not describe the market appropriately, since detergent with cleaning power 3 in the figure cannot be on the efficiency frontier. But with a third characteristic, detergent 3 could be adjacent to detergents 2 and 1 in an extra dimension, and we could build up an efficiency frontier in three characteristics.

Other evidence could, of course, be used to determine the efficiency frontier for a given market situation. Among this evidence is that arising from ordinary activity-analysis theory, that, with r characteristics we would expect to find some consumers who used r commodities at the same time, unless all consumers were on corners or edges of the efficiency frontier.

Last, but possibly not least, simply asking consumers about the characteristics associated with various commodities may be much more productive than attempts to extract information concerning preferences within the context of conventional theory.

In general, if consumer preferences are well dispersed (so that all facets of the efficiency frontier are represented in some consumer's choice pattern), a combination of information concerning interpersonal variances in the collections of goods chosen and of the effects of price changes on both aggregate and individual choices can, in principle, be used to ferret out the nature of the consumption technology. Some of the problems that arise are similar to those met by psychologists in measuring intelligence, personality, and other

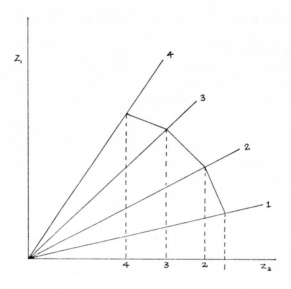

Figure 2-7*a*

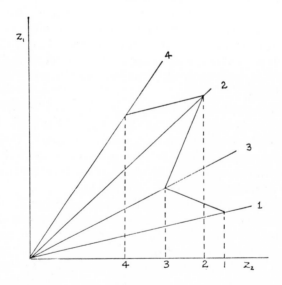

Figure 2-7*b*

multidimensional traits, so that techniques similar to those used in psychology, such as factor analysis, might prove useful.

Even without specification of the consumption technology, the present theory makes many predictions of a structural kind which may be contrasted with the predictions of conventional theory. Some of these are set out in Chart 1.

Chart 1

This Theory	*Conventional Theory*
Wood will not be a close substitute for bread, since characteristics are dissimilar	No reason except "tastes" why they should not be close substitutes
A red Buick will be a close substitute for a gray Buick	No reason why they should be any closer substitutes than wood and bread
Substitution (for example, butter and margarine) is frequently intrinsic and objective, will be observed in many societies under many market conditions	No reasons why close substitutes in one context should be close substitutes in another
A good may be displaced from the market by new goods or by price changes	No presumption that goods will be completely displaced
The labor-leisure choice may have a marked occupational pattern	Labor-leisure choice determined solely by individual preferences; no pattern, other than between individuals, would be predicted
(Gresham's Law) A monetary asset may cease to be on the efficiency frontier, and will disappear from the economy	No ex ante presumption that any good or asset will disappear from the economy
An individual is completely unaffected by price changes that leave unchanged the portion of the efficiency frontier on which his choice rests	An individual is affected by changes in all prices
Some commodity groups may be intrinsic, and universally so	No presumption that commodities forming a group (defined by a break in spectrum of cross-elasticities) in one context will form a group in another context

14. Conclusion

In this model we have extended into consumption theory activity analysis, which has proved so penetrating in its application to production theory. The crucial assumption in making this application has been the assumption that goods possess, or give rise to, multiple characteristics in fixed proportions and that it is these characteristics, not goods themselves, on which the consumer's preferences are exercised.

The result, as this brief survey of the possibilities has shown, is a model very many times richer in heuristic explanatory and predictive power than the conventional model of consumer behavior and one that deals easily with those many common-sense characteristics of actual behavior that have found no place in traditional exposition.

This paper is nothing more than a condensed presentation of some of the great number of possible ways in which the model can be used. It is hoped that a door has been opened to a new, rich treasure house of ideas for the future development of the most refined and least powerful branch of economic theory, the theory of the consumer himself.

Appendix

1. Transformation of the Utility Function into G-Space

Consider some characteristics vector z^* which does have an image x^* in G-space, and consider the set P of all vectors z preferred or indifferent to z^*. If U has the traditional properties, the set P is convex with an inner boundary which is the indifference surface through z^*. Now $z \geqslant z^*$ implies z is in P so that every x such that $Bx \geqslant z^*$, a set S, is preferred or indifferent to x^*. If we take some other z' in P, every x in S' such that $Bx \geqslant z'$ is also preferred or indifferent to x'^*. Similarly for z'' in P and S'' such that that $Bx \geqslant z''$, and so on. From the theory of inequalities, the sets $S, S', S'' \ldots$ are all convex, and since P is convex, a linear combination of z', z'', is in P, so that a linear combination of x's in S', S'' is also preferred or indifferent to x^*. Hence the set $\bar{P}$ of all x preferred or indifferent to x^* is the linear combination of all the sets $S, S', S'', \ldots$ and so is convex.

Thus the utility function transformed into G-space retains its essential convexity. A more intuitive way of looking at the situation is to note that all characteristics collections which are actually available are contained in an *n*-dimensional slice through the *r*-dimensional utility function and that all slices through a convex function are themselves convex. The transformation of this *n*-dimensional slice into G-space preserves this convexity.

2. Revealed Preference in
a Complex Economy

We shall use the structural properties of the consumption technology *A, B* (dropping the assumption of a one-to-one relationship between goods and activities) to show that in a complex economy with more activities than characteristics the efficiency choice always satisfies the weak axiom of revealed preference and will satisfy the strong axiom for sufficiently large price changes, so that satisfaction of even the strong axiom does not "reveal" convexity of the preference function itself.

Consider an economy with a consumption technology defined by

$$z = By,$$

$$x = Ay,$$

and a consumer subject to a budget constraint of the form $p^*x \leqslant k$ who has chosen goods x^* for activities y^*, giving characteristics z^*.

We know that if the consumer has made an efficient choice, y^* is the solution of the program (the value of which is k).

Minimize $p^*Ay \, (= p^*x)$:

$$By = z^*, \, y \geqslant 0, \tag{8.1a}$$

which has a dual (solution v^*).

$$\text{Maximize } vz^* : vB \leqslant p^*A. \tag{8.1b}$$

The dual variables v can be interpreted as the implicit prices of the characteristics themselves. From the Kuhn-Tucker Theorem, we can associate the vector v with the slope of the separating hyperplane

EDINBURGH UNIVERSITY WITHDRAWN

between the set of attainable z's and the set of z's preferred or indifferent to z^*.

For the same satisfactions vector Z^* and a new price vector p^{**} the efficiency choice will be the solution y^{**} (giving x^{**}), v^{**}, of

$$\text{Min } p^{**}Ay : By = z^*, \ y \geqslant 0,$$

$$\text{Max } vz^* : vb \leqslant p^{**}A. \qquad (8.2)$$

Since z^* is the same in (8.1) and (8.2), y^{**} is a feasible solution of (8.1) and y^* of (8.2). From the fundamental theorem of linear programming we have

$$p^{**}Ay^* \geqslant v^{**}z^* = p^{**}Ay^{**}, \qquad (8.3)$$

$$p^*Ay^{**} \geqslant v^*z^* = p^*Ay^*. \qquad (8.4)$$

A program identical with (8.2) except that z^* is replaced by hz^* will have a solution hy^{**}, v^{**}. Choose h so that $hp^{**}Ay^{**} = p^{**}Ay^*$. From (8.3) $h \geqslant 1$. From (8.4),

$$hp^*Ay^{**} \geqslant p^*Ay^{**} \geqslant p^*Ay^*. \qquad (8.5)$$

If we now write p for p^*, p' for p^{**}; $x = Ay^*$, $x' = hAy^{**}$, we have

$$p'x' = p'x \text{ implies } px' \geqslant px, \qquad (8.6)$$

satisfying the *weak axiom of revealed preference*.

The equality will occur on the right in (8.6) only if equalities hold in *both* (8.3) and (8.4) and these will hold only if y^{**} is optimal as well as feasible in (8.1), and y^* is optimal as well as feasible in (8.2). In general, if the number of activities exceeds the number of characteristics, we can always find two prices p^*, p^{**} so related that neither of the solutions y^{**}, y^* is optimal in the other's program.

Hence, if the number of activities exceeds the number of characteristics (representing the number of primary constraints in the program), we can find prices so related that the strong axiom of revealed preference is satisfied, even though the consumer has obtained characteristics in unchanged proportions (z^*, hz^*) and has revealed nothing of his preference map.

The above effect represents an *efficiency substitution effect* which would occur even if characteristics were consumed in absolutely fixed proportions. If the consumer substitutes between different satisfactions bundles when his budget constraint changes, this private substitution effect is additional to the efficiency substitution effect.

Just as the conceptual experiment implicit in revealed preference implies "overcompensation" in the conventional analysis (see Samuelson 1948, 1953*a*), so the efficiency effect leads to "external overcompensation" additional to private overcompensation.

References

Becker, Gary S. "A Theory of the Allocation of Time," *Econ. J.,* September, 1965.

Debreu, Gerald. *Theory of Value.* Cowles Foundation Monograph 17, 1959.

_____. "Topological Methods in Cardinal Utility Theory," in K. J. Arrow, S. Karlin, and P. Suppes (eds.). *Mathematical Methods in the Social Sciences, 1959.* Stanford, Calif.: Stanford Univ. Press, 1960.

Friedman, Milton, and Savage, L. J. "The Expected-Utility Hypothesis and the Measurability of Utility," *J.P.E.,* Vol. LX (December, 1952).

Gorman, W. M. "Separable Utility and Aggregation," *Econometrica,* Vol. XXVII (July, 1959).

Johnson, Harry G. "Demand Theory Further Revised or Goods Are Goods," *Economica,* N.S. 25 (May, 1958).

Karlin, S. *Mathematical Methods and Theory in Games, Programming and Economics.* New York: Pergamon Press, 1959.

Koopmans, T. C. "Stationary Ordinal Utility and Impatience," *Econometrica,* Vol. XXIII (April, 1960).

Koopmans, T. C., Diamond, P. A., and Williamson, R. E. "Stationary Utility and Time Perspective," *ibid.,* Vol. XXXII (January-April, 1964).

Lancaster, Kelvin J. "Revising Demand Theory," *Economica,* N.S. 24 (November, 1957).

_____. "The Scope of Qualitative Economics," *Rev. Econ. Studies,* Vol. XXIX (1962).

_____. "An Axiomatic Theory of Consumer Time Preference," *Internat. Econ. Rev.,* Vol. IV (May, 1963).

_____. "The Theory of Qualitative Linear Systems," *Econometrica,* Vol. XXXIII (April, 1965).

_____. "Change and Innovation in the Technology of Consumption," *A.E.R.,* Papers and Proceedings, May, 1966.

Morishima, M. "The Problem of Intrinsic Complementarity and Separability of Goods," *Metroeconomica,* Vol. XI (December, 1959).

Pearce, I. F. *A Contribution to Demand Analysis.* New York: Oxford Univ. Press, 1964.

Quandt, R. E. "A Probabilistic Theory of Consumer Behaviour," *Q.J.E.,* Vol. LXX (November, 1956).

Samuelson, P. A. "Consumption Theory in Terms of Revealed Preference," *Economica,* N.S. 15 (November, 1948).

_____. "Consumption Theorems in Terms of Over-Compensation Rather than Indifference Comparisons," *ibid.,* N.S. 20 (February, 1953). (*a*)

_____. "Prices of Factors and Goods in General Equilibrium," *Rev. Econ. Studies*, Vol. XXI (1953). (*b*)

Stigler, G. J. "The Cost of Subsistence," *J. Farm Econ.,* Vol. XXVII (1945).

Strotz, Robert, "The Empirical Implications of a Utility Tree," *Econometrica,* Vol. XXV (April, 1957).

_____. "The Utility Tree: A Correction and Further Appraisal," *ibid.,* Vol. XXVII (July, 1959).

Thrall, Robert M., Coombs, C., and Davis, R. L. *Decision Processes.* New York: Wiley & Sons, 1954.

Uzawa, H., "Preference and Rational Choice in the Theory of Consumption," in K. J. Arrow, S. Karlin, and P. Suppes (eds.). *Mathematical Methods in the Social Sciences, 1959.* Stanford, Calif.: Stanford Univ. Press, 1960.

Von Neumann, J., and Morgenstern, O. *Theory of Games and Economic Behaviour.* Princeton, N.J.: Princeton Univ. Press, 1944.

3 A Statistical Theory of Spatial Distribution Models

A. G. Wilson

1. Introduction

This paper offers a theoretical basis for some spatial distribution models which are in common use in locational analysis, and uses the new methodology to generate new models. Such analysis is likely to be concerned with the spatial location of activities among the zones of a region, and measures of interaction between the zones. For example, there may be an interest in zonal activity levels in the form of numbers of workers in residential zones, and the numbers of jobs in employment zones; the interaction between these activities is the journey to work. To fix ideas, this example will be used to illustrate the methods proposed in this paper.

Let T_{ij} be the number of (work) trips, and d_{ij} the distance, between zones i and j, let O_i be the total number of work trip origins in i, and let D_j be the total number of work trip destinations in j. A spatial distribution model then estimates T_{ij} as a function of the O_i's, the D_j's and the d_{ij}'s. These variables could, of course, themselves be functions of other independent variables.

The simplest such model is the so-called gravity model developed by analogy with Newton's law of the gravitational force F_{ij} between two masses m_i and m_j separated by a distance d_{ij}.

$$F_{ij} = \gamma \frac{m_i m_j}{d_{ij}^2} \tag{1}$$

where γ is a constant. The analogous transport gravity model is then

$$T_{ij} = k \frac{O_i D_j}{d_{ij}^2} \tag{2}$$

Reprinted from *Transportation Research*, Vol. I (1967), pp. 253-269. Copyright © by the Pergamon Press. Used with permission.

using the variables defined above, and where k is a constant. This model has some sensible properties: T_{ij} is proportional to each of O_i and D_j and inversely proportional to the square of the distance between them. But the equation has at least one obvious deficiency: if a particular O_i and a particular D_j are each doubled, then the number of trips between these zones would quadruple according to the equation (2), when it would be expected that they would double also. To put this criticism of (2) more precisely, the following constraint equations on T_{ij} should always be satisfied, and they are not satisfied by (2):

$$\sum_j T_{ij} = O_i \qquad (3)$$

$$\sum_i T_{ij} = D_j \qquad (4)$$

That is, the row and column sums of the trip matrix should be the numbers of trips generated in each zone, and the number of trips attracted, respectively. These constraint equations can be satisfied if sets of constants A_i and B_j associated with production zones and attraction zones respectively are introduced. They are sometimes called balancing factors. Also, there is no reason to think that distance plays its part in the transport equation (2) as it does in the world of Newtonian physics, and so a general function of distance is introduced. The modified gravity model is then

$$T_{ij} = A_i B_j O_i D_j f(d_{ij}) \qquad (5)$$

where

$$A_i = \left[\sum_j B_j D_j f(d_{ij}) \right]^{-1} \qquad (6)$$

and

$$B_j = \left[\sum_i A_i O_i f(d_{ij}) \right]^{-1} \qquad (7)$$

The equations for A_i and B_j are solved iteratively, and it can easily be checked that they ensure that the T_{ij} given in equation (5) satisfies the constraint equations (3) and (4). Note also that d_{ij} in such a model should be interpreted as a general measure of impedance between i and j, which may be measured as actual distance, as travel time, as cost, or as some weighted combination of such factors sometimes referred to as a "generalized cost". With this proviso, equations (5)-(7) describe a gravity model which has been extensively used, and the discussion above has shown its heuristic derivation by analogy with Newton's gravitational law.

A second approach to trip distribution uses the intervening opportunities model. Interzonal impedance does not appear explicitly in this model, but possible destination zones away from an origin zone i have to be ranked in order of increasing impedance from i. A notation is needed to describe this. Let $j_\mu(i)$ be the μth destination zone in this rank order away from i; $j_\mu(i)$ will be referred to simply as j_μ in cases where it is clear to which i it refers. The intervening opportunities model was first developed by Stouffler (1940) in a simple form, assuming that the number of trips from an origin zone to a destination zone is proportional to the number of opportunities at the destination zone, and inversely proportional to the number of intervening opportunities. The underlying assumption of the model is that the tripper considers each opportunity, as reached, in turn, and has a definite probability that his needs will be satisfied. The model will be derived here in the form developed by Schneider, originally for use in the Chicago Area Transportation Study (1960). To see how the basic assumption operates, consider a situation in which destination zones are rank ordered away from an origin zone as defined earlier. Let U_{ij_μ} be the probability that one tripper will continue beyond the μth zone away from i. Suppose there is a chance L that an opportunity will satisfy this single tripper when it is offered. Then, to the first order in L,

$$U_{ij_1} = 1 - LD_{j_1}$$

where D_{j_1} is the number of opportunities in the zone j_1, nearest to i. Then combining successive probabilities multiplicatively,

$$U_{ij_2} = U_{ij_1}(1 - LD_{j_2})$$

$$U_{ij_3} = U_{ij_2}(1 - LD_{j_3})$$

and so on. In general

$$U_{ij_\mu} = U_{ij_{\mu-1}}(1 - LD_{j_\mu}) \tag{8}$$

This equation can be written

$$\frac{U_{ij_\mu} - U_{ij_{\mu-1}}}{U_{ij_{\mu-1}}} = -LD_{j_\mu} \tag{9}$$

Let A_{j_μ} be the number of opportunities passed up to and including zone j_μ. Then

$$D_{j_\mu} = A_{j_\mu} - A_{j_{\mu-1}} \tag{10}$$

and (9) can be written

$$\frac{U_{ij_\mu} - U_{ij_{\mu-1}}}{U_{ij_{\mu-1}}} = -L(A_{j_\mu} - A_{j_{\mu-1}}) \tag{11}$$

This equation can be written, assuming continuous variation, as

$$dU/U = -LdA \tag{12}$$

which integrates to

$$\log U = -LA + \text{constant}$$

so that

$$U_{ij_\mu} = k_i \exp(-LA_{j_\mu}) \tag{13}$$

where k_i is a constant. But

$$T_{ij_\mu} = O_i(U_{ij_{\mu-1}} - U_{ij_\mu}) \tag{14}$$

where T_{ij_μ} is the number of trips from i to the μth destination away from i, for a total of O_i trips originating at i. Substitution from (13) to (14) gives

$$T_{ij_\mu} = k_i O_i [\exp(-LA_{j_{\mu-1}}) - \exp(-LA_{j_\mu})] \tag{15}$$

and this is the usual statement of the intervening opportunities model.

Note that k_i can be chosen so that the resulting matrix T_{ij} satisfies the constraint equation (3):

$$\sum_j T_{ij} = k_i O_i [1 - \exp(-A_{j_N})] = O_i$$

where N is the total number of zones. Since $\exp(-LA_{j_N})$ should be very small, k_i will be very nearly one for each i. The constraint equation (4) on the total number of trip attractions cannot be satisfied, however, within the model structure itself, but if actual D_j's are known, the matrix can be adjusted by the same balancing process as that implied by equations (6) and (7).

(Thus, in general, if there is a matrix $T_{ij}{}^*$ and it is required to transform it to a matrix T_{ij} whose columns and rows sum to O_i and D_j, then this can be done by the transformation

$$T_{ij} = A_i B_j T_{ij}{}^* \tag{16}$$

where

$$A_i = O_i \left(\sum_j B_j T_{ij}{}^* \right)^{-1} \tag{17}$$

$$B_j = D_j \left(\sum_i A_i T_{ij}{}^* \right)^{-1} \tag{18}$$

and these equations can be seen to reduce to (6) and (7) for the gravity model. This process is accomplished in practice by factoring rows and columns successively by $D_j/D_j{}^*$ and $O_i/O_i{}^*$ where the $D_j{}^*$ are the column sums, and $O_i{}^*$ the row sums, of the matrix reached after the immediately preceding operation. This is the balancing process which can be applied, if required, to the intervening opportunities model trip matrix.)

It is often argued that the intervening opportunities model is "better" than the gravity model because the theoretical derivation (as outlined above) is sound, whereas the derivation of the gravity model is at best heuristic and based on an analogy with Newton's gravitational law in the physical sciences. The statistical theory of spatial distribution models proposed in this paper is based on an analogy with a different branch of physics, statistical mechanics, and does offer a sound theoretical base for the gravity model. It is also possible, by changing the assumptions, to derive the intervening opportunities model. In fact, the proposed method provides a reasonably general rule for deriving appropriate spatial distribution models for a variety of purposes and situations, and for comparing different models which are supposed to apply to the same situation.

The key to the method is to define a set of variables which completely specify the system, and to enumerate any constraints on these variables. It will usually be possible to do this using the variables T_{ij} defined previously, the number of trips between i and j (still assuming that this is for one purpose and a reasonably homogeneous set of travellers). A set of T_{ij}'s defined by $\{T_{ij}\}$ then defines a *distribution* of trips. It is also possible to define a *state* of the system as one of the ways in which a distribution is brought about at the microlevel: thus, if the system is made up of individual trippers, a state of the system, for example for the journey to work, is just one way in which these trippers decide on their journey to work in a consistent way (that is, subject to the usual constraints). Note that, at the end of the analysis, the only interest is in distributions — total numbers of trips between points — and not in states — that is, the individual trippers who are making up these trip bundles. The crucial assumption of the new method can now be stated: that the probability of a distribution $\{T_{ij}\}$ occurring is proportional to the number of states of the system which give rise to the distribution $\{T_{ij}\}$. Thus, if $w(T_{ij})$ is the number of ways in which individuals can arrange themselves to produce the overall distribution $\{T_{ij}\}$, then the probability of $\{T_{ij}\}$ occurring is proportional to $w(T_{ij})$. The total number of such arrangements is

$$\Sigma w(T_{ij}) \tag{19}$$

where the summation is over the distributions which satisfy the constraints of the problem. It will be shown that in most cases there is one distribution $\{T_{ij}\}$ for which $w(T_{ij})$ dominates all other terms of the sum (19) overwhelmingly, and so forms the most probable distribution.

Section 2 of this paper states and discusses this theory for the usual gravity model; Section 3 then applies the theory to a variety of new situations, including an application to multimodal distribution, and also including a derivation of the intervening opportunities model. The final section summarizes the conclusions.

2. A Statistical Theory of
the Gravity Model

2.1. The "conventional" gravity model. The new method is most easily illustrated by a single-purpose example, such as the journey to work example discussed above, and so the previously defined example and notation are used. The trip matrix, T_{ij}, must satisfy the two constraint equations (3) and (4), which, for convenience, are stated again here:

$$\sum_j T_{ij} = O_i \tag{20}$$

$$\sum_i T_{ij} = D_j \tag{21}$$

It will also be assumed that another constraint equation is satisfied:

$$\sum_i \sum_j T_{ij} c_{ij} = C \tag{22}$$

where c_{ij} is the impedance, or generalized cost, of travelling between i and j, and so replaces the d_{ij} of the introduction to emphasize that the measure of impedance need not be distance. This constraint, then, implies that the total amount spent on trips in the region at this point in time, is a fixed amount C. The use of, and need for, this constraint will be made clear as the method develops.

The basic assumption of the method is that the probability of the distribution $\{T_{ij}\}$ occurring is proportional to the number of states of the system which give rise to this distribution, and which satisfy the constraints. Suppose

$$T = \sum_i O_i = \sum_j D_j \tag{23}$$

is the total number of trips. Then the number of distinct arrangements of individuals which give rise to the distribution $\{T_{ij}\}$ is

$$w(T_{ij}) = (T!) \Big/ \left(\prod_{ij} T_{ij}! \right) \tag{24}$$

since there is no interest in arrangements within a particular trip bundle. The total number of possible states is then

$$W = \Sigma w(T_{ij}) \tag{25}$$

where the summation is over T_{ij} satisfying (20)-(22). However, the maximum value of $w(T_{ij})$ turns out to dominate the other terms of the sum to such an extent that the distribution $\{T_{ij}\}$, which gives rise to this maximum is overwhelmingly the most probable distribution. This maximum will now be obtained, and its sharpness, and the validity of the method in general, will then be discussed in Section 2.3 below, following a section which discusses the interpretation of particular terms.

To obtain the set of T_{ij}'s which maximizes $w(T_{ij})$ as defined in (24) subject to the constraints (20)-(22), the function M has to be maximized, where

$$M = \log w + \sum_i \lambda_i^{(1)} \left(O_i - \sum_j T_{ij} \right) + \sum_j \lambda_j^{(2)} \left(D_j - \sum_i T_{ij} \right)$$

$$+ \beta \left(C - \sum_i \sum_j T_{ij} c_{ij} \right) \tag{26}$$

and where $\lambda_i^{(1)}$, $\lambda_j^{(2)}$ and β are Lagrangian multipliers. Note that it is more convenient to maximize $\log w$ rather than w, and then it is possible to use Stirling's approximation

$$\log N! = N \log N - N \tag{27}$$

to estimate the factorial terms. The T_{ij}'s which maximize M, and which therefore constitute the most probable distribution of trips, are the solutions of

$$\frac{\partial M}{\partial T_{ij}} = 0 \tag{28}$$

and the constraint equations (20)-(22). Using Stirling's approximation, (27), note that

$$\frac{\partial \log N!}{\partial N} = \log N \tag{29}$$

and so

$$\frac{\partial M}{\partial T_{ij}} = -\log T_{ij} - \lambda_i^{(1)} - \lambda_j^{(2)} - \beta c_{ij} \qquad (30)$$

and this vanishes when

$$T_{ij} = \exp(-\lambda_i^{(1)} - \lambda_j^{(2)} - \beta c_{ij}) \qquad (31)$$

Substitute in (20) and (21) to obtain $\lambda_i^{(1)}$ and $\lambda_j^{(2)}$:

$$\exp\,[-\lambda_i^{(1)}] = O_i \bigg/ \left[\sum_j \exp(-\lambda_j^{(2)} - \beta c_{ij})\right] \qquad (32)$$

$$\exp\,[-\lambda_j^{(2)}] = D_j \bigg/ \left[\sum_i \exp(-\lambda_i^{(1)} - \beta c_{ij})\right] \qquad (33)$$

To obtain the final result in more familiar form, write

$$A_i = \exp(-\lambda_i^{(1)})/O_i \qquad (34)$$

and

$$B_j = \exp(-\lambda_j^{(2)})/D_j \qquad (35)$$

and then

$$T_{ij} = A_i B_j O_i D_j \exp(-\beta c_{ij}) \qquad (36)$$

where, using equations (32)-(35),

$$A_i = \left[\sum_j B_j D_j \exp(-\beta c_{ij})\right]^{-1} \qquad (37)$$

$$B_j = \left[\sum_i A_i O_i \exp(-\beta c_{ij})\right]^{-1} \qquad (38)$$

Thus the most probable distribution of trips is the same as the gravity model distribution discussed earlier, and defined in equations (5)-(7), and so this statistical derivation constitutes a new theoretical base for the gravity model. Note that C in the cost constraint equation (22) need not actually be known, as this equation is not in practice solved for β. This parameter would be found by the normal calibration methods. However, if C was known, then (22) could be solved numerically for β.

This statistical theory is effectively saying that, given total numbers of trip origins and destinations for each zone for a homogeneous person-trip purpose category, given the costs of travelling between each zone, and given that there is some fixed total expenditure on transport in the region, then there is a most probable distribution of trips between zones, and this distribution is the same as the one normally described as the gravity model distribution. Students of statistical mechanics will recognize the method as a variation of the micro-canonical ensemble method for analysing systems of particles, for example, the molecules of a gas.

2.2 Interpretation of terms. It has always been a feature of statistical mechanics that the terms which occur in the equation giving the most probable distribution are then seen to have physical significance. This is true here also. O_i, D_j and c_{ij} were defined previously, The expression $\exp(-\beta c_{ij})$ appears in this formulation as the preferred form of distance deterrence function, and the parameter β is determined in theory by the cost constraint equation (22). It does, however, have its usual interpretation: it is closely related to the average distance travelled. The greater β, the less is the average distance travelled. This is then obviously related to C of equation (22). If C is increased, then more is spent on travelling and distances will increase, but an examination of the left-hand side of (22) shows that β would decrease. The remaining task is to interpret A_i and B_j.

Suppose one of the D_j's changes, say D_1. Then

$$T_{i1} = A_i B_1 O_i D_1 \exp\left(-\beta c_{i1}\right) \tag{39}$$

and if D_1 changes substantially, the trips from each i to zone 1 would change in proportion. The next largest change will be in the A_i's as defined by (37), but the change will not be large as the expression involving D_1 in each A_i is only one of a number of terms. The B_j's will probably be affected even less, as any change is brought about through changes in the A_i's.

Suppose, then, that D_1 is substantially increased. Then the T_{i1}'s will increase more or less in proportion. The A_i's will decrease by a lesser amount relatively, and the B_j's will increase even more slightly. The role of the A_i's, then, will be to reduce all trips slightly to compensate for the increase in trips to zone 1. A_i can thus be seen as a competition term which reduces most trips due to the increased attractiveness of one zone. The denominator of A_i is also commonly used as a measure of accessibility, and the increase in D_1 could be said to increase the accessibility of everyone to opportunities at 1, though more usually such an interpretation would be reserved for changes in the c_{ij}'s. Thus, this analysis establishes a competition-accessibility interpretation of the A_i's. The B_j's play a similar role, and would be responsible for the main adjustments if the major change was in an O_i rather than a D_j. A change in the c_{ij}'s, or several O_i's and D_j's simultaneously, would bring about complex readjustments through the A_i's and the B_j's.

One consequence of this interpretation, and of the use of the new method which gives a fundamental role to the A_i's and B_j's, is that it shows that the interpretation of the A_i's and B_j's suggested by Dieter (1962) is wrong. Dieter suggested that the A_i's and B_j's should be associated with terminal costs, say a_i and b_j in origin and destination zones i and j respectively. This can be checked by replacing c_{ij} by $a_i + b_j + c_{ij}$ in the preceding analysis, and this gives for T_{ij}:

$$T_{ij} = A_i B_j O_i D_j \exp(-\beta a_i - \beta b_j - \beta c_{ij}) \tag{40}$$

Thus, new terms $\exp(-\beta a_i)$ and $\exp(-\beta b_j)$ are introduced, but the A_i's and B_j's are still present independently of the existence of terminal costs.

2.3. Validity of the method. There are two possible points of weakness in the method. Firstly, is Stirling's approximation, in equation (27), valid for the sort of T_{ij}'s that occur in practice? Secondly, is the maximum value of

$$\frac{T!}{\prod_{ij} T_{ij}!}$$

a very sharp maximum?

The first of the doubts can be answered by analogy. The use of Stirling's approximation underlies one particular approach in statistical mechanics and is used, as here, to produce most probable distributions. There is, however, a second method, the Darwin-Fowler method, which actually calculates the individual terms of the sum in equation (19) by using a generating function and complex integration. These terms are then used as weights to calculate the means of all the distributions, and these mean values have been shown to be the same as the most probable values obtained by using Stirling's approximation, even in the cases where the numbers involved are obviously so small that Stirling's theorem is not valid. It is a safe conjecture that the same result applies here: that theoretically valid results can be obtained, using the method above, at all times.

The second question can be answered explicitly if small changes in $\log w(T_{ij})$ are examined near the maximum. At, or very near, the maximum the terms of $d[\log w(T_{ij})]$ which are linear in dT_{ij} vanish, and

$$d[\log w(T_{ij})] = \frac{1}{2}\sum_i \sum_j \frac{\partial^2 \log w}{\partial T_{ij}^2}(dT_{ij})^2 \qquad (41)$$

It will be recalled that

$$\frac{\partial \log w}{\partial T_{ij}} = -\log T_{ij}$$

and so

$$\frac{\partial^2 \log w}{\partial T_{ij}^2} = -T_{ij}^{-1} \qquad (42)$$

Substituting in equation (41),

$$d[\log w(T_{ij})] = -\frac{1}{2}\sum_i \sum_j \frac{(dT_{ij})^2}{T_{ij}} = -\frac{1}{2}\sum_i \sum_j \left(\frac{dT_{ij}}{T_{ij}}\right)^2 T_{ij} \qquad (43)$$

Thus (43) can be written

$$d[\log w(T_{ij})] = -\frac{1}{2}\sum_i \sum_j p^2 T_{ij} \qquad (44)$$

where p is the percentage change in each T_{ij} away from the most probable distribution.

To evaluate this expression, the size distribution of elements of the trip matrix is needed. Suppose there are N size groups, and that the nth group has T_{ij}'s with a mean value T_n, and there are S_n such trip matrix elements in this group. Then, (44) can be written

$$d[\log w(T_{ij})] = -\frac{1}{2} p^2 \sum_n S_n T_n \qquad (45)$$

Now consider a typical example: take a large urban area with, say 1000 zones. Suppose 1000 trip interchanges have each got 10^4 trips, 10,000 have 10^3 and 100,000 have 10^2. Let $p = 10^{-3}$. Then

$$d(\log w) \approx -\frac{1}{2} 10^{-6}(10^7 + 10^7 + 10^7) \approx -15$$

Thus, $\log w$ changes by -15 for a change of one part in a thousand of each element of the trip matrix away from the most probable distribution. Thus w drops by the enormous factor of e^{-15}, which gives an indication of just how sharp the maximum can be. Such an estimate of d $(\log w)$ can be calculated as a check in any particular case. One of the advantages of this new approach is that it gives the possibility of doing this check, and ruling out certain situations as being unsuitable for the gravity model approach should the maximum turn out not to be a sharp one.

A third result of interest can also be stated by analogy with the corresponding result in statistical mechanics (cf. Tolman, 1938). That is:

$$\frac{\overline{(T_{ij} - \overline{T}_{ij})^2}}{\overline{T}_{ij}^2} = T_{ij}^{-1} - T^{-1} \qquad (46)$$

This gives the dispersion of T_{ij} and indicates, as is well known in practice, that estimates are better for large flows than for small ones.

This analysis has shown that the gravity model has a sound base. However, it should be recalled that the whole analysis has been for a single trip purpose, and for a homogeneous group of travellers. People are not identical in the way that particles in physics are identical, and so no theory of this form (indeed, no theory period) can be expected to apply exactly. This analysis has shown, in effect, that good results can be expected if trips can be classified by purpose and by person type in a reasonably uniform way.

3. New Applications of the Statistical Theory

3.1. Rules for constructing distribution models. The previous sections have shown that a statistical theoretical base can be given to the conventional gravity model. The principle on which this derivation is based is, however, quite general. The only assumption is that the probability of a distribution occurring is proportional to the number of states of the system which give rise to that distribution, subject to a number of constraints. It can easily be seen that if there were no constraints at all, then all the T_{ij}'s would have an equal share of the total number of trips. In other words, it is the constraints which have the effect of giving a distribution of trips other than a trivial one. One of the remarkable features of this statistical theory is that it produces the conventional gravity model using constraints which really say relatively little, that is, are relatively unrestrictive. The new theory reveals that an effective way of developing better models is to refine the constraints which are applied to behaviourable variables to make them more restrictive. This makes more precise for this problem what is simply the normal method of scientific research. (See, for example, Popper, 1959.) This new theory is a powerful general method for constructing spatial distribution models: the main task to produce a model in this framework is to discover the constraints on the variables which describe the spatial distribution problem, and then to maximize, as a function of the distribution variables, the number of states which can give rise to the distribution subject to the constraints.

The derivation of the conventional gravity model above followed this pattern. The following sections of the paper apply the general theory to a number of situations, ranging from new ones being tackled for the first time to a derivation of the intervening opportunities model.

3.2. The single competition term gravity model. The so-called conventional gravity model was described by equations (5)-(7) above. A much-used variant of this simply takes all the B_j's as one at the expense of failing to satisfy the constraints (4). So this model is

$$T_{ij} = A_i O_i D_j f(c_{ij}) \tag{47}$$

where

$$A_i = \left[\sum_j D_j f(c_{ij}) \right]^{-1} \tag{48}$$

to ensure that

$$\sum_j T_{ij} = O_i \tag{49}$$

but where, if

$$D_j{}^* = \sum_i T_{ij} ,$$

$D_j{}^*$ is not necessarily equal to D_j. This model may be used in a variety of special circumstances: for example, when D_j is simply some measure of attraction, and $D_j{}^*$ is then *defined* to be the resulting number of trips produced in the model. That is, no constraint of the form (4) is assumed to hold. The new method can be applied to this situation easily: maximize

$$\frac{T!}{\prod_{ij} T_{ij}!}$$

subject to the constraints (49), and subject to a generalized cost constraint (22). The resulting distribution, which is analogous to (31) as derived from (30), is

$$T_{ij} = \exp(-\lambda_i^{(1)} - \beta c_{ij}) \tag{50}$$

where the $\lambda_i^{(1)}$'s and β are Lagrangian multipliers. The $\lambda_i^{(1)}$ can be found by substituting in (49) with the result

$$T_{ij} = \frac{O_i \exp(-\beta c_{ij})}{\sum_k \exp(-\beta c_{ik})} \tag{51}$$

Now this equation resembles (47) and (48), but the D_j term of the latter equation is now missing. However, it will be recalled that in this case D_j is likely to be a measure of attraction, and not a number of trip ends. Such a term can be introduced into equation (51) by the following interesting device. Assume that the traveller to j receives some benefit W_j which can be set against the transport cost c_{ij} over and above the benefit which can be obtained from going to other zones. (So W_j may be a measure of the scale economies available to the shopper in large shopping centres.) Equation (51) can then be rewritten with c_{ij} being replaced by $c_{ij} - W_j$ as

$$T_{ij} = \frac{O_i \exp(\beta W_j - \beta c_{ij})}{\sum\limits_k \exp(\beta W_k - \beta c_{ik})} \qquad (52)$$

so that we can now identify the new model with that of equations (47)-(48) by taking $\exp(\beta W_j)$ as the attractive measure D_j. Since D_j in such applications is usually taken as a zonal size variable which is a proxy for scale benefits of the form W_j, it seems intuitively reasonable to expect W_j to vary as $\log D_j$, as implied here, rather than D_j.

3.3. Distribution of trips when there are several transport modes. This section discusses a more important problem. Consider the basic situation illustrated earlier by the journey to work, and described by variables T_{ij}, O_i, D_j and c_{ij}. Suppose now, however, that there are several possible modes of transport between i and j, and the cost of travelling by the kth mode is c_{ij}^k. Let T_{ij}, O_i and D_j be defined as before, and let T_{ij}^k, O_i^k and D_j^k be the proportions of these trip totals carried by mode k.

The constraint equations which describe this situation are

$$\sum_i \sum_k T_{ij}^k = D_j \qquad (53)$$

$$\sum_j \sum_k T_{ij}^k = O_i \qquad (54)$$

$$\sum_i \sum_j \sum_k T_{ij}^k c_{ij}^k = C \qquad (55)$$

and the maximand, subject to these constraints, is

$$\frac{T!}{\prod_{ijk} T_{ij}{}^k !}$$

Note that the constraint equations (53) and (54) do not use any knowledge of trip end modal split, and because of this, there are the same number of Lagrangian multipliers as for the single-mode case. The most probable distribution, obtained in the usual way, is

$$T_{ij}{}^k = \exp(-\lambda_i{}^{(1)} - \lambda_j{}^{(2)} - \beta c_{ij}{}^k) \tag{56}$$

and, substituting in (53) and (54),

$$\exp(-\lambda_j{}^{(2)}) = \frac{D_j}{\sum_i \sum_k \exp(-\lambda_i{}^{(1)} - \beta c_{ij}{}^k)} \tag{57}$$

$$\exp(-\lambda_i{}^{(1)}) = \frac{O_i}{\sum_j \sum_k \exp(-\lambda_j{}^{(2)} - \beta c_{ij}{}^k)} \tag{58}$$

So, putting

$$A_i = \exp(-\lambda_i{}^{(1)})/O_i , \quad B_j = \exp(-\lambda_j{}^{(2)})/D_j$$

as before,

$$T_{ij}{}^k = A_i B_j O_i D_j \exp(-\beta c_{ij}{}^k) \tag{59}$$

where

$$A_i = \left[\sum_j \sum_k B_j D_j \exp(-\beta c_{ij}{}^k) \right]^{-1}$$

$$= \left[\sum_j B_j D_j \sum_k \exp(-\beta c_{ij}{}^k) \right]^{-1} \tag{60}$$

$$B_j = \left[\sum_i \sum_k A_i O_i \exp(-\beta c_{ij}{}^k) \right]^{-1}$$

$$= \left[\sum_i A_i O_i \sum_k \exp(-\beta c_{ij}{}^k) \right]^{-1} \tag{61}$$

Note also that

$$T_{ij} = \sum_k T_{ij}{}^k = A_i B_j O_i D_j \sum_k \exp(-\beta c_{ij}{}^k) \tag{62}$$

Thus, equations (59)-(61) define a multi-mode distribution model. $T_{ij}{}^k$ and T_{ij} can be divided, using equations (59) and (62), to give the modal split as

$$\frac{T_{ij}{}^k}{T_{ij}} = \frac{\exp(-\beta c_{ij}{}^k)}{\sum_k \exp(-\beta c_{ij}{}^k)} \tag{63}$$

as the proportion travelling by mode k between i and j. Note that in the two-mode case, say with modes 1 and 2 representing public and private transport, a plot of, say, $T_{ij}{}^1/T_{ij}$ would give a curve which has the shape of the usual diversion curve.

Note further that the T_{ij} derived in (62) above can be wholly identified with the T_{ij} derived in the conventional gravity model in equation (36) provided that

$$\exp(-\beta c_{ij}) = \sum_k \exp(-\beta c_{ij}{}^k) \tag{64}$$

This equation is of the greatest importance because it shows how a composite measure of impedance, $\exp(-\beta c_{ij})$, or average generalized cost, c_{ij}, can be derived from the modal impedances $\exp(-\beta c_{ij}{}^k)$ where these are known individually. Such composite impedances are valuable in a variety of planning models, but past practice has been to use one of a number of arbitrary averaging procedures.

It should also be remarked that the modal split formula (63) is identical in form to that derived from a statistical approach to modal split using discriminant analysis (Quarmby, 1967). There could be complete identification if the generalized cost $c_{ij}{}^k$ could be identified with the discriminant function used by the statisticians. If such an identification can be made, then discriminant analysis would provide a method for determining the generalized costs.

Finally, let us examine the case where there is independent information on trip end estimation by mode. Suppose it is known that not only are there O_i trips in total from zone i, but that O_i^k are by mode k, and that similarly there are D_j^k trips by mode k into zone j. The constraints analogous to (53) and (54) can be written as

$$\sum_i T_{ij}^k = D_j^k \tag{65}$$

$$\sum_j T_{ij}^k = O_i^k \tag{66}$$

Sets of Lagrangian multipliers $\lambda_j^{(2)k}$, $\lambda_i^{(1)k}$ are now defined to be associated with these constraints. The maximization process is carried through in the usual way giving

$$T_{ij}^k = A_i^k B_j^k O_i^k D_j^k \exp(-\beta c_{ik}^k) \tag{67}$$

where

$$A_i^k = \left[\sum_j B_j^k D_j^k \exp(-\beta c_{ij}^k) \right]^{-1} \tag{68}$$

$$B_j^k = \left[\sum_i A_i^k O_i^k \exp(-\beta c_{ij}^k) \right]^{-1} \tag{69}$$

Notice that in this case, T_{ij}^k / T_{ij} is not as simple a ratio as with the previous one and no longer agrees with the results of the discriminant analysis approach.

An alternative result is obtained if the constraint (53) is used with (66) together with the usual cost constraint (55). (This represents the situation where trip generations are known by mode but trip attractions only in total for each zone.) This can be worked out in the usual way and the result is

$$T_{ij}^k = A_i^k B_j O_i^k D_j \exp(-\beta c_{ij}^k) \tag{70}$$

where

$$A_i^k = \left[\sum_j B_j D_j \exp(-\beta c_{ij}^k) \right]^{-1} \qquad (71)$$

and

$$B_j = \left[\sum_i \sum_k A_i^k O_i^k \exp(-\beta c_{ij}^k) \right]^{-1} \qquad (72)$$

The objective of obtaining these results and comparing them is to assess their importance for modal split applications in transportation studies, since in some cases it is assumed that trip ends by mode can be estimated, for example by regression analysis.

The model represented by equations (67)-(69), that is assuming that trip end modal split is known, is commonly used. Examination of the structure of these equations shows that they are completely separated for each mode: the trip ends are estimated separately, and then each mode is distributed separately. The weakness of this method arises in the need for forecasting as well as to explain the present, or in any situation where some of the parameters change: any aggregate switching of mode can only be brought about by changes in the O_i^k's and D_j^k's. By contrast, with the first multi-modal distribution model derived above, described by equations (53)-(55), the aggregate levels of modal choice are determined, given only total O_i's and D_j's by the relative costs, the c_{ij}^k's. This seems a much more fundamental mechanism than the separate mode methods, and is directly related to the sort of inter-modal comparison a traveller may be expected to make. Its connection with the discriminant analysis approach also adds weight to the view that it is a preferable method.

The intermediate method, that is the use of the model described by equations (70)-(72), falls between the two stools, and is probably not in current use anyway. However, it will be seen in the next section that a model of this structure will become important in the case where two types of traveller are considered: car owners and non-car owners.

3.4 Extension of the multi-mode model to the case where some users have access to only a subset of all modes. The multi-mode distribution models produced in Sections 3.3 assume implicitly that all travellers have access to all modes. There is at least one obvious case in real life where this is not so: non-car owners do not have the possibility of travel by car. This is important for current transportation study models, where usual practice is often to assume that trip ends for car owners, for example, can be separately estimated, and the trips separately distributed. This suffers from the same forecasting deficiency as the separate modal distributions of the previous section. It is, in fact, an exactly analogous assumption. However, once again the situation can be described by the appropriate constraints and a model can be produced which seems more appropriate to the situation. The basis of the constraint equations will be that, if any set of travellers should have only a subset of the modes available, then the trip end productions should be similarly categorized, but not trip attractions, so that all travellers compete for the same attractions, but non-car owners, for example, cannot generate trips by car. Thus trip productions would be generated separately for car owners and non-car owners, but only total trip attractions would be estimated.

The first step, however, is to get a general formulation of the problem and to develop an appropriate notation. Let n represent a class of travellers, and let $\gamma(n)$ be the set of modes available to travellers in category n, k will denote mode as usual, and

$$\sum_{k \, \epsilon \, \gamma(n)}$$

denotes summation over the subset of modes k available to persons of the type n. The new constraints, embodying the principles discussed above, are then

$$\sum_{j} \sum_{k \, \epsilon \, \gamma(n)} T_{ij}^{kn} = O_i^n \qquad (73)$$

$$\sum_{i} \sum_{n} \sum_{k \, \epsilon \, \gamma(n)} T_{ij}^{kn} = D_j \qquad (74)$$

$$\sum_{i} \sum_{j} \sum_{n} \sum_{k \, \epsilon \, \gamma(n)} T_{ij}^{kn} = C \qquad (75)$$

where, in an obvious notation, T_{ij}^{kn} is the number of trips from i to j by mode k by traveller type n, O_i^n is the number of trip generations at i by travellers of type n, and other variables have been defined before. The maximand is now

$$\frac{T!}{\underset{ijkn}{\Pi} \ T_{ij}^{kn}!} \tag{76}$$

subject to the constraints (73)-(75). Introduce Lagrangian multipliers $\lambda_i^{(1)n}$, $\lambda_j^{(2)}$ and β in the usual way and the maximizing condition is

$$-\log T_{ij}^{kn} - \lambda_i^{(1)n} - \lambda_j^{(2)} - \beta c_{ij}^k = 0 \tag{77}$$

so

$$T_{ij}^{kn} = \exp(-\lambda_i^{(1)n} - \lambda_j^{(2)} - \beta c_{ij}^k) \tag{78}$$

and writing

$$A_i^n = \exp(-\lambda_i^{(1)n})/O_i^n \tag{79}$$

and

$$B_j = \exp(-\lambda_j^{(2)})/D_j \tag{80}$$

the usual manipulation gives

$$T_{ij}^{kn} = A_i^n B_j O_i^n D_j \exp(-\beta c_{ij}^k) \tag{81}$$

where

$$A_i^n = \left[\sum_j \sum_{k \in \gamma(n)} B_j D_j \exp(-\beta c_{ij}^k) \right]^{-1} \tag{82}$$

and

$$B_j = \left[\sum_j \sum_n \sum_{k \in \gamma(n)} A_i^n O_i^n \exp(-\beta c_{ij}^k) \right]^{-1} \tag{83}$$

Note that we can now get the total inter-zonal trips by mode (by summing over n, denoted by $T_{ij}{}^k$), by traveller type (by summing over $k \epsilon \gamma(n)$, denoted by $T_{ij}{}^n$), and in total (by summing over $k \epsilon \gamma(n)$ and n denoted by T_{ij}). Thus:

$$T_{ij}{}^k = B_j D_j \left(\sum_n A_i{}^n O_i{}^n \right) \exp(-\beta c_{ij}{}^k) \qquad (84)$$

$$T_{ij}{}^n = A_i{}^n B_j O_i{}^n D_j \sum_{k \epsilon \gamma(n)} \exp(-\beta c_{ij}{}^k) \qquad (85)$$

$$T_{ij} = B_j D_j \sum_n \sum_{k \epsilon \gamma(n)} A_i{}^n O_i{}^n \exp(-\beta c_{ij}{}^k) \qquad (86)$$

Note that in equation (85), the results for one person category n is linked to the other person type variables through the B_j's defined in (83). This arises because different person categories are competing for the same attractions.

A result which is suitable for a car owner/non-car owner split can now be obtained easily from these general equations.

3.5 Derivation of the intervening opportunities model. The intervening opportunities model was derived in the traditional way in the introduction to this paper and its main equation was derived as equation (15). It is of some interest to attempt to derive this using the new methodology, since, if this is possible, the gravity and opportunities models are related by this common base and can be compared in a new light.

Using the variables defined in the introduction, it is also possible to define in addition

$$S_{ij_\mu} = O_i U_{ij_\mu} \qquad (87)$$

as the number of trips from i continuing beyond the μth ranked zone away from i. Note that, since

$$T_{ij_\mu} = S_{ij_{\mu-1}} - S_{ij_\mu} \qquad (88)$$

the variables S_{ij_μ} define the new system as a possible alternative to T_{ij_μ}. To derive the opportunities model, the new method is applied to the variables S_{ij_μ}. Thus if S is the total number of states for a given distribution $\{S_{ij_\mu}\}$, then the maximand will be

$$\frac{S}{\prod_{ij_\mu} S_{ij_\mu}!}$$

It is now necessary to establish appropriate constraints. As seen earlier, the opportunities model does not have a constraint on trip attractions of the form of equation (4), but does need a constraint on trip generations of the form (3). For the variables S_{ij_μ}, the strictly analogous constraint to (3) is the inequality

$$S_{ij_\mu} \leqslant O_i \tag{89}$$

as there cannot be more trips continuing beyond a point from i than originally set out from i. If these are summed over j_μ to get a constraint of the form (3), the resulting equation is

$$\sum_{j_\mu} S_{ij_\mu} = k_i' O_i \tag{90}$$

where k_i' is some constant, and $1 \leqslant k_i' \leqslant N$, where N is the total number of zones. Finally, a constraint analogous to the gravity model cost constraint, equation (22), is needed. The main assumption of the intervening opportunities model, as commonly stated, is that the number of trips between i and j is determined by the number of opportunities at j, and varies inversely as the number of intervening opportunities. This gives the clue for the cost constraint: to use intervening opportunities as a proxy for cost. Thus, if S_{ij_μ} trips are to be made beyond j_μ, then these will incur costs greater than those for trips which have been made to nearer zones. Suppose, then, for trips from i, we take the number of opportunities passed as a measure of the cost of getting so far. Thus, the minimum cost for the remaining trips beyond j_μ is $A_{j_\mu} S_{ij_\mu}$. If this is summed over j_μ and then over all origin zones i, this gives a function which behaves in some ways like a total cost function, and the corresponding constraint is

$$\sum_{i} \sum_{j\mu} A_{ij\mu} S_{ij\mu} = C \qquad (91)$$

Since, as can be derived from the definitional equation (10),

$$A_{j\mu} = \sum_{n=1}^{\mu} D_{jn} \qquad (92)$$

and, as can be derived from the definition of $S_{ij\mu}$,

$$S_{ij\mu} = \sum_{n=\mu+1}^{N} T_{ijn} \qquad (93)$$

where N is the total number of zones, it can easily be seen that the coefficient of $T_{ij\mu}$ in the summation in equation (91) is [substituting for $S_{ij\mu}$ from (93)]

$$(\mu - 1) D_{j_1} + (\mu - 2) D_{j_2} + \ldots + D_{j_{\mu-1}} \qquad (94)$$

and so the opportunities passed contribute to the cost associated with a particular element of the trip matrix weighted by the number of times they have been "passed" or "have intervened".

Now, maximizing

$$\frac{S}{\prod_{ij\mu} S_{ij\mu}!}$$

subject to the constraints (90) and (91), introducing Lagrangian multipliers $\lambda_i^{(1)}$ and L for these constraints, the most probable distribution occurs when

$$- \log S_{ij\mu} - LA_{j\mu} - \lambda_i^{(1)} = 0$$

so

$$S_{ij} = \exp(-LA_{j\mu} - \lambda_i^{(1)}). \qquad (95)$$

$\lambda_i{}^{(1)}$ can be obtained in the usual way by substituting from (95) into (90):

$$\exp(-\lambda_i{}^{(1)}) = \frac{k_i{}'O_i}{\sum\limits_{j_\mu} \exp(-LA_{j_\mu})} \tag{96}$$

and so, writing

$$k_i = \frac{k_i{}'}{\sum\limits_{j_\mu} \exp(-LA_{j_\mu})} \tag{97}$$

$$S_{ij_\mu} = k_i O_i \exp(-LA_{j_\mu}) \tag{98}$$

and, using equation (88),

$$T_{ij_\mu} = k_i O_i [\exp(-LA_{j_{\mu-1}}) - \exp(-LA_{j_\mu})] \tag{99}$$

which is identical to equation (15). Thus, the main equation of the intervening opportunities model has been obtained using the new method.

This derivation has been made at the expense of using a rather strange cost constraint equation (92), and assuming a cost of getting from i to j_μ implied by equation (94). Perhaps this is an argument in itself for preferring the gravity model to the intervening opportunities model.

3.6. A distribution model of gravity type which uses intervening opportunities as a measure of cost. As a final example of the application of the new method, consider the distribution model which is obtained if intervening opportunities are used as a measure of cost, but not weighted in the form (94). This is perhaps a more plausible assumption.

Note that j_μ, as originally defined, is properly a function of i and should be written as $j_\mu(i)$. The assumption now proposed is

$$c_{ij} = A_{j_\mu(i)} \tag{100}$$

This cost can now be substituted in either of the two gravity models derived above, the so-called conventional model described by equations (36)-(38), or the so-called single competition term model described by equations (47)-(48) with $f(c_{ij})$ as $\exp(-\beta c_{ij})$. Thus, substituting for c_{ij} from (100), the double competition term "gravity/opportunity" model is

$$T_{ij_\mu} = a_i b_{j_\mu} O_i D_{j_\mu} \exp(-\beta A_{j_\mu(i)}) \qquad (101)$$

$$a_i = \left[\sum_{j_\mu} b_{j_\mu} D_{j_\mu} \exp(-\beta A_{j_\mu(i)}) \right]^{-1} \qquad (102)$$

$$b_{j_\mu} = \left[\sum_i a_i O_i \exp(-\beta A_{j_\mu(i)}) \right]^{-1} \qquad (103)$$

Small a's and b's are used for the balancing factors to avoid confusion with the A_{j_μ}'s.

The single competition term "gravity/opportunity" model is

$$T_{ij_\mu} = a_i O_i D_{j_\mu} \exp(-\beta A_{j_\mu(i)}) \qquad (104)$$

$$a_i = \left[\sum_{j_\mu} D_{j_\mu} \exp(-\beta A_{j_\mu(i)}) \right]^{-1} \qquad (105)$$

If it could be argued that (100) represents a better account of cost than (94), then the models represented by equations (101)-(103) and (104)-(105) may give better answers than the conventional intervening opportunities model. A test of these new models would be welcomed.

4. Conclusions

A new statistical theory of spatial distribution models has been demonstrated. This gives a new method for constructing such models to meet a wide variety of circumstances. It appears to show that the gravity model has a more plausible theoretical base than the intervening opportunities model. But above all, the new method offers a technique for extending conventional spatial distribution models to cover new situations which now often present serious problems, especially in transportation study models: for example, modal split, especially in the multi-mode case, and the necessity of separating car owners and non-car owners, but allowing them to compete for the same attractions. Finally, a comparison of the gravity models and intervening opportunities model leads to a suggestion of a completely different type of model for quite simple and conventional situations.

References

Chicago Area Transportation Study (1960). Final report, Vol. II.

Dieter, K. H. (1962). Distribution of work trips in Toronto. *Proc. Am. Soc. Civ. Engrs.* 88, 9-28.

Popper, K. R. (1959). *The Logic of Scientific Discovery.* Hutchinson, London.

Quarmby, D. A. (1967). Choice of travel mode for the journey to work: some findings. *J. Transp. Economics and Policy* 1, 1-42; also Chapter 12 in this volume.

Stouffler, S. A. (1940). Intervening opportunities: A theory relating mobility and distance. *Am. Soc. Rev.* 5, No. 6.

Tolman, R. C. (1938). *Principles of Statistical Mechanics.* Clarendon Press, Oxford.

4

The Demand for Abstract Transport Modes: Theory and Measurement

Richard E. Quandt and William J. Baumol

1. Introduction

A variety of techniques has been employed in estimating statistical relationships which might be used to predict the amount of travel that will take place at some future time.* Some of these attempts involve the formulation of traditional demand functions according to the dictates of *a priori* economic theorizing.[1] Others depend upon careful stratification of the population and subsequent pragmatic extrapolation of travel propensities observed on the basis of direct samples of the various strata.[2] Distinctions may be drawn among the various approaches according to whether they employ (a) time series data or cross-sectional information; (b) data available largely from public sources or data from samples collected for special purposes; (c) models of the gravity-type or modal split models or others.[3]

The variety of techniques one encounters in the field of travel demand estimation is at least partly a result of the scarcity and heterogeneity of the data. Studies which are intended to describe and predict behavior in some particular geographic area may not be able to utilize the same types of data as studies referring to some other area. Thus many *ad hoc* techniques, models, and methods of measurement have been employed. Clearly, the larger the geographic area which must be encompassed by a model, the less likely it is that required data of uniform quality can be found.

Reprinted from *Journal of Regional Science* Vol 6, No. 2 (1966), pp. 13-26. Copyright© by the Regional Science Research Institute. Used with permission.

*Presented at the Second Latin American Regional Science Congress, Rio de Janeiro, August, 1966. The authors are indebted to Anthony Blackburn, Jack L. Rutner and Francis Sand for valuable comments, and to Mark Rose for providing usable data. This study was performed through MATHEMATICA for the Transport Systems Division of the Office of High Speed Ground Transportation, U.S. Department of Commerce, under Contract No. C-187-66.

[1] See Fisher [1].

[2] See Port of New York Authority [2].

[3] See Isard *et al.* [3].

The basic purposes of this paper are (a) to make a theoretical contribution to the study of travel demand and (b) to make a contribution to the estimation and measurement of demand which, in some sense, minimizes the effect of incompleteness of data. The content of this paper is somewhat speculative in that the ideas expressed here have not been fully tested on a variety of data. However, some initial tests have already been carried out. Section 2 is devoted to theoretical discussion of the abstract mode approach. Section 3 explores the implications of the notion of abstract modes for estimation. Section 4 briefly discusses relevant variables in the context of a concrete model. Section 5 presents some empirical results, and Section 6 contains some concluding comments.

2. The Theory of Abstract Modes

Our analysis of transportation demand is not formulated in terms of the demand for travel by trains, airplanes, and other conventional means of transportation; it utilizes instead a number of abstract modal types, none of which may correspond entirely to any specific present or future mode of transportation. In a world of changing technology in which tomorrow's vehicles may differ radically from those of today such an approach offers obvious advantages if one seeks to produce an analysis pertinent to the future. Thus, we will find it useful to define a mode in terms of the type of service it provides to the traveler and not in terms of the administrative entity that controls its operations or the sort of physical equipment it employs.

An abstract mode is characterized by the values of the several variables that affect the desirability of the mode's service to the public: speed, frequency of service, comfort and cost. Thus one can define a continuum of abstract modes; most of them may have no current counterpart, although some of them will become realities in the future. More important, it should be recognized that an actual mode may in one type of service correspond to some abstract mode *A*, while in another usage it may be related to an entirely different abstract mode *B*. A trivial example can make this clear. Between New York and San Francisco among commercially operated vehicles the scheduled airplane is currently the highest speed abstract mode, while between Trenton and Philadelphia the railroad probably takes that position.

To illustrate the characterization of an abstract mode let us consider a pair of nodes in a network, such as Princeton and New York, and list the various characteristics of travel from the center of one node to the center of the other.

Table 1

Performance Characteristics of Modes Operating Between Princeton and New York

Mode	Travel Time (minutes)	Round Trip Cost (dollars)	Number of Departures from Princeton (per day)
A	70	23.00	10
B	80	4.50	17
C	90	2.80	39
D	80	5.40	not applicable

Only minimal experience is necessary to identify A as airplane, B as railroad, C as bus and D as private automobile.[4] A mode can be thought of in *abstract* terms if it is characterized only in terms of features such as travel time, cost, departure frequency, other convenience factors, etc. The choice of a mode by a traveler as well as the decision to undertake travel can then be regarded as depending (in addition to the usual exogenous motivations for travel) on (a) the absolute performance level of the "best" mode on each criterion and (b) the performance level of each mode on each criterion *relative* to the "best" mode. Table 1 can then be transformed as shown in Table 2.

We now consider the amount of travel between all pairs of nodes and by all modes during a given period of time to represent the outcome of the same basic generating mechanism. In a formulation

---

[4] Since the example is just illustrative, the figures are only approximate. Of course, the mode designation in our interpretation of the example refers to the mode by which the interurban portion of the trip is undertaken. Thus, the cost of A includes the cost of a limousine trip from airport to the center of the city. The cost of automobile travel is calculated at 8 cents a mile plus tolls.

Table 2

Relative Performance Characteristics of
Modes between Princeton and
New York

Mode	Relative Travel Time	Relative Cost	Relative Departure Frequency
A	1.0	8.2	.26
B	1.1	1.6	.44
C	1.3	1.0	1.00
D	1.1	1.9	—

of the gravity type the demand for travel along a particular arc is taken to be increased by the attraction exerted by the population masses in the two terminal nodes and to be impeded by the distance between them. Apart from these factors, travel by any mode along that arc will be influenced by the absolute levels of the variable values characterizing the best available mode — though clearly, which is the best mode depends on which characteristic we are considering — and by the relative characteristics of the mode in question. In a cross-sectional sense the mechanism works as follows. First, disregard the effect on travel of population and distance; i.e., for simplicity consider two pairs of nodes which have the same (pairwise) populations and the same arc length. Then, if relative modal performances are the same, the arc with the best (faster, cheaper, more conveniently scheduled) mode will exhibit more travel along it by every mode. If, however, the best modes along two arcs have identical absolute performance levels but some other modes have differential relative standings, this will show up in a relative reduction in travel by the mode which is relatively inferior.

It is a characteristic of this approach that at no point is it necessary to identify any of the modes in terms of institutional characteristics — i.e., it is not necessary for the analyst to know which of the abstract modes is the railroad or airplane. The present theory therefore presupposes that individuals are characterized by a *modal neutrality* which is substantially comparable to the neutrality towards risk exhibited by persons who have a von Neumann-Morgenstern utility index. In other words, our modally neutral person chooses among modes purely on the basis of their characteristics and not on the basis of what they are called.

In theory this assumption may be very desirable but, in practice, it may be difficult to characterize modes so completely that what would otherwise appear as modal nonneutrality is, in fact, encompassed by the characteristics of the various modes. It is well known, for example, that a substantial aversion to flying has characterized, and perhaps still influences, some segments of the population. In order to avoid violating the assumption of modal neutrality, we would have to introduce a characteristic, represented by a dummy variable taking the values of zero or one, which describes whether travel is by air or on the ground. This dummy variable would then have one value for all forms of air travel (conventional airplane and helicopter, one-man back-pack rocket kit, Gemini space capsule, etc.) and another value for all forms of ground level transportation. Clearly, we have not yet resolved all the problems arising from these considerations although possibly many will be solved if sufficiently ingenious measures of the "convenience" provided by various modes are designed.

3. Estimating the Demand for Travel by
Abstract Modes: Model Specification

The first task that has to be accomplished is the specification of the demand equations. Clearly, the demand for travel along any arc in a network and a particular (abstract) mode will depend upon the characteristics of that mode and a number of variables which can be considered to be exogeneous except over very long periods of time. These exogeneous variables are the socio-economic, geographic and demographic characteristics of the origin and destination nodes such as populations, incomes and the institutional character of cities, the distance between them, etc.[5] As a first approximation we shall assume that these factors enter the demand function in the same manner in which they do in generalized gravity models, i.e., the logarithm of the demand is linear in the logarithms of these variables. It is then possible to argue plausibly that the remaining variables, i.e., those which describe the (relative or absolute) positions of the modes should enter in similar fashion.

---

[5] See Kessler [5].

The nature of these additional variables and the conceptual aspects of the manner in which they enter the demand function will be discussed in terms of examples. For the sake of easier computation, the form of the equations in the examples will be arithmetic rather than logarithmic. Assume, first of all, that for a given pair of nodes the initially existing travel modes can be described by the figures in Table 3A. The corresponding relative performance factors are given in Table 3B.

Table 3A					Table 3B				
Performance Characteristics of Hypothetical Modes					**Relative Performance Characteristics of Hypothetical Modes**				
		Mode					*Mode*		
	1	*2*	*3*				*1*	*2*	*3*
Travel time (hours)	1	2	3		Travel time		1	2	3
Travel cost (dollars)	5	3	2		Travel cost		2.5	1.5	1

Let us denote by H_b and C_b the absolutely best travel time and cost by any mode and by H_{rk} and C_{rk} the relative travel time and cost for mode k. Let N measure the number of modes serving an arc.[6] Then, for the arc under consideration $H_b = 1$, $C_b = 2$, $N = 3$ and H_{rk} and C_{rk} have different values depending upon the mode in question. Finally we denote by T_k the number of trips along an arc by mode k.[7] Suppose that on the basis of statistical information covering many pairs of nodes, the following equation predicting travel by mode k has been estimated (say, by least squares)[8]:

$$T_k = 1000 - 100H_b - 60C_b - 60H_{rk} - 50C_{rk} - 50N \qquad (1)$$

---

[6]The presence of the variable N has one disadvantage — it implies that travel demand will be affected by the availability of "irrelevant modes" — modes that would not even be considered by the class of travelers in question. It also makes the calculation dependent on fineness of classification — whether, e.g., we consider local and express trains to constitute one mode or two. Perhaps more useful variables might be the *range* and *density* of the available mode set, where the range might be described as the Euclidian distance between the furthest pair of points representing the available modes in abstract mode space, and density might be measured as $N/range$.

[7]Clearly, all these variables require an additional (ij) subscript to identify the two terminal nodes. These have been omitted for simplicity.

[8]No significance should be attached to the form of the equation in this illustrative example.

Denoting by M_i the predicted volume of travel by the ith mode, the equation then predicts for the arc in question (the modal characteristics of which are displayed in Tables 3A and B) the following travel volumes:

$$
\begin{aligned}
M_1 &= 445 \\
M_2 &= 435 \\
M_3 &= \underline{400} \\
\text{Total} &= 1280
\end{aligned}
$$

Consider now the hypothetical introduction of a fourth (abstract) mode with absolute characteristics of 1.5 for travel time and 1.0 for travel cost. This alters the value of C_b for this arc as well as the values of C_r but leaves the values of H_b and H_r unchanged. Substituting in (1) and remembering that now $N = 4$, we obtain

$$
\begin{aligned}
M_1 &= 330 \\
M_2 &= 370 \\
M_3 &= 360 \\
M_4 &= \underline{500} \\
\text{Total} &= 1560
\end{aligned}
$$

There is a predicted increase of 280 in total traffic but the new mode clearly makes inroads on some existing modes since it alone accommodates 500 trips.

As an alternative consider mode 5 with characteristics of 0.5 for travel time and 2.0 for cost. This yields a result as follows:

$$
\begin{aligned}
M_1 &= 385 \\
M_2 &= 315 \\
M_3 &= 220 \\
M_5 &= \underline{520} \\
\text{Total} &= 1440
\end{aligned}
$$

Finally, if we were to introduce both modes 4 and 5, the same reasoning would yield the result

$$
\begin{aligned}
M_1 &= 270 \\
M_2 &= 250 \\
M_3 &= 180 \\
M_4 &= 410 \\
M_5 &= \underline{480} \\
\text{Total} &= 1590
\end{aligned}
$$

The method therefore has the following advantages: (a) It permits us to predict for every existing mode the effect of the introduction of a new mode; (b) It allows us to introduce a new mode simply by specifying its cost, travel time, and other major characteristics; (c) It makes the forecast of total travel demand a function of the range of travel alternatives.

4. Variables and Models

The discussion of the variables which express the effect of the socio-economic environment upon travel demand need not be extremely detailed at this point. We shall chiefly adopt the procedures outlined in an earlier paper.[9] The demand for travel between nodes i and j will thus be assumed to depend upon

(a) The populations P_i, P_j of the two nodes. The population variable is central to interaction models of the gravity type, and it seems safe to hypothesize that, other things being equal, population has an increasing effect upon travel. Since, however, nodes are often merely transit points in travel, the measurement of flows along arcs does not unambiguously imply node-to-node movements. Hence the proper definition of the area, the population of which is thought to give rise to an observed volume of travel along some arc, is a problem of considerable importance that has not been fully resolved.

(b) The mean (or median) incomes Y_i, Y_j at the two nodes.

(c) The institutional (industrial) character indices M_i, M_j of the two nodes. It has been observed that cities with a high concentration of service industries, governmental or educational institutions give rise to higher travel propensities than predominantly manufacturing centers.[10]

The variables which characterize the modes of travel will certainly include

(a) The least required travel time between i and j, $H_{ij}{}^b$, and relative travel time for; the kth mode, $H_{kij}{}^r$.

---

[9] See Quandt [9].

[10] See Kessler [5; p. 50]. A fully satisfactory way of defining M_i and M_j has not yet been determined. A possible measure may be the fraction of the labor force employed in mining and manufacturing.

(b) The least cost of travel between i and j, $C_{ij}{}^b$, and the relative cost for the kth mode.

Convenience of travel between i and j must certainly be included but it is no longer too clear how this factor ought to be measured. It is not even clear that a single variable is capable of measuring convenience in an acceptable manner. One relevant variable may be:

(c) Relative departure frequency of each mode, denoted by $D_{kij}{}^r$ and the best departure frequency $D_{ij}{}^b$. A better measure of this might be the average time a person has to wait for a departure if he decides to travel at a randomly selected point in time. This may be a preferable measure since it has a natural value of zero for the private automobile, whereas $D_{kij}{}^r$ is not defined if k denotes automobiles.

Finally, we require

(d) The number of modes serving i and j, denoted by N_{ij}.

On the basis of this simple list of variables, a reasonable formulation of the model becomes

$$T_{kij} = \alpha_0 P_i^{\alpha_1} P_j^{\alpha_2} Y_i^{\alpha_3} Y_j^{\alpha_4} M_i^{\alpha_5} M_j^{\alpha_6} N_{ij}^{\alpha_7} f_1(H) f_2(C) f_3(D) \qquad (2)$$

where

$$f_1(H) = (H_{ij}{}^b)^{\beta_0} (H_{kij}{}^r)^{\beta_1}$$

$$f_2(C) = (C_{ij}{}^b)^{\gamma_0} (C_{kij}{}^r)^{\gamma_1}$$

$$f_3(D) = (D_{ij}{}^b)^{\delta_0} (D_{kij}{}^r)^{\delta_1}$$

In this model the total number of parameters to be estimated is 14.

Several things should be noted about the model.

(a) For the sake of convenience we have adopted temporarily a formulation which yields an estimating equation linear in the logarithms of the variables. This may be considered a residue of the gravity model approach.

(b) If the number of arcs is m and the number of existing modes is n, the number of observations is of the order of nm; i.e., substantially larger than the number of observations m which would be available for the estimation of a standard gravity model.

(c) It is not required that an exhaustive set of data be available; i.e., if the relevant observations on the variables pertaining to some arcs and modes are not available the model and its coefficients can still be estimated.

(d) Whereas disaggregation by modes in a standard gravity model is undesirable[11], such disaggregation is essential for the present model.

Examples such as the one in the previous section may exhibit the somewhat peculiar characteristic that the introduction of a new mode can, under certain circumstances, lead to an increase of travel by some other, already existing, mode. Thus, we may have a situation in which the introduction of air travel on a route actually increases the number of rail trips. Readers may verify that this occurs if the first four modes discussed in the illustration in Section 3 are used in conjunction with the demand equation

$$T_k = 1000 - 100H_b - 200C_b - 60H_{rk} - 50C_{rk} - 10N.$$

On the face of it this kind of behavior seems to constitute a violation of a frequently employed axiom in the theory of choice, namely the axiom of the independence of irrelevant alternatives. Specifically, if the introduction of a new mode increases travel by an old mode, some consumers for whom travel by that old mode (or any mode) was not an optimal choice before the introduction of the new mode now find it to be optimal.[12] It is, therefore, important that we investigate at least briefly the nature of the conditions which can guarantee that this result does not occur.

For simplicity we shall concentrate on the travel time variable H. Let there be two existing modes, with $H_1 < H_2$, and let the function forecasting travel volume by an abstract mode have the following simple form:

$$T_k = H_b{}^{\beta_0} H_{kr}{}^{\beta_1} N^{\alpha} \qquad (3)$$

where H_b is the best travel time $(=H_1)$, H_{kr} is the relative travel time by mode k, and N is the number of modes. When only two modes exist

---

[11] See Quandt [9].

[12] For more detailed discussion of these concepts see Luce and Raiffa [6].

$$T_1 = H_1{}^{\beta_0} 2^{\alpha}$$

$$T_2 = H_1{}^{\beta_0} \left(\frac{H_2}{H_1}\right)^{\beta_1} 2^{\alpha}$$

and total travel T is

$$T = 2^{\alpha} H_1{}^{\beta_0} \left[1 + \left(\frac{H_2}{H_1}\right)^{\beta_1}\right] \tag{4}$$

If we introduce a third mode, there are two possibilities:

(a) The third mode does not become the best mode, i.e., $H_3 > H_1$. Then travel by each existing mode does not increase if $\alpha < 0$. Since the introduction of a new mode may reasonably be expected to increase the total volume of travel, the requirement that $\alpha < 0$ imposes a further restriction on β_1. Using (4) and its analogue for three modes, the requirement that total travel increase is equivalent to

$$3^{\alpha} H_1{}^{\beta_0} \left[1 + \left(\frac{H_2}{H_1}\right)^{\beta_1} + \left(\frac{H_3}{H_1}\right)^{\beta_1}\right] < 2^{\alpha} H_1{}^{\beta_0} \left[1 + \left(\frac{H_2}{H_1}\right)^{\beta_1}\right]$$

or

$$\left(\frac{3}{2}\right)^{\alpha} > \frac{1}{1 + \dfrac{H_3{}^{\beta_1}}{H_1{}^{\beta_1} + H_2{}^{\beta_1}}}$$

(b) If the new mode becomes the best mode, $H_3 < H_1$. Then the independence of irrelevant alternatives requires that

$$H_1{}^{\beta_0} 2^{\alpha} \geqslant H_3{}^{\beta_0} \left(\frac{H_1}{H_3}\right)^{\beta_1} 3^{\alpha}$$

$$H_1{}^{\beta_0} \left(\frac{H_2}{H_1}\right)^{\beta_1} 2^{\alpha} \geqslant H_3{}^{\beta_0} \left(\frac{H_2}{H_3}\right)^{\beta_1} 3^{\alpha}$$

Both of these inequalities require

$$\left(\frac{H_1}{H_3}\right)^{\beta_0 - \beta_1} \geqslant \left(\frac{3}{2}\right)^{\alpha}$$

This implies that if $\alpha > 0$, since $H_1 > H_3$, then $\beta_0 > \beta_1$. Since β_0 and β_1 are both likely to be negative, this implies $|\beta_0| < |\beta_1|$. It then follows from the independence of irrelevant alternatives and a positive value of α that travel demand is more sensitive to relative time than to the best travel time — an observation which makes sense intuitively. As in case (a) a further restriction is also implied by the requirement that the introduction of a new mode increase total travel.

Other variants of the model also merit investigation. One immediate modification would consist of deletion of the variable N and the introduction into the functions f_1, f_2 and f_3 of measures of the range or density of the mode configurations. *Ceteris paribus,* we would expect total travel volume to be an increasing function of the range and density of alternatives and volume traveled by any one mode a decreasing function of the density of alternatives.

Perhaps a more significant modification arises out of the observation that, although cross-sectional approaches of the type being discussed here often yield good correlations, they frequently result in very bad predictions for the future. This may occur because the parameters characterizing the cross-sectional relation may themselves change over time. A long run theory ought to be able to predict the manner in which the coefficients change over time.[13] In fact, we ought to be able to relate the coefficients to various socio-economic variables. Arguing more crudely, the coefficients may be expressed as functions of time. As a first approximation, these functions may be assumed to exhibit linear or perhaps quadratic trends in time. This device would increase the number of parameters to be estimated but the number of observations upon which regressions are based will increase even more since time series and cross-section data would now be pooled. In effect, if we have a cross-section for two distinct years, the data can be lumped together in a single regression, taking care that each variable now carries a time subscript as well. Ultimately the true dependence of the various coefficients may be replaced by a dependence on other variables considered exogeneous to the model. Thus, if it were argued that as personal incomes increase relative to travel costs, the travel costs become relatively unimportant, the coefficient of travel cost may be made an increasing function of $C_{ij}/(Y_i + Y_j)$ where Y_i and Y_j measure income in nodes i and j and C_{ij} the travel cost between the nodes. The coefficient of the variable N_{ij}, the number of modes serving the arc

---

[13] See also Quandt [9].

from i to j, may be a decreasing function of the travel time by the fastest means over the travel time by the slowest means.

The estimation of the coefficients that are functions of time poses no particular problems as long as they are polynomials in time. Assume, for example, that they are linear functions of time. A typical term in our basic equation can then be represented by $x^{\alpha+\beta t}$. Upon taking logarithms, this becomes $(\alpha + \beta t) \log x$ which can be written as $\alpha(\log x) + \beta(t \log x)$; i.e., the corresponding part of the logarithmic regression equation is linear in the parameters to be estimated.

If more complicated hypotheses are to be explored and the coefficients to be estimated appear in nonlinear fashion, the estimation problem becomes a nonlinear minimization problem of possibly great complexity. Although efficient algorithms are available for the solution of these problems,[14] they are not solved as routinely as is the linear estimation problem.

5. Empirical Results

The foregoing ideas and analysis have been subjected so far to only one empirical test. Data appropriate for the testing of such models are extremely scarce. The best sample that was available for initial testing consisted of figures for twenty city pairs in California in 1960.

The information which was available for some of these city pairs is as follows:

1. Traffic volumes by air, rail, bus and car.[15] Four of the city pairs had to be eliminated because volumes by automobile or bus were unobtainable for them. All rail passenger volume (for all city pairs) had to be eliminated because these figures were missing for about half the remaining sixteen city pairs. We thus tested the model on sixteen city pairs for air, bus and automobile travel.

2. Travel times and travel costs. Times and costs can both be

---

[14] See Goldfeld, Quandt and Trotter [2].

[15] Traffic volumes were derived from a variety of sources such as the *CAB Domestic Origin and Destination Survey of Airline Passenger Traffic*, 1960; various railroad companies; Western Greyhound Lines; the California Division of Highways, *LARTS* Survey of 1960. These data were obtained from the Northeast Corridor Transportation Project through the courtesy of the Stanford Research Institute. Since the rail data were incomplete, railroad travel was deleted from the analysis.

broken down into the "access to terminal" portion and interurban portion of the trip.[16] Costs were calculated on a per capita basis; i.e., total automobile costs were divided by the mean number of persons per car (a figure that varies from city pair to city pair).

3. Economic-demographic variables. These include, for each city, population figures, per capita incomes, percentage of total employment in manufacturing, percentage in white collar occupations, and bank deposits per capita.[17] The last three of these variables are intended to measure, at least crudely, the institutional character of the cities involved.

Since we are dealing with sixteen city pairs and three modes, the number of observations is 48 for all basic estimating equations. In order to describe the equations estimated we introduce the following notation:

T_{kij} : Travel volume from city i to city j by mode k;

P_i : Population (in millions) of the ith city;

Y_i : Per capita income in the ith city;

D_i : Per capita deposits in the ith city;

M_i : Per cent of employment in manufacturing in the ith city;

W_i : Per cent of employment in white-collar occupations in the ith city;

H_{ij}^b : Best travel time between i and j;

H_{kij}^r : Relative travel time between i and j by mode k;

C_{ij}^b : Least travel cost between i and j;

C_{kij}^r : Relative travel cost between i and j by mode k;

A_k : A dummy variable indicating the availability of a car at the end of the trip, if one takes mode k; if k refers to automobile, the value of A_k was set $= e = 2.718 \ldots$, otherwise $A_k = 1$.[18]

F_{kij}^r : Relative frequency of departures from i to j by mode k. Since the private automobile is always "best" in terms of departure frequency, the variable F_{ij}^b has to be omitted since it is in effect a constant. It was assumed arbitrarily for the purpose of calculating F_{kij}^r that the number of potential daily departures by automobile is 96 (i.e., one every quarter hour).

---

[16]Derived from Joseph and Haikalis [4]; the *Los Angeles Metropolitan Peak Hour Driving Study — 1960*; various rail, bus and air schedules and estimates prepared by Mr. J. Goodman, Traffic Research Corporation.

[17]Data were derived from the U.S. Bureau of the Census, *County and City Data Book* 1962.

[18]Hence, log $A_k = 1$ or 0 depending on whether k refers to automobile travel or not.

It may be noted that, since all city pairs are served by all modes, the variable N_{ij}, the number of modes serving the ij^{th} arc, was redundant and was not used.

Regression Calculated. The regressions which were calculated are listed below in Table 4. Each column represents a separate regression. The variables entering the various regressions are listed in the left-hand column, together with the coefficient of correlation and the F-statistic for testing the general linear hypothesis. Numbers in the cells are the coefficients of the variable in question for the particular regression together with the corresponding t-value (in parentheses). Blanks indicate that the particular variable was not included in the regression in question. The dependent variable was log T_{kij} in every case.

Interpretation of Results. The results are incomplete at this point, not only with respect to the various hypotheses that can be tested but also with respect to the sturdiness of the forecasts that can be made from the estimated relations. These tests will continue to be carried out.

However, the present results permit a number of interesting and encouraging conclusions:

(1) In every regression estimated the coefficients of population are highly significant and have the correct (*a priori* expected) sign; that is, travel demand is seen to increase with the population of the locations served.

(2) From regressions 1, 2 and 3 it appears that variables D_i, W_i and M_i (bank deposits, per cent of white collar workers and per cent employed in manufacturing) contribute no significant explanatory power to the equations. In the case of D_i and W_i this is perhaps a little surprising but not seriously so. It is interesting to note, however, that the coefficients of D_i and M_i have the *a priori* expected signs (*ceteris paribus*, the greater the per capita liquid wealth and the more the area relies on services as opposed to manufacturing, the more travel it generates). In one case the W_i coefficient had the expected sign but in another it did not.

(3) Separate inclusion of per capita income in i and j yields coefficients with the right signs in regressions 1, 2, 3 and 4 although they are not statistically significant. In regression 5, Y_i and Y_j are replaced by a naive average $(Y_i + Y_j)/2$ and in regression 6 and 7 by a properly weighted average. In all three of these cases the income variable has the correct sign and is either significant or barely misses being so.

(4) The dummy variable A_{ij} has the correct sign (the availability of a car at the end of the trip increases travel demand) but is not significant.

Table 4

Results of Regressions on California Data

Variable	Regression						
	1	2	3	4	5	6	7
Constant	−31.91	−38.04	−40.71	−33.82	−36.57	−32.56	−28.73
	(−.95)	(−1.14)	(−.69)	(1.45)	(−1.62)	(−1.37)	(−1.25)
$\log P_i$	.95	.92	.94	.93	.91	.95	.88
	(5.88)	(4.44)	(3.71)	(6.99)	(7.40)	(7.54)	(6.95)
$\log P_j$	1.08	1.14	1.14	1.12	1.14	.99	.88
	(5.14)	(6.20)	(6.37)	(6.38)	(6.95)	(6.41)	(5.47)
$\log Y_i$	1.75	4.59	3.32	2.64			
	(.53)	(1.30)	(.33)	(1.05)			
$\log Y_j$	3.71	3.11	3.02	3.72			
	(.99)	(1.01)	(.99)	(1.43)			
$\log D_i$	.67						
	(.57)						
$\log D_j$	(.17)						
	(.19)						
$\log W_i$			−.36				
			(−.05)				
$\log W_j$			2.38				
			(.76)				
M_i		−.73					
		(−.53)					
M_j		−.96					
		(−1.15)					
$\log (Y_i + Y_j)/2$					6.83		
					(2.35)		
$\log C_{ij}^{\,b}$	−.99	−.61	−1.57	−1.20	−1.12	−.62	−.57
	(−1.19)	(−.70)	(−1.75)	(−1.69)	(−1.68)	(−1.04)	(−.99)
$\log C_{kij}^{\,r}$	−3.17	−3.15	−3.18	−2.62	−3.17	−3.15	−2.34
	(−11.40)	(−11.51)	(−11.48)	(3.59)	(11.82)	(−11.62)	(−4.54)
$\log H_{ij}^{\,b}$	−.32	−.92	.59	−.15	−.20	−1.19	−1.20
	(−.21)	(−.59)	(.36)	(−.12)	(−.16)	(−1.17)	(−1.23)
$\log H_{kij}^{\,r}$	−2.04	−2.01	−2.05	−1.73	−2.04	−2.01	−1.75
	(−5.45)	(−5.45)	(−5.51)	(−3.23)	(−5.66)	(−5.51)	(−4.59)
$\log F_{kij}^{\,r}$							.44
							(1.83)
$\log A_{ij}$				.66			
				(.81)			
$\log [(P_iY_i + P_jY_j)/ (P_i + P_j)]$						6.33	5.82
						(2.08)	(1.96)
R	.9355	.9376	.9360	.9361	.9350	.9331	.9386
F	25.94	26.91	26.18	29.92	39.70	38.49	36.09

(5) The best cost and time variable and the relative cost and time variables all have the correct (negative) signs (a single exception occurring in regression 3). As indicated in Section 4, we expect demand to be more sensitive to the relative cost and time variables than to the best cost and time variables. This is indeed the case, with the relative cost and times being highly significant in all regressions.

(6) The relative departure frequency in regression 7 has the correct sign and is nearly significant.

(7) The correlation coefficients indicate that we are successfully explaining a very substantial fraction of the variations in the dependent variable.

(8) The F-values are all significant.

(9) The regressions are quite robust in the sense that the values of particular regression coefficients are very stable from regression to regression.

(10) Regression 7 from which the bank deposit, per cent white collar, per cent manufacturing and car availability variables were omitted seems best not only on the grounds that it yields the smallest unexplained residual (although not the highest F-value) but also on the grounds that the coefficients of P_i and P_j are the same, which is what we would expect on *a priori* grounds.

(11) There are no problems of multicollinearity.

6. Concluding Comments

This paper has described a new theoretical approach to the analysis of travel demand. Apparently by coincidence, a number of other writings have recently taken the same point of view: one in which goods and services are specified as abstract bundles of characteristics.[19] Our first empirical test of this approach has also been described, and one can only conclude that its results are highly encouraging. Insofar as so limited a test can provide any basis of judgment it suggests that the approach is highly promising.

The abstract mode approach promises to enable us to obtain a far more satisfactory explanation of the current situation than is presently available and to draw from our models much stronger inferences about the future. Whereas the long-run models of straight-forward gravity variety generally require for efficient forecasting that travel by different modes along a given arc be aggregated, the abstract mode approach permits travel by different modes to be kept separate. We can thus treat the quantities of travel by different modes as separate observations, but we submerge the institutional

---

[19] See Lancaster [6].

identity of the mode, retaining only its characteristics expressed in terms of relative speed, cost, etc. Moreover, the abstract mode approach permits meaningful comparisons of travel behavior along different arcs of the transportation network that might otherwise not be possible. In terms of our Trenton-Philadelphia, New York-San Francisco illustration, we note that the data describing air travel demand along the two arcs have no obvious common interpretation, whereas data on demand for the fastest abstract modes along the two routes may very well permit an illuminating common analysis. The approach may then make it possible for regression analysis to deal cross-sectionally with a wide variety of areas, employing as variables the length of arcs and the characteristics of the abstract mode sets. The abstract mode approach will then play a role not only in estimating the future demand for each mode, but also estimating the total demand for travel.

References

1. Fisher, F. *A Priori Information and Time Series Analysis.* North-Holland Publishing Co., 1962.

2. Goldfeld, S. M., R. E. Quandt, and H. F. Trotter, "Maximization by Quadratic Hill-Climbing" *Econometrica*, 34 (1966), 541-51.

3. Isard, W. *et al. Methods of Regional Analysis: An Introduction to Regional Science.* New York: The Technology Press of M.I.T. and John Wiley and Sons, Inc., 1960.

4. Joseph, Hyman and George Haikalis. "Economic Evaluation of Traffic Networks," delivered at the 40th Annual Meeting, Highway Research Board, Washington, D.C., January, 1961.

5. Kessler, D. S. *Relationships Between Intercity Air Passengers and Economic and Demographic Factors — A Multiple Linear Regression Analysis,* MSE Thesis, Princeton University, 1965.

6. Lancaster, K. J. "A New Approach to Consumer Theory," *Journal of Political Economy,* 14 (1966), 132-157; also Chapter 2 in this volume.

7. Luce, D. and H. Raiffa. *Games and Decisions.* New York: John Wiley and Sons, Inc., 1957.

8. Port of New York Authority. *Air Travel Forecasting: Market Analysis Method, Domestic Air Passenger Market, 1965-1975.* Saugatuck, Conn.: The Eno Foundation for Highway Traffic Control, 1957.

9. Quandt, R. E. "Some Perspectives of Gravity Models" in *Studies in Travel Demand*. (Prepared by MATHEMATICA for the Department of Commerce under Contract No. C-247-65 (Neg): September 1965.)

5 Structural Requirements for Abstract-Mode Models of Passenger Transportation

John P. Mayberry

1. Introduction

Whenever we attempt to develop a formal model of a real situation, we are attempting to express a conviction as to which factors of the real situation are central and which are peripheral. These convictions may be contradicted by comparing their implications with actual observations or data, but can never be finally verified. It is worth noting, however, that even a contradiction or rejection must rest on some interpretation of our observations ([10]) so that there must always be uncertainty in both directions.

This paper describes some efforts to deduce a plausible set of algebraic models which could be useful for predicting inter-urban passenger travel. The models described here may be regarded as "second-generation" models, the need for which was made evident by the shortcomings of an earlier ("first-generation") set of abstract mode models of transportation ([3], [4], [5], [6], [7], [8], [9], [14]).

The original hope, perhaps somewhat naive [13], was that a set of desiderata could be assembled, against which algebraic models could be measured; thus models which have the potential for producing unacceptable qualitative behavior could be excluded in advance, and quantitative predictions could be attempted in the full confidence that common sense would not reject their conclusions out of hand. Unfortunately, the usual reason for proposing a more complex model is to repair the shortcomings of an *unacceptable* simpler model, rather than to build upon the firm foundation of an *acceptable* simpler model; and often the unacceptability is only discovered after data have been collected and predictions made.

We do hope, in this present chapter, to point out the kind of counter-intuitive results which may be expected from certain sets of assumptions, and thus from certain models; and we hope to clarify, if not to remove, the shortcomings of models suggested earlier. We may typically find ourselves attempting to "make the best of a bad job"

[12], because we will seldom be able to resolve the paradoxes and shortcomings of our models as rapidly as new flaws can be discovered.

Section 2 of this chapter presents the basic axioms on which the models presented are based. Several general results are derived or quoted, including a close relationship between a standard type of formula used in several modal-split proposals and the homogeneity of the population of potential travelers. A class of "attractiveness functions" is described, and a family of functions is proposed which can explain the dependence of total travel on total attractiveness of all modes.

In section 3, alternatives to the basic homogeneous population models are presented. The only inhomogeneity explicitly discussed is the variation in income within the population; but the same methods could be applied to any other sort of diversity which was believed (or suspected) to be important. The resulting formulae are displayed.

In section 4, the problem of predicting two-way traffic between two cities is attacked; among the proposals which were investigated, only one appears to possess the desired consistency with the axioms and with the simpler models.

Section 5 presents the formulae which result when the problem of two-way traffic between two cities with diverse income-structures is attacked.

Section 6 shows how the problem of capacity limitation (sell-out) can be resolved when the population is homogeneous. A diverse population, which requires that "attractiveness" of a mode be related to a particular element of the population, will need more detailed assumptions if the sell-out problem is to be clarified.

Section 7 is a set of conclusions and proposals for further investigation.

2. The Principal Axioms

We begin by assuming that the amount of passenger travel among a set of cities can usefully be approximated by some deterministic function of a finite set of parameters. In particular, if we focus our attention on the travel between a specific pair of cities A and B, and assume that indirect travel between them (which involves a change of mode or of carrier at an intermediate point) is negligible in comparison with direct travel, then the travel between those cities will primarily depend on the characteristics of the several passenger-transport modes which connect the two cities.

If we adopt the abstract-mode approach, whose central tenet is that the total travel from A to B and its distribution among competing modes should be determined only by the attributes of the mode, which may within our model influence total travel, we can produce more comprehensive versions of the Abstract Mode Model by enlarging the set of attributes considered and more restrictive versions by reducing the set of attributes considered.

We will distinguish the M alternative modes by the index $m = 1, 2, \ldots, M$. Initially, we will consider these characteristics of a mode:

h_m, the elapsed time per trip (in hours);
c_m, the dollar cost per trip; and
v_m, the frequency of trips per week.

Then total travel from A to B (in passenger-trips per week) is given by

$$D = D(v_1, c_1, h_1, v_2, c_2, h_2, \ldots, v_M, c_M, h_M); \qquad (2.1)$$

and the amount of travel by mode m is given by

$$DS_m = DS_m(v_m, c_m, h_m; v_1, c_1, h_1, \ldots, v_M, c_M, h_M). \qquad (2.2)$$

Now we shall investigate properties which the functions D and DS_m should have, as a consequence of the qualitative conditions (axioms) which we shall impose.

A. Total travel must equal the sum, over all modes, of travel by that mode:

$$D = \Sigma_m DS_m. \qquad (2.3)$$

Reason: Self-evident.

B. Total travel must not depend on the names given the modes:

The function $D(\cdot)$ must be invariant under
any permutation of mode names. $\qquad (2.4)$

Reason: None of the predictions made by our models may depend on the names given to the various modes. This axiom is absolutely fundamental to the whole Abstract-Mode approach; if we believe that demand for trains behaves differently from demand for buses, we cannot simply incorporate a mode-specific parameter, but we must rather determine what *characteristics* of the trains vs. the buses cause that distinction, and then formulate a model which incorporates that *characteristic*. Not only is this essential in order to justify the name of "abstract mode", but it is essential if we are to be able to predict demand for modes not yet introduced.

C. Travel by the mth mode must not depend on the names given to the other modes:

$$\text{The function } DS_m(\cdot) \text{ must be invariant under any}$$
$$\text{permutation of the other modes}$$
$$[1, 2, \ldots, m-1, m+1, \ldots, M]. \tag{2.5}$$

Reason: Same as for (B) above.

D. Travel by the mth mode must not depend on the name given to that mode:

$$\text{The function } DS_m(v_m, c_m, h_m; v_1, c_1, \ldots, h_M) \text{ must in fact}$$
$$\text{all be the same function of their arguments:}$$
$$\text{we may call it } DS(v_m, c_m, h_m; v_1, c_1, \ldots, h_M). \tag{2.6}$$

Reason: Same as for (B) above

E. The share $S(\cdot)$ of the travel which is performed by the mth mode should satisfy the conditions (C) and (D) above; defining

$$S(\cdot) = \frac{DS(\cdot)}{D(\cdot)} \tag{2.7}$$

we have the algebraic statement that

$$S(v_m, c_m, h_m; v_1, c_1, \ldots, h_M)$$
$$\text{must be invariant under any permutation}$$
$$\text{of the modes in its second group of arguments.} \tag{2.8}$$

Reason: Same as for (B) above.

F. Now suppose that some one mode — say, "bus" — is divided into two modes — say, "red bus" and "blue bus". Then we wish our model to possess a structure which will assure that the predicted travel by all other modes will be unchanged, and that the predicted travel by red bus, *plus* the predicted travel by blue bus, will equal the previously predicted travel by bus. To formulate this algebraically requires that $D(\cdot)$ and $S(\cdot,\cdot,\cdot;\cdot)$ be defined for variable numbers of modes — i.e., for variable M. Then we may assume that mode m is to be divided into two modes m' and m'', which have the same cost and the same duration as mode m, while the sum of the frequencies $v_{m'}$ and $v_{m''}$ must equal the original frequency v_m ; in other words,

$$v_m = v_{m'} + v_{m''};$$
$$c_m = c_{m'} = c_{m''}; \qquad\qquad (2.9)$$
$$b_m = b_{m'} = b_{m''}.$$

Then our verbal conditions require that these equations must imply

$$D(\cdot, v_m, c_m, b_m, \cdot) = D(\cdot, v_{m'}, c_{m'}, b_{m'}, v_{m''}, c_{m''}, b_{m''}, \cdot)$$

$$(2.10)$$

and also

$$S(v_m, c_m, b_m ; \cdot) = S(v_{m'}, c_{m'}, b_{m'}; \cdot) + S(v_{m''}, c_{m''}, b_{m''} ;\cdot).$$

$$(2.11)$$

When we break every mode down as far as possible, we are in effect identifying each trip within the base period — for us, one week — as a separate mode. Then all the $v_{m'}$ will be equal to 1, and we conclude that

$$S(v_m, c_m, b_m ;\cdot) = v_m S(1, c_m, b_m ;\cdot). \qquad (2.12)$$

Note that dots in these last expressions refer to the spectrum of available modes — or, what is the same thing, the spectrum of available trips — among which there are v_m trips of mode m.

Reason: The predictions may not depend on how we classify the trips into modes, but must depend only on the *characteristics* of the trips. This axiom has been called the "Red-Bus/Blue-Bus Axiom" in previous work by Ku and Mayberry, because of the following informal but equivalent statement:

> If some of our buses are red, and the rest blue, and if we regard the red buses and blue buses as separate modes, our predictions should not change.

G. The predicted passenger travel on each mode should depend continuously on the set of characteristics of all the modes, as long as none of the parameters (v_m, c_m, or b_m) become equal to 0.

The functions $DS(\cdot)$ and $D(\cdot)$ are continuous functions
when all their arguments are non-zero.　　　　(2.13)

Reason: Although an *individual's* decisions might be discontinuous functions of the parameters describing his alternatives (*e.g.,* he might always choose the cheaper, no matter how small the difference in total cost to him), when we attempt to analyze the behavior of many individuals I cannot imagine that significant discontinuities will be observable from the aggregated data. The apparent cost of each alternative to each individual will depend on a variety of minor factors, which will smooth out any discontinuities.

H. If the frequency v_m of some mode m decreases gradually to zero, the demand for passenger travel on that mode must decrease continuously to zero, and there should not be a sudden change in total travel, nor a sudden shift in the allocation of that travel among the various modes. (N.B.: This might not be an automatic consequence of an otherwise reasonable model, since we have not incorporated the notion of capacity, or saturation, or congestion).

Formally,

If $v_m \to 0$, then
$$DS(v_m, c_m, b_m; v_1, c_1, b_1, \ldots, v_M, c_M, b_M) \to 0 \text{ and}$$
$$DS(v_m', c_m', b_m'; v_1, c_1, b_1, \ldots, v_M, c_M, b_M) \quad (2.14)$$
should be continuous for $m' \neq m$ as well as for $m' = m$.

This condition is in some danger of being violated whenever modal split is based on $\min_m c_m$ and/or $\min_m b_m$, since if service on either the cheapest or the fastest mode dwindles away gradually and finally vanishes, those minima will change discontinuously.[1]

Reason: A mode with vanishingly small number of trips per week should have little influence on total travel, or on its distribution.

I. Let us consider the following assumption:

"If the characteristics of mode m change, while the characteristics of all other modes remain unchanged, then *either* the attractiveness of mode m will *increase* (in which case the travel on mode m increases and the travel on all other modes decreases), *or the opposite occurs.*"

This assumption is very strong; from it conclusions can be drawn which drastically limit the possible algebraic forms of $S(\cdot)$. Some of those conclusions are at variance with common sense (at least with mine) in a rather subtle way. To illustrate, let us consider the consequences of a change in the characteristics of mode m, which happens not to cause a change in the travel by mode m itself. Then Assumption I would imply that *no change* would occur in the predicted travel by *any mode,* because the change under consideration lies on the boundary between "travel on all other modes increases" and "travel by all other modes decreases." I feel that this conclusion is not plausible in view of the following imaginary experiment. Let us take some of the buses (say the "blue buses" of (F) above), and consider them as a separate mode (say the mth). Then let us change the *characteristics* of that mode so that it resembles an airplane mode (i.e., has the same cost c_m and travel time b_m as an airplane mode), adjusting v_m so that it has the same amount of travel as the previous blue bus mode. (The new mode may be called "flying blue buses."). Then Assumption I would imply that no change in travel pattern would result from exchanging the "blue buses" for the "flying blue buses;" I believe, on the contrary, that the red buses would gain travelers (who formerly traveled by blue buses), while the previous airplane flights would lose travelers (to the flying blue buses).

---

[1] The same occurs if a new mode (either cheaper than any old mode, or faster than any old mode) appears. This is a crucial consideration in attempting to predict demand for the SST or the ultra-high-speed tube train.

From this example I conclude that we must not assume Assumption I; neither can we assume the following formula, which can be shown to be *equivalent* to Assumption I:

$$S(v_m, c_m\, b_m\, ;\cdot\,) = \frac{f(v_m, c_m, b_m)}{\Sigma_m f(v_m, c_m, b_m)} \qquad (2.15)$$

for some function f which depends only on the characteristics of a single mode.

Alan Goldman has pointed out a more obvious problem with the last expression; it implies that the ratio of travel by one mode to travel by another depends only on characteristics of those two modes, and not on characteristics of any other mode; but this implication is inconsistent with the qualitative argument, given above, concerning flying blue buses.

J. For the above reasons, we will make this weaker assumption instead of Assumption I: if any one characteristic of mode m changes, while all characteristics of all other modes and all other characteristics of mode m remain fixed, then *either* the travel on mode m increases, total travel increases, and travel on all other modes decreases (this happens if c_m decreases, if v_m increases, or if b_m decreases) *or* the opposite occurs.

> If c_m decreases, b_m decreases, or v_m increases, and there is no change in any other argument of $D(\cdot)$, then $D(\cdot)$ increases, and $DS(v_m', c_m', b_m'; \cdot)$ decreases for $m' \neq m$.

K. Because the objections to Assumption I all seem to rest on the *inhomogeneity* of the population of potential travelers, we can make that assumption, and also assume (2.15), *within* a homogeneous subset of the population. *Within such a subset*, we can use Assumption I to prove that the total travel D must depend only on the total attractiveness $F = \Sigma_m f(v_m, c_m, b_m)$ to the members of that subset.

[For proof, we need only change the characteristics of one mode at a time, so that its cost c_m becomes equal to a standard c_o, its time b_m becomes equal to a standard b_o, and its frequency v_m is adjusted so that travel by that mode is unchanged. By Assumption I, none of those changes will alter the travel by any mode; and the attractiveness $f_m = f(v_m, c_m, b_m)$ will also be unchanged for each mode. But 2.12) implies that travel, and attractiveness, are both now proportional to the new v_m ; we have in effect replaced the original diverse trips by replicas of a single standard trip. Thus any two sets of modes which have the same total attractiveness can be converted one into another by changes which do not change total travel; thus $D(\cdot)$ must in fact be a function of F only.]

Now $D(F)$ must be a function which increases with F; but Assumption I (or even the weaker form found as Assumption J above) will limit the form of possible functions of D, since adding a new mode (of attractiveness ΔF) must *decrease* the travel by the old modes; it can be shown that a set of necessary and sufficient conditions on the function $D(F)$ is that [2]

$$0 < \frac{d\ell D(F)}{d\ell F} < 1. \tag{2.16}$$

It can be shown that, if a new mode (with attractiveness ΔF) becomes available, the above expression gives the fraction of the travel on the new mode which is newly-generated as a result of the increased attractiveness; the rest of the travel on the new mode must have been diverted from the previously existing modes. If that fraction is a *constant,* then

$$D(F) = F^{\alpha}, \tag{2.17}$$

and we must have

$$0 < \alpha < 1 \tag{2.18}$$

to satisfy (2.16).

Other reasonably simple functions D satisfying (2.16) can be found; for example,

$$D(F) = \frac{BF^{\alpha}}{A + F^{\beta}} \tag{2.19}$$

satisfies (2.16) if we have

$$\begin{array}{c} A, B > 0, \\ 0 < \alpha \leqslant 1, \text{ and} \\ \alpha - 1 < \beta \leqslant \alpha. \end{array} \tag{2.20}$$

---

[2] We use $\ell(x)$ to denote the natural logarithm of x.

We shall assume, when definiteness on the form of $D(F)$ is necessary, that the form (2.17) is used; but (2.19) would have all of the same advantages except for being less simple than (2.17).

3. Influence of Population and Income-Distribution

The conclusions of Assumption I above seem to be exactly equivalent to the verbal concept that the consumers of transportation make up a homogeneous population. Consider the flying blue bus paradox. If a radical change occurs in the characteristics of the blue buses, without a change in the total travel on them, then that change could not influence the travel by other modes if demand were homogeneous. On the other hand, if demand were inhomogeneous (e.g., if people with more money than time would tend to take airplanes, and people with more time than money would tend to take buses), then the former customers would be gained when the blue buses flew and the latter customers would be lost, resulting in a shift of customers from airplanes to the flying blue buses, and from the previous blue buses to the red buses. It seems very reasonable (as suggested by this argument) that the principal inhomogeneity of the population should be with respect to its income (which will govern the indifference curves between time and money). Therefore, we might imagine that Assumption I would hold with regard to *any one particular slice* of potential travelers of approximately equal income.

This viewpoint permits us to retain some of the simplicity of formula (2.15), while still incorporating income effects and permitting the rejection of Assumption I as it would apply to the *whole* population.

Suppose (to simplify the notation) that we consider a finite number N of income-strata, indexed by $n = 1, 2, \ldots, N$, where the representative income of an individual in the nth stratum is Y_n dollars per year.

We might reasonably have called the function $f(v_m, c_m, b_m)$ of expression (2.15) the *attractiveness* of the mth mode. Now, if we are to apply a breakdown like that of (2.15) *to each income-stratum separately*, we must define a function $f_n(v_m, c_m, b_m)$, the *attractiveness* of the mth mode to an individual in the nth income-stratum. Then the total travel by residents of city A will presumably be proportional to the population of A, on the reasonable assumption that individuals make their travel decisions independently. Ku, in

[7] , and Blackburn in chapter 8, suggest that if P_A is the population of city A and P_B is that of city B, the influence of population on the total passenger travel might more reasonably be approximated by a factor of the form

$$K'(P_A P_B{}^\beta + P_B P_A{}^\beta) \qquad (3.1)$$

than by a factor of the form

$$K'(P_A P_B)^\beta; \qquad (3.2)$$

(Of course, the numerical values of K' and of β would be different in the two cases.) Ku also found that those formulae fit the data about equally well — and therefore recommended the former as being intuitively more satisfactory.

The K' above is intended to be independent of population; although it might be made to depend on other characteristics of the city-pair (principally the distance between them) we may hope that K' could be independent of distance, since the major influence of distance is likely to be in the large values of c_m and h_m, cost per trip and duration of trip, and those are captured already in the function f.

We will consider that the populations of cities A and B are characterized by the following distributions of income Y; P_{An} is the population of A in the nth income-stratum, and P_{Bn} is the population of B in the nth income-stratum. Then

$$P_A = \Sigma_n P_{An} \qquad (3.3)$$

and

$$P_B = \Sigma_n P_{Bn} \qquad (3.4)$$

since every individual must be in *some* income-stratum.

We shall presume that the attractiveness of a trip by mode m to an individual residing in A, having income-level Y_n, is given by some diminishing function of the *total* cost of a trip. The total cost is the sum of the dollar cost and the time cost; and I feel it is reasonable to weight these costs in proportion to the individual's income, so that we are in effect comparing the value of one man's hours to him, against the value of another man's hours to *him*. Then, recognizing that attractiveness of a number of trips must satisfy (2.12), we may propose

$$f_n(v_m, c_m, b_m) = v_m(b_m + v_1 Y_n^{-1} c_m)^{v_2}, \qquad (3.5)$$

where v_1, v_2, are parameters to be determined from all available data; of course we will presume $v_1 > 0$, $v_2 < 0$.

This implies that, for persons in the nth income-stratum, the share of travel by mode m would be

$$S_{mn} = \frac{f_n(v_m, c_m, b_m)}{\Sigma_m f_n(v_m, c_m, b_m)} = \frac{f_n(v_m, c_m, b_m)}{F_n} \qquad (3.6)$$

where

$$F_n = \Sigma_m f_n(v_m, c_m, b_m) ,$$

and the total travel between A and B by residents of A in the nth income-stratum will be

$$D_{An} = K' P_B{}^\beta P_{An} F_n{}^\alpha \qquad (3.7)$$

passenger trips per week.

Then the actual travel between A and B by mode m, by residents of A in the nth income-stratum, will be

$$DS_{Amn} = S_{mn} D_{An}$$

$$= K' P_B{}^\beta P_{An} f_n(v_m, c_m, b_m) F_n{}^{\alpha-1} \qquad (3.8)$$

Similarly, travel between A and B by residents of B in income-stratum Y_n is

$$DS_{Bmn} = S_{mn} D_{Bn}$$

$$= K' P_A{}^\beta P_{Bn} f_n(v_m, c_m, b_m) F_n{}^{\alpha-1} \qquad (3.9)$$

Then the total travel between A and B via mode m by travelers in income-stratum Y_n is

$$DS_{mn} = DS_{Amn} + DS_{Bmn}$$
$$= S_{mn}(D_{An} + D_{Bn})$$
$$= \frac{f_n(v_m,c_m,b_m)}{F_n} K'F_n{}^{\alpha}(P_B{}^{\beta}P_{An} + P_A{}^{\beta}P_{Bn}).$$

$$(3.10)$$

Then the total travel between A and B by mode m is given by

$$\Sigma_n DS_{mn} = K'P_B{}^{\beta}(\Sigma_n P_{An} f_n(v_m,c_m,b_m)F_n{}^{\alpha-1})$$

$$+ K'P_A{}^{\beta}(\Sigma_n P_{Bn} f_n(v_m,c_m,b_m)F_n{}^{\alpha-1}),$$

$$= K'\Sigma_n [(P_B{}^{\beta}P_{An} + P_A{}^{\beta}P_{Bn} f_n(v_m,c_m,b_m)F_n{}^{\alpha-1}]$$

$$(3.11)$$

Each of these depends only on a few parameters (assuming that the population/income data are available); α, β, and K' appear explicitly in (3.11), and v_1, v_2 are buried within the function f_n. Of course, the estimation of those parameters will be tedious. The results are likely to be of interest, because all available data will be used in a single coherent estimation process; and any simpler model could generate predictions which would be unreasonable in the various specific senses identified above.

4. Two-Way Flow of Passenger Traffic

As long as the attractiveness of a mode, for travel from city A to city B, is defined to depend only on the *frequency* of trips from A to B, and not on the *schedule* through the day, then the attractiveness of each mode for travel from A to B is likely to be equal to the attractiveness of that mode for travel from B to A.

However, we wish to be prepared for the possibility that the attractiveness of the same mode in the two directions might be different. We will analyze the effect of different attractivenesses, assuming that total passenger *travel* from A to B must equal that from B to A. Initially, we will disregard the dependence of modal preferences on income; we combine the two considerations in Section 5 below.

We continue to denote by f_m the attractiveness of the mth mode for the "forward" travel (i.e., from A to B), and let $\overline{f}_m$ denote the corresponding attractiveness of the mth mode for "reverse" travel (i.e., from B to A). In general, all barred symbols will refer to the reverse direction:

$$F = \Sigma_m f_m , \tag{4.1}$$

and

$$\overline{F} = \Sigma_m \overline{f}_m . \tag{4.2}$$

Then the total travel D in the forward direction would be given by[3]

$$D = K F^\alpha \tag{4.3}$$

if there were no return-trip constraint, and the return travel $\overline{D}$ would be given by

$$\overline{D} = K \overline{F}^\alpha ; \tag{4.4}$$

but when we impose the condition

$$\overline{D} = D, \tag{4.5}$$

we must make an adjustment (unless it should accidentally happen that $F = \overline{F}$).

Suppose

$$F > \overline{F}; \tag{4.6}$$

then the most natural form of adjustment seems to be one of these: *either* to inflate $\overline{D}$ and deflate D by the same factor, *or* to increase the reverse exponent α and decrease the forward exponent α by the same amount. Surprisingly enough, a little deeper thought makes the choice (between these two alternatives, at least) easy.

The first alternative would make

---

[3]The constant K in the following formulae is intended to incorporate both the K' of formulae (3.1) to (3.11) and the population-factors; in Section 5 we will make that dependence explicit.

$$\overline{D} = XK\overline{F}^{\alpha},$$

$$D = X^{-1}K F^{\alpha},$$

$$D = \overline{D} , \tag{4.7}$$

whence

$$D^2 = (\overline{D})^2 = K^2 (F\overline{F})^{\alpha}, \tag{4.8}$$

so that we may calculate

$$D = \overline{D} = K(F\overline{F})^{\alpha/2} . \tag{4.9}$$

The second alternative would imply

$$K F^{\alpha-\epsilon} = D$$

$$= \overline{D}$$

$$= K\overline{F}^{\alpha+\epsilon} \tag{4.10}$$

whence

$$\epsilon = \alpha \, \frac{\ell(F/\overline{F})}{\ell(F\cdot\overline{F})} \tag{4.11}$$

(In either case, if it happens that $F = \overline{F}$, the new formula — (4.8) or (4.10) — reduces to (4.3).) Not only is the second more complex, but there exists the possibility that a large difference between F and $\overline{F}$ could cause the exponent $\alpha + \epsilon$ to exceed 1, and/or cause the exponent $\alpha - \epsilon$ to be less than 0. (Either would cause the modified model to violate axioms J and K and (2.18) above.)

Explicitly,

$$\alpha+\epsilon = \alpha \left(1 + \frac{\ell(F/\overline{F})}{\ell(F/\overline{F})} \right)$$

$$= \alpha \, \frac{2 \, \ell(F)}{\ell(F) + \ell(\overline{F})} \; ;$$

$$\alpha - \epsilon = \alpha \left(1 - \frac{\ell(F/\overline{F})}{\ell(F\overline{F})} \right)$$

$$= \alpha \frac{2 \ell(\overline{F})}{\ell(F) + \ell(\overline{F})} \quad . \tag{4.12}$$

Consider this example of how those axioms could be violated; if we had both

$$F\overline{F} > 1 \quad \text{and}$$
$$\tag{4.13}$$
$$F > 1 > \overline{F}$$

then we would have

$$\ell(F) > \ell(F) + \ell(\overline{F}) > 0 > \ell(\overline{F}),$$

so that the exponent of F would be given by

$$\alpha - \epsilon < 0, \tag{4.15}$$

which would cause total travel both ways to *decrease* if one or more modes in the forward direction became more attractive. This is ridiculous, but could not be excluded *a priori* since its truth would depend on the actual observed values.[4]

In accordance with the general principle that a model which is capable of generating ridiculous predictions from plausible data is an unacceptable model, we therefore must reject the second alternative suggested above. What about the first alternative?

From (4.8) we cannot deduce any foolishness comparable to (4.15). We can be sure of that, because the dependence of

$$(F\overline{F})^{\alpha/2} = (\overline{F})^{\alpha/2} F^{\alpha/2} \tag{4.16}$$

on F alone, or on $\overline{F}$ alone, is of the same kind as the standard model (4.3); and if α lies strictly between 0 and 1, then so must $\alpha/2$, so that axioms J and K, and condition (2.16), will be satisfied by this new model.

---

[4]It is clear that the case illustrated in (4.13) *could* occur with reasonable data, because the absolute sizes of F and $\overline{F}$ depend on the units in which they are expressed; consequently, if $F \neq \overline{F}$, some changes of units could make (4.13) true.

5. Combined Effect of Two-Way Flow and Income-Distribution

In this section we analyze the combined effect of the two-way flow of traffic (as expressed in (4.9) above) with the income-distribution (as expressed in (3.11) above.) Omitting the algebra, we find the following expressions for DS_m, the total travel from A to B via mode m, and $\overline{DS}_m$, the total travel from B to A via mode m. In these expressions, the barred symbols refer to the characteristics of the reverse modes (i.e., from B to A.)

$$DS_m = K' \Sigma_n \left[(P_B{}^\beta P_{An} + P_A{}^\beta P_{Bn}) \frac{f_n(v_m, c_m, b_m)}{F_n} \right.$$

$$\left. \times (F_n \overline{F}_n)^{\alpha/2} \right],$$

$$\overline{DS}_m = K' \Sigma_n \left[(P_B{}^\beta P_{An} + P_A{}^\beta P_{Bn}) \frac{f_n(\overline{v}_m, \overline{c}_m, \overline{b}_m)}{\overline{F}_n} \right.$$

$$\left. \times (F_n \overline{F}_n)^{\alpha/2} \right]. \tag{5.1}$$

6. Capacity Limitation: (Sell-Out)

The models described in the preceding sections would permit travel by each of the modes $m = 1, 2, \ldots, M$, as influenced by the characteristics of all the modes available. Our axioms required that, as a mode became more attractive, travel by that mode would continually increase; in fact, as the total attractiveness F increased (see discussion following Axiom K), the specific algebraic forms suggested in (2.17) and (2.19) for $D(F)$ would generally imply that total passenger travel would increase without limit. (The exception is the case $\alpha = \beta$ in (2.19).) Consequently, our models would surely predict that the limits on available passenger capacity in the mth mode would be exceeded if the cost c_m and the time b_m both became small enough. This section proposes modifications to the models, which allow us to incorporate one aspect of capacity — the "sell-out" problem.

(Congestion, which is the other aspect of capacity-limitation, is much more difficult[5] to model in an explicit manner, because congestion has the effect of increasing the effective cost (in dollars or in time) for all users, due to the increase in trip duration and/or the

---

[5] See [2] for a major contribution to this topic.

increased time and money expended in getting to and from the terminus. The net effect of congestion is therefore to make the cost c_m and time h_m dependent on the travel DS_m by mode m — or even possibly to influence the cost and duration of trips by other modes, since auto congestion may increase bus trip time. Sell-out, however, does not change the cost or duration of the mode[6] for those who use it — the mode simply becomes unavailable to travelers who would have used it.)

The logical basis for our model of limited-capacity transportation networks, incorporating the capacity-limits CL_m for the mth mode, consists of three assumptions:

First, we assume that the characteristics of a sold-out mode would have no influence on travel by any other mode if the population were homogeneous, as long as the capacity limits do not change. (In the case where some trips within a given mode sell out, while others do not, we must break the mode into several modes — in the limit perhaps considering each trip as a separate mode.) This presumes that passengers do not to a significant extent travel by a non-sold-out mode as a result of planning to travel by a mode which happens to be sold out.

Second, we assume that the *possibility* of a sell-out is unimportant unless it actually occurs; i.e., we assume that passengers are not at all deterred from planning to travel by a mode which is *almost* sold out. (Both those assumptions might introduce errors, but the errors would tend to operate in opposite directions, so that ignoring both is rather a "neutral" position.)

Third, we assume that the travel by each mode is a continuous function of the characteristics of all modes — even when one mode is just on the borderline of being sold out. (This is actually a special case of Axion G above.)

From these three assumptions it follows that the influence of a sold-out mode on travel by other modes is exactly the influence which that mode would have had if it had been less attractive, so that it had exactly sold out with no excess demand.

We present below a computational scheme (i.e., an algorithm) which permits the calculation of travel by each mode, given the characteristics (including the capacity limits) of each mode, *if* the population is homogeneous. Unfortunately, the result cannot be expressed in a closed algebraic form, even for the homogeneous population and simple form (2.17) of the function $D(F)$. Under

---

[6]Except for such minor effects as those caused by passengers who arrive early at the airport in case their flight is oversold, thereby increasing the effective total duration of their trip.

those circumstances, the actual travel DS_m by the mth mode would be (in the absence of capacity limits).[7]

$$DS_m = Kf_m F^{\alpha-1}. \tag{6.1}$$

Now suppose there are capacity limits CL_m on each mode ($m = 1,\ldots,M$). If $DS_m \leqslant CL_m$ for all $m = 1,\ldots,M$, then the capacity limits have no effect. But if $DS_m > CL_m$ for any m, then we must conceptually replace the attractiveness f_m of the mth mode by an "equivalent attractiveness" $f_m{}^*$, which has the property that

$$\left.\begin{array}{l} f_m{}^* = f_m \\[6pt] DS_m \leqslant CL_m \end{array}\right\} \text{ if sell-out does not occur on the } m^{\text{th}} \text{ mode,} \tag{6.2}$$

$$\left.\begin{array}{l} f_m{}^* < f_m \\[6pt] DS_m = CL_m \end{array}\right\} \text{ if sell-out does occur,} \tag{6.3}$$

where the DS_m in each case is computed using the starred values. To be more precise, we can express DS_m in terms of the $f_m{}^*$, using the concept of total equivalent attractiveness

$$F^* = \Sigma_m f_m{}^*. \tag{6.4}$$

Then

$$\left.\begin{array}{l} f_m{}^* = f_m \\[6pt] K\, f_m{}^*\, (F^*)^{\alpha-1} \leqslant CL_m \end{array}\right\} \begin{array}{l} \text{if sell-out does not occur on the } m^{\text{th}} \\ \text{mode,} \end{array} \tag{6.5}$$

$$\left.\begin{array}{l} f_m{}^* < f_m \\[6pt] K\, f_m{}^*\, (F^*)^{\alpha-1} = CL_m \end{array}\right\} \text{ if sell-out does occur.} \tag{6.6}$$

We can combine (6.5) and (6.6) into one statement:

$$f_m{}^* = \min(f_m, CL_m (F^*)^{1-\alpha} K^{-1}), \tag{6.7}$$

which can be used as a computational scheme; initially, $f_m{}^*$ is taken as equal to f_m for all m; sold-out modes (those modes for which the

---

[7] Here again, the factor K incorporates the necessary population terms.

second argument of the "min" function is smaller than the first) will modify those f_m * values, and a sequence of values can be determined. That sequence will converge to the only non-zero set of stable solutions to equations (6.7) for the M variables f_m *, which then can be used to compute the resulting passenger travel by each mode. No analogous result has been found for the inhomogeneous case.

7. Conclusion

There are several other significant aspects of the modeling of passenger transportation which have not yet been successfully attacked by the methods described in this paper. They are mentioned here to indicate that much still remains to be done.

A model which incorporates explicit schedules, rather than merely a quantitative measure of frequency (trips per week), would be of major importance; airport congestion, caused by heavy flight schedules at peak hours, prevents many travelers from reaching their destination at the desired time – but the airline which schedules its flights in off-hours will suffer if the other airlines do not follow suit. A concerted effort to adjust schedules in a equitable manner requires an appropriate definition of "equitable", such as would be provided by a successful model of this type.

Some modes of passenger transportation do not possess schedules – chief of these, for interurban travel, is the privately owned automobile, although private aircraft, rental cars, taxis, and others may be significant in some cases. Analysis of demand for these modes requires additional assumptions, over and above those made in the preceding sections of this chapter.

Actual travel takes place in richly-structured networks, whose analysis probably requires algorithms which resemble simulations more than algebraic formulae. But there must exist relations between characteristics of available modes, and actual demand, in networks more complex than the basic $A \rightarrow B \rightarrow A$ cycle which implicitly formed the basis for Section 4.

The process of employing the above models to predict transportation requirements, and the utilization of future transport systems, will be fruitful to the extent that the qualitative axioms have been successful in identifying the most significant factors, and exploiting the meager data to the fullest extent.

Glossary

A,B	cities
c_m	cost of mode m (\$/trip)
CL_m	capacity limit on travel by mode m (passenger trips/week)
D	demand for total travel by all modes (passenger trips/week)
D_{An}	demand for travel by potential passengers residing in city A with incomes in the nth stratum
DS_m	demand for travel by mode m (passenger trips/week)
$f(\cdot)$	attractiveness function
f_m	$= f(v_m, c_m, b_m)$; attractiveness of mode m
$\overline{f}_m$	barred symbols, such as $\overline{f}_m$, $\overline{F}$, refer to reverse travel
F	total attractiveness of all modes
$f_n(\cdot)$	attractiveness function for potential travelers in n^{th} income stratum
$f_m{}^*$	equivalent attractiveness of mode m when sell-out is considered
F^*	total equivalent attractiveness of all modes when sell-out is considered
b_m	duration of travel by mode m (hours/trip)
K	parameter incorporating population
K'	parameter excluding population
$\ell(\ )$	natural logarithm function
m	mode index; $m = 1, \ldots, M$
M	number of modes
n	income-stratum index; $n = 1, \ldots, N$
N	number of income-level strata
P	population
P_A, P_B	population of city A, of city B
P_{An}	population of city A in n^{th} income stratum

S_m	fractional share, of the total passenger trips, which employ mode m
S_{mn}	fractional share, of the total passenger trips by persons in the nth income-stratum, which employ mode m
v_m	effective frequency of mode m (vehicle trips/week)
X	adjustment-factor to reconcile two-way flow (dimensionless)
Y	income ($/year)
Y_n	average income in nth income stratum ($/year)

$\left.\begin{array}{l} \alpha \\ \beta, \beta_1, \beta_2, \beta_3, \\ v_1, v_2 \end{array}\right\}$ parameters

Bibliography

[1] Beer, Sir Stafford, *Decision and Control,* Wiley, 1966.

[2] Dafermos, S. C. and F. T. Sparrow, "The Traffic Assignment Problem for a General Network", *Journal of Res. of the NBS-B Math. Sci.* 73B (1969), 91-118.

[3] Ku, Richard, "Experiments with Abstract-Mode Models I", NBS Memorandum, May 31, 1968.

[4] ———, "Experiments with Abstract-Mode Models II", NBS Memorandum, July 31, 1968.

[5] ———, "Experiments with Abstract-Mode Models III", NBS Memorandum, August 30, 1968.

[6] ———, "Experiments with Abstract-Mode Models IV", NBS Memorandum, April 11, 1969.

[7] ———, "Experiments with Abstract-Mode Models V," NBS Memorandum, July 22, 1969.

[8] Mayberry, John P., "Axioms for Abstract-Mode Models I" Mathematica Working Paper WP-1035, Sept. 26, 1969.

[9] ———, "Axioms for Abstract-Mode Models II", Mathematica Working Paper WP-1039, Nov. 14, 1969.

[10] ———, "On the Use of Models in Interpretation of Data and the Use of Data in Interpretation of Models", *Proceedings of U. S. Army Operations Research Symposium,* Durham, N. C., May 1969.

125

[11] ————, "Simulation and Dissimulation", *Proceedings of the Department of Defense Logistics Research Conference*, Warrenton, Va., May 26-28, 1965; Office of the Assistant Secretary of Defense for Installations and Logistics, August 1965.

[12] ————, "Valid Uses of Invalid Models", Paper presented to a Symposium held by the College on Logistics of the Institute for Management Sciences, Washington, D. C., 2 March 1970.

[13] ————, "Variants of Abstract-Mode Models", Mathematica Working Paper WP-1006, July 11, 1969.

[14] Quandt, R. E. and W. J. Baumol, "The Demand for Abstract Transport Modes: Some Hopes", *Journal of Regional Science,* 9 (1969), 159-162.

6

Cross-Sectional Travel Demand Models: Estimates and Tests

Richard E. Quandt and Kan Hua Young

1. Introduction

The cross-sectional demand model for passenger transportation known as the "abstract mode model" and exemplified in Quandt [6] and [7] and Quandt and Baumol [8] represents only a first step in estimating cross-sectional models with the general characteristic that the demand is a function of various attributes of the commodity in question.[*,1]

Since the original formulation of the abstract mode model, a large number of variants have been formulated and estimated. These variants all bear a family resemblance to each other. The purpose of examining a large number of different formulations was to improve the basic theory. The formulations described in this paper differ from one another in terms of the explanatory variables included, in terms of the functional form in which these variables enter the models, and in terms of the techniques employed for obtaining the estimates.

Section 2 contains a description of each of the formulations. Section 3 describes briefly problems of estimation. In Section 4 we present the results and attempt to combine *a priori* knowledge and *a posteriori* evidence for interpreting these results. Finally, in Section 5 we present the results of generalized least squares estimation based upon the assumption that city-pairs have intrinsic characteristics.

Reprinted from *Journal of Regional Science*. Vol. 9, No. 2, 1969, pp. 201-214. Copyright © by the Regional Science Research Institute. Used with permission.

*This study was performed under MATHEMATICA's contract with the Office of High Speed Ground Transportation, under Contract No. C-187-66.

[1] In a way it may be unfortunate that the term "abstract mode" has become attached to models of this variety; not only because of some of the difficulties associated with this notion, but because some preliminary tests have indicated that the "abstract mode model" in its simple formulation may not be all that abstract. See Quandt [7] and particularly Young [10].

2. Models

The following notation will be employed throughout.

T_{ijk} = volume of travel, measured in terms of number of trips, between nodes i and j by mode k;

P_i, P_j = population at node i or j;

Y_{ij} = weighted average of per capita income in nodes i and j;

C_{ij}^b = "best" (cheapest) cost of traveling from i to j by any mode;

C_{ijk}^r = cost of the kth mode divided by the best cost between i and j;

H_{ij}^b = "best" (fastest) journey time from i to j by any mode;

H_{ijk}^r = journey time of the kth mode divided by the best journey time between i and j;

D_{ijk}^r = departure frequency of the kth mode divided by the best departure frequency between i and j;

R_{ij} = a measure of the range and density of the distributions of costs and journey times;[2]

A_{ijk} = automobile dummy variable with value one if k refers to automobiles and value zero if it does not;

B_{ijk} = bus dummy variable with value one if k refers to bus and value zero if it does not;

I_{ijc} = cost of the cheapest trip one can take by any mode from i or j to any point in the network;

I_{ijb} = journey time of the fastest trip one can take by any mode from either i or j to any point in the network.

The following models were estimated, using both California and Northeast Corridor data.

$$T_{ijk} = \alpha_0 (P_i P_j)^{\alpha_1} (C_{ij}^b)^{\alpha_2} (C_{ijk}^r)^{\alpha_3} (H_{ij}^b)^{\alpha_4} (H_{ijk}^r)^{\alpha_5} (D_{ijk}^r)^{\alpha_6}$$
$$R_{ij}^{\alpha_7} Y_{ij}^{\alpha_8} \tag{2.1}$$

$$T_{ijk} = \alpha_0 (P_i P_j)^{\alpha_1} (C_{ij}^b)^{\alpha_2} (C_{ijk}^r)^{\alpha_3} (H_{ij}^b)^{\alpha_4} (H_{ijk}^r)^{\alpha_5} (D_{ijk}^r)^{\alpha_6}$$
$$R_{ij}^{\alpha_7} Y_{ij}^{(\alpha_8 + \alpha_9 A_{ijk} + \alpha_{10} B_{ijk})} \tag{2.2}$$

$$T_{ijk} = \alpha_0 (P_i P_j)^{\alpha_1} (C_{ijk}^r)^{\alpha_3} (H_{ijk}^r)^{\alpha_5} (D_{ijk}^r)^{\alpha_6}$$
$$e^{[\alpha_{11}(C_{ij}^b / Y_{ij}) + \alpha_{12}(H_{ij}^b / Y_{ij})]} \tag{2.3}$$

$$T_{ijk} = \alpha_0 (P_i P_j)^{\alpha_1} (C_{ijk}^r)^{\alpha_3} (H_{ijk}^r)^{\alpha_5} (D_{ijk}^r)^{\alpha_6} Y_{ij}^{\alpha_8}$$
$$e^{[\alpha_{11}(C_{ij}^b / Y_{ij}) + \alpha_{12}(H_{ij}^b / Y_{ij})]} \tag{2.4}$$

---

[2] See Quandt [7] for details.

$$T_{ijk} = \alpha_0 (P_i P_j)^{\alpha_1} (C_{ijk}{}^r)^{\alpha_3} (H_{ijk}{}^r)^{\alpha_5} (D_{ijk}{}^r)^{\alpha_6}$$
$$Y_{ij}{}^{(\alpha_8 + \alpha_9 A_{ijk} + \alpha_{10} B_{ijk})}$$
$$e^{[\alpha_{11}(C_{ij}{}^b / Y_{ij}) + \alpha_{12}(H_{ij}{}^b / Y_{ij})]} \tag{2.5}$$

$$T_{ijk} = \alpha_0 (P_i P_j)^{\alpha_1} (C_{ijk}{}^r)^{\alpha_3} (H_{ijk}{}^r)^{\alpha_5} (D_{ijk}{}^r)^{\alpha_6}$$
$$R_{ij}{}^{\alpha_7} Y_{ij}{}^{(\alpha_8 + \alpha_9 A_{ijk} + \alpha_{10} B_{ijk})}$$
$$e^{[\alpha_{11}(C_{ij}{}^b / Y_{ij}) + \alpha_{12}(H_{ij}{}^b / Y_{ij})]} \tag{2.6}$$

$$T_{ijk} = \alpha_0 (P_i P_j)^{\alpha_1} (C_{ij}{}^b)^{\alpha_2} (H_{ij}{}^b)^{\alpha_4}$$
$$e^{[\alpha_{13}(\log C_{ijk}{}^r / \log Y_{ij}) + \alpha_{14}(\log H_{ijk}{}^r / \log Y_{ij})}$$
$$+ \alpha_{15}(\log D_{ijk}{}^r / \log Y_{ij})]} \tag{2.7}$$

$$T_{ijk} = \alpha_0 (P_i P_j)^{\alpha_1} (C_{ij}{}^b)^{\alpha_2} (H_{ij}{}^b)^{\alpha_4} Y_{ij}{}^{\alpha_8}$$
$$e^{[\alpha_{13}(\log C_{ijk}{}^r / \log Y_{ij}) + \alpha_{14}(\log H_{ijk}{}^r / \log Y_{ij})}$$
$$+ \alpha_{15}(\log D_{ijk}{}^r / \log Y_{ij})]} \tag{2.8}$$

$$T_{ijk} = \alpha_0 (P_i P_j)^{\alpha_1} (C_{ijk}{}^r)^{\alpha_3} (H_{ijk}{}^r)^{\alpha_5} (D_{ijk}{}^r)^{\alpha_6}$$
$$(Y_{ij}{}^{\alpha_8} (C_{ij}{}^b / I_{ijc})^{\alpha_{16}} (H_{ij}{}^b / I_{ijb})^{\alpha_{17}} \tag{2.9}$$

Equation (2-1) is one of the earliest versions of the abstract mode model. The remaining formulations attempt in various ways to introduce "non-abstractness" by the use of dummy variables or by the other modifications of the functional form. Equation (2-2) is a modification of Equation (2-1) achieved by introducing two dummy variables for auto and bus travel respectively. Equations (2-3) to (2-6) all express, in various ways, the hypothesis that it is not the "best" cost and journey time that are relevant for travel, but these same figures relative to income as measured by $C_{ij}{}^b / Y_{ij}$ and $H_{ij}{}^b / Y_{ij}$. Equations (2-3) and (2-4) assume that the income elasticities for travel along different routes may be different but that they are the same for different modes on the same route. Equations (2-5) and (2-6) relax the assumption of equal income elasticities for different modes on the same route by introducing two dummy variables. Equations (2-7) and (2-8) represent an alternative approach to relaxing this assumption, the hypothesis being that it is the ratio of relative cost, journey time and departure frequency to income that is relevant in travel demand. Finally, equation (2-9) is a preliminary and relatively simple formulation of the notion of intervening opportunities.[3]

3. Problems of Estimation

Each of the models in Section 2 can have the stochastic term specified multiplicatively or additively, as in $y_i = \alpha x_i^\beta e^{u_i}$ or $y_i = \alpha x_i^\beta + v_i$. In the former case parameter estimates are obtained by taking logarithms on both sides and using the standard linear regression theory. In the latter case the sum of squares of deviations must be minimized directly by employing some suitable algorithm. The algorithms described in Marquardt [5] and Goldfeld, Quandt and Trotter [2] were employed for this purpose. The latter performed better on the whole, although in some cases it also failed to achieve satisfactory convergence.

In the case of nonlinear estimation, approximations to the variances of the estimates can be obtained in various ways. We experimented with two methods. (1) One can minimize the sum of squares of deviations, which is equivalent to maximizing the likelihood function under the assumption of normality, and then the asymptotic covariance matrix of estimates can be approximated by the Cramer-Rao lower bound (See Wilks [9, Chap. 12].) (2) One can expand the original estimating equation in Taylor Series, truncate after the linear term and then compute the covariance matrix of estimates as in the case of ordinary linear regression. This was the technique actually employed in the computations.

4. Analysis of Results and Choice of Model

All the equations (described in Section 2) yield good results in the sense that the correlation coefficient is invariably higher than .80. The size of the correlation coefficient is not a satisfactory measure of the goodness of a model. Our choices amongst models are based partly on a priori considerations and partly on their predictive power.[4]

---

[3] More complicated formulations would allow traffic patterns to be derived from models of generalized gravitational equilibrium. For a more explicit model of this type see Blackburn [1].

[4] For somewhat similar concerns see Howrey [4].

4.1. Preliminary Considerations and A Priori Judgments. The basic results are shown in Tables 1 and 2, representing California and Northeast Corridor data respectively. The California data include air, bus, and car travel for 16 city pairs; the Northeast Corridor data include air, bus, car and rail travel for 32 city pairs. Both refer to 1960 travel volumes. In each of these tables the equation numbers appear on top and the coefficients are listed on the left hand margin. The column corresponding to each equation is divided into two subcolumns, A and B. The first one contains the results of loglinear minimization of the sum of squares and the second has the results of direct nonlinear minimization of the sum of squares. These will be referred to as methods A and B, respectively.

Considering first Table 1, certain uniformities are striking. The elasticity of travel demand with respect to population (α_1) is between .62 and 1.08. These estimates are significant and we may conclude that α_1 is slightly less than 1.0, say .90 ± .10. The coefficients of best and relative travel time (α_4, α_5) are almost invariably negative, as one would hypothesize. But some estimates of the coefficient of best travel cost (α_2) and relative travel cost (α_3) are positive. Most of them are, however, not statistically significant. The elasticity with respect to the relative departure frequency (α_6) falls mostly between .2 and .5 but is rarely significant. Somewhat less uniform is the behavior of (α_7), the coefficient of the range variable R_{ij}; it is mostly positive but also generally not statistically significant.

A difficult problem arises when we consider the income elasticity of demand denoted by η. For Equations (2-1) and (2-9), the coefficient α_8 is the income elasticity. For the other equations, this elasticity has to be calculated in each instance. Depending on the equation, the income elasticity may depend on the mode or on the city pair or both. A priori reasoning leads us to conjecture that $\eta > 0$ but less than some figure approximately between 3 and 4. We further hypothesize that the income elasticity for travel by air is not lower than for travel by bus and auto.[5] The only two equations of type A not ruled out by either of these two a priori criteria are (2-3) and (2-7). As far as equations of type B are concerned, Equation (2-5) violates the criterion that the income elasticities with respect to air

---

[5]This restriction may be questioned if it is assumed that an increase in income not only induces some bus travelers to go by air but also induces low-income non-travelers to start traveling by bus in sufficiently large numbers.

Table 1

Linear and Nonlinear Estimates of Coefficients and Related Statistics, California*

Equation

Parameter	(2-1)		(2-2)		(2-3)		(2-4)	
	A	B	A	B	A	B	A	B
α_1	1.03 (6.77)	.85	1.08 (7.45)		.87 (7.22)	.62 (12.40)	.90 (7.66)	
α_2	.60 (.64)	2.85	2.49 (2.23)					
α_3	-2.79 (-4.87)	-4.79	.40 (.31)		-2.34 (-4.60)	-2.62 (-4.16)	-2.45 (-4.95)	
α_4	-3.21 (-1.99)	-4.10	-5.09 (-3.07)					
α_5	-1.95 (-4.99)	-4.97	-3.74 (-4.58)		-1.72 (-4.58)	-2.46 (-5.59)	-1.78 (-4.87)	
α_6	.22 (.81)	.84	.04 (.04)		.42 (1.77)	.88 (.85)	.38 (1.63)	
α_7	5.72 (1.54)	-2.01	5.29 (7.53)					
α_8	6.14 (2.14)	2.28	3.61 (1.27)				5.83 (1.94)	
α_9			.62 (2.80)					
α_{10}			.91 (2.72)					
α_{11}					-401.96 (-1.33)	429.33 (1.23)	-597.65 (-1.93)	
α_{12}					-1413.57 (-2.52)	-2250.44 (-5.40)	-765.66 (-1.20)	
α_{13}								
α_{14}								
α_{15}								
α_{16}								
α_{17}								

Equation

(2-5) A	(2-5) B	(2-6) A	(2-6) B	(2-7) A	(2-7) B	(2-8) A	(2-8) B	(2-9) A	(2-9) B
.97	.62	1.05		.86	.67	.88		.86	
(8.16)		(6.85)		(6.38)	(8.37)	(7.25)		(7.07)	
				-.24	1.81	-.57			
				(-.43)	(2.03)	(-1.00)			
.24	-.65	-.04						-2.38	
(.18)		(-.03)						(-4.71)	
				-1.98	-3.14	-1.20			
				(-2.23)	(-3.61)	(-1.24)			
-3.10	-2.47	-3.13						-1.83	
(-4.03)		(-4.65)						(-4.80)	
.20	.87	.08						.43	
(.76)		(.27)						(1.82)	
		2.98							
		(.85)							
3.26	-.44	3.19				5.35		5.62	
(1.04)		(1.02)				(1.84)		(1.98)	
.75	.37	.74							
(2.23)		(2.18)							
.50	.14	.48							
(2.28)		(2.20)							
301.93	448.51	589.74							
(.61)		(.98)							
-1734.38	-2299.99	-2387.83							
(-2.33)		(-2.22)							
				-17.21	-3440.06	-18.11			
				(-4.35)	(-4.76)	(-4.67)			
				-13.17	-3950.73	-13.58			
				(-4.41)	(-4.32)	(-4.67)			
				3.72	2472.85	3.35			
				(2.02)	(2.09)	(1.86)			
								-.11	
								(-.21)	
								-1.86	
								(-2.01)	

*Numbers in parentheses represent *t*-values. For Columns B they were not always computed.

Table 2

Linear and Nonlinear Estimates of Coefficients and Related Statistics, Northeast Corridor

| | Equation | | | | | | | |
| Param-eter | (2-1) | | (2-2) | | (2-3) | | (2-4) | |
	A	B	A	B	A	B	A	B
α_1	1.00 (7.15)	.78	.90 (7.64)	.88	.73 (7.23)	1.77 (16.09)	.71 (6.81)	2.07
α_2	−.83 (−1.63)	−5.29	−1.32 (−3.05)	−5.53				
α_3	−2.26 (−4.97)	−3.62	−3.09 (−7.75)	−4.43	−1.72 (−3.74)	−3.83 (−9.57)	−1.67 (−3.61)	−3.94
α_4	.52 (1.14)	.51	1.03 (2.66)	1.31				
α_5	−.55 (−2.09)	.52	.06 (.25)	1.51	−.46 (−1.63)	−.26 (−.96)	−.45 (−1.57)	−.82
α_6	.80 (6.12)	.55	1.16 (8.95)	.95	.95 (7.17)	.35 (1.59)	.96 (7.18)	1.73
α_7	2.62 (1.44)	−7.16	2.72 (1.79)	−5.97				
α_8	2.43 (1.92)	−.34	2.46 (2.32)	−1.71			.84 (.62)	.28
α_9			−.27 (−6.47)	−.36				
α_{10}			−.37 (−6.79)	−.35				
α_{11}					−3.28 (−2.82)	74.25 (21.28)	−3.24 (−2.77)	−73.42
α_{12}					−7.17 (−.71)	117.52 (5.91)	−6.78 (−.67)	108.55
α_{13}								
α_{14}								
α_{15}								
α_{16}								
α_{17}								

Equation

(2-5)		(2-6)		(2-7)		(2-8)		(2-9)	
A	*B*	*A*	*B*	*A*	*B*	*A*	*B*	*A*	*R*
.57	3.37	.87	1.42	.93		.89		.77	
(5.99)		(7.89)		(8.05)		(7.61)		(5.55)	
				−1.30		−1.35			
				(−3.59)		(−3.73)			
−2.31	−5.12	−3.04	−4.63					−1.84	
(−5.46)		(−7.17)						(−3.98)	
				.43		.47			
				(.94)		(1.03)			
.15	9.02	−.09	3.35					−.51	
(.56)		(−.35)						(−1.83)	
1.33	5.09	1.19	1.49					.93	
(9.43)		(8.86)						(7.02)	
		5.02	−5.60						
		(4.53)							
.62	−35.57	2.21	−11.78			2.25		1.86	
(.52)		(1.90)				(1.77)		(1.38)	
−.25	−1.25	−.26	−.52						
(−5.24)		(−5.89)							
−.36	−1.39	−.36	−.53						
(−5.77)		(−6.33)							
−4.69	119.89	−1.12	−80.86						
(−4.40)		(−.89)							
2.18	329.60	11.68	118.30						
(.24)		(1.35)							
				−16.84		−16.26			
				(−4.92)		(−4.77)			
				−4.14		−3.64			
				(−2.09)		(−1.84)			
				6.26		6.24			
				(6.21)		(6.26)			
								−.75	
								(−1.74)	
								−.03	
								(−.06)	

travel should exceed those with respect to bus and auto travel. Among those remaining, Equation (2-3) yields reasonable estimates of the income elasticity varying between 1.1 and 3.5 for different city pairs. However, Equation (2-7) does not provide acceptable estimates.

The results presented in Table 2 pertain to the Northeast Corridor. The coefficient α_1 ranges between 0.57 and 0.93, and is significant for method A. The corresponding results from method B, however, fluctuate more widely. The coefficients α_2 and α_3 are negative and highly significant in many cases. The coefficient α_5 is positive, although it is generally not statistically significant. The coefficient estimates for α_7 are positive for method A, but negative for method B. In fact, every one of the equations computed for the Northeast Corridor gives *a priori* unacceptable results for method B; the results of method A are mostly quite reasonable.

Certain general conclusions emerge from comparison of Tables 1 and 2: (a) The population elasticities are substantially the same in the Northeast Corridor as in California; (b) the elasticity with respect to departure frequency is less in California than in the Northeast Corridor, where it is mostly between .7 and 1.00 and also highly statistically significant; (c) the elasticity with respect to journey time, contrary to our expectation, is often positive but not statistically significant in the Northeast Corridor. Perhaps conclusions (b) and (c) make sense in the light of the fact that average distances in the Northeast Corridor are smaller than in California; hence travel time becomes less significant but departure frequency more important. (d) This is perhaps further supported by the finding that α_{16} is much more significant relative to α_{17} in the Northeast Corridor than in California; i.e., the availability of alternative short trips (compared to a given trip) in the Northeast Corridor does not have as much a discouraging effect on trips along the given arc as in California. Finally, (e) for the Northeast Corridor, the income elasticities are of reasonable orders of magnitude ($0 < \eta < 3$) but vary from model to model.[6] It must be noted that Equations (2-3) and (2-7), selected from the California results using log-linear regression, also provide more or less reasonable estimates of the income elasticity from Northeast Corridor data; they are slightly higher or lower than one, respectively.

---

[6] If we compare the results of these equations with those obtained by using the average of the median incomes in city pairs instead of the weighted mean per capita income in the two cities, we find that the estimates of coefficients of variables *not* involving income are more or less unchanged but that the estimates of coefficients of the variables which do involve income sometimes change rather erratically.

In view of the fact that method B does not always converge for California data, and that its results fluctuate rather widely compared with those of the method A for Northeast Corridor data, we conclude that method A seems to be relatively more reliable. This is equivalent to the conclusion that multiplicative error is more important than additive error. We therefore exclude method B from further serious consideration.

4.2. The Choice Among Equations on A Priori Grounds. Equation (2-2) assumes that the income elasticity for distinct modes is different, though it is the same within each mode for distinct city pairs. Both dummy variables in (2-2) are highly statistically significant for both California and also Northeast Corridor data. These results strongly suggest that the income elasticities for distinct modes are different from one another.

Equations (2-3) and (2-4) attempt to examine another hypothesis, namely that income elasticities are the same for distinct city pairs. The choice between (2-3) and (2-4) is somewhat difficult. Empirical results for California data yield bad estimates of the income elasticity of (2-4), though both equations provide reasonable estimates of the income elasticity for Northeast Corridor data. For this reason one may prefer (2-3) to (2-4) but it seems difficult to argue convincingly that (2-4) ought to be rejected completely.

Equations (2-5) and (2-6) as well as (2-7) and (2-8) attempt in alternative ways to combine both the features of (2-2) and (2-3) or (2-4). According to these models, income elasticities are different not only for different modes but also for different city pairs. Both (2-5) and (2-6) violate several *a priori* expectations concerning the sign and size of certain coefficients and for these reasons, neither can be regarded as an adequate formulation.

Finally, consider Equations (2-7) and (2-8). The application of these formulations to both California and Northeast Corridor data provide very reasonable results, except that the elasticity of best travel time is estimated to be positive for Northeast Corridor data. However, this result is not statistically different from zero. The choice between (2-7) and (2-8) is again difficult. Based on the empirical evidence that (2-8) yielded unreasonably high estimates of income elasticities for California data, we may prefer (2-7). This choice, as the one between (2-3) and (2-4), is based entirely on the empirical evidence and is tentative at best.[7]

---

[7]It must be noted that although Equations (2-3) and (2-7) resulted in very reasonable estimates of income elasticities by method A (log-linear regression), the same formulas did not always provide reasonable estimates if the estimation is by method B (direct minimization).

The results from Equation (2-7) indicate that air and rail travel have a higher income elasticity than the other modes and that auto travel has the lowest income elasticity. The estimates of income elasticity are extremely sensitive to both the statistical method employed and the functional form specified.

Finally, Equation (2-9) also yields very reasonable results except for the income elasticity as estimated from California data. The various *a priori* considerations employed thus leave us with Equations (2-3), (2-4), (2-7), (2-8) and (2-9). Although all of these equations seem to be reasonably applicable for both California and Northeast Corridor data we shall concentrate our further efforts on testing these equations based on Northeast Corridor data alone.

4.3. The Choice Among Equations on Forecasting Grounds. The forecasts from Equations (2-3), (2-4), (2-7), (2-8) and (2-9) may be considered as forecasts from competing formulas. Consider a situation in which the actual values of the dependent variable are denoted by y, the forecasts by one formula by f_1 and those from another by f_2. Hoel [3] has suggested a t-test for testing f_2 against f_1 which is equivalent to finding a significant β in the regression $y - f_1 = \alpha + \beta(f_2 - f_1)$. A significantly positive β implies rejection of f_1 in favor of f_2. Obviously the roles of f_1 and f_2 may be interchanged and the regression $y - f_2 = \alpha' + \beta'(f_1 - f_2)$ computed. If β is significantly positive and β' significantly negative, the rejection of f_1 in favor of f_2 is doubly confirmed. If β and β' are both significant and of the same sign an ambiguous situation exists and no clear choice can be made.

The forecasts from the five equations to be evaluated may be either in logarithmic or in natural form. In other words, if the equation $y = \alpha_0 x^{\alpha_1}$ is estimated as a linear regression after logarithms are taken, i.e., as $\log y = \log \alpha_0 + \alpha_1 \log x$, then the quantity $\widehat{\log y} = \widehat{\log \alpha_0} + \hat{\alpha}_1 \log x$ is best linear unbiased prediction for $\log y$. An unbiased prediction for y, however, is given by $\hat{y} = \exp\{\widehat{\log \alpha_0} + \hat{\alpha}_1 \log x + \hat{\sigma}^2/2\}$ where $\hat{\sigma}^2$ is the estimated error variance. The computations for the final test were performed pairwise for all five equations using both the logarithmic and the unbiased natural predictions. The corresponding t-values for β are displayed in Tables 3 and 4. A positive entry in the Tables indicates rejection of the null hypothesis. Double confirmation for the rejection of null

Table 3

t-Values for Hoel Test Using
Logarithmic Prediction

Null Hypothesis Equation	Alternative Hypothesis Equation				
	(2-3)	(2-4)	(2-7)	(2-8)	(2-9)
(2-3)	—	0.63	3.69	4.43	1.11
(2-4)	0.00	—	3.51	4.48	1.01
(2-7)	−1.02	−0.50	—	1.81	0.45
(2-8)	−1.76	−1.78	−0.00	—	−0.05
(2-9)	7.21	7.23	8.25	8.53	—

Table 4

t-Values for Hoel Test Using
Unbiased Natural Prediction

Null Hypothesis Equation	Alternative Hypothesis Equation				
	(2-3)	(2-4)	(2-7)	(2-8)	(2-9)
(2-3)	—	2.29	0.68	0.83	0.47
(2-4)	−1.85	—	0.84	0.94	0.40
(2-7)	3.87	4.15	—	2.59	3.05
(2-8)	3.40	3.70	−1.81	—	2.41
(2-9)	2.24	2.61	0.02	0.17	—

hypothesis i by alternative hypothesis j requires that the entry in the ith row and jth column be significantly positive and the entry in the jth row and ith column be significantly negative.

Either table may be used to deduce an implied ordering of equations.[8] Table 3 implies the following ordering from best to

---

[8]The orderings will, of course, depend on whether they are based on the signs of the t-values, on significant t-values, or on pairs of significant t-values (ith row and jth column paired with jth row and ith column). The orderings determined here rest on significant t-values.

worst models: (2-7) and (2-8) tied, then (2-3) and (2-4) tied and finally (2-9). The corresponding ordering from Table 4 is (2-4) best, then (2-3), (2-9), (2-8), and finally (2-7). The two orderings are quite different. Since the natural value of travel volume seems the more relevant quantity rather than its logarithm, the results of Table 4 should be considered decisive.

5. Generalized Least Squares Estimates and the Theory of Intrinsic Characteristics

In the previous sections, we have considered two different specifications of the error terms, i.e., multiplicative error and additive error. The empirical analyses of both the California and Northeast Corridor data suggest that the specification of multiplicative error yields more reasonable results than the alternative specification of additive error. In view of the fact that the error term may include the effect of all omitted variables which might be utilized for forecasting purposes, we shall examine how this effect can be estimated even though the omitted variables cannot be explicitly included. It is important to note that, in our present study, the effect of some of the omitted variables may be considered as "intrinsic characteristics" of city pairs. Obviously, if we assume that these intrinsic characteristics do not change substantially over time, then they should also be utilized for purposes of forecasting.

The modification of the error term required for an estimation of the intrinsic characteristics consists of the decomposition of the error term into two independent components, representing the intrinsic characteristics and the random errors respectively.[9] We further assume that the intrinsic characteristics are the same for the same city pair regardless of the mode of transportation. In symbols, we have $U_{ijk} = \epsilon_{ij} + V_{ijk}$, where ϵ_{ij} and V_{ijk} are the intrinsic characteristics and random errors respectively. Assuming, in general, that there are n city pairs and m modes, and denoting by I_n the identity matrix of order n, the total error terms U_{ijk} may be represented as follows:

$$U = [I_n I_n \ldots I_n]' \epsilon + V \qquad (5-1)$$

where U and V are column vectors with nm elements consisting of U_{ijk} and V_{ijk} respectively, and ϵ a column vector with n elements

[9]The discussion to follow is related only to the specification of the error terms. Therefore, the appropriate estimating and forecasting procedures to be proposed would be applicable to all models which can be transformed into linear regressions.

consisting of ϵ_{ij}. The assumptions of our modified specification can be summarized as:

$$(i) \quad E(U) \quad = [I_n \ I_n \ldots I_n]'E(\epsilon) = 0 \qquad (5.2a)$$

$$(ii) \quad E(UU') \quad = \Omega = \sigma_\epsilon^2 M + \sigma_\nu^2 I_{nm}$$

$$= \sigma_\nu^2 [I_{nm} + \delta M] \qquad (5.2b)$$

where $\sigma_\epsilon^2 = E(\epsilon_{ij}^2)$ and $\sigma_\nu^2 = E(V_{ijk}^2)$ are the variances of the intrinsic characteristics and random errors respectively. The quantity δ denotes the ratio of variances of the two components of the error term, i.e., $\delta = \sigma_\epsilon^2/\sigma_\nu^2$. Finally, the matrix M is defined as follows:

$$\underset{(nm \ \times \ nm)}{M =} \begin{bmatrix} I_n & I_n & \cdots & I_n \\ I_n & I_n & \cdots & I_n \\ \multicolumn{4}{c}{\cdots\cdots\cdots\cdots} \\ I_n & I_n & \cdots & I_n \end{bmatrix}$$

Assumption (i) implies that there is an intrinsic characteristic ϵ_{ij} for each city pair. In fact, ϵ_{ij} is the mean of the error terms associated with different modes for the same city pair. Assumption (ii) asserts that the variance-covariance matrix of the error terms is no longer diagonal, in general. Clearly if the intrinsic characteristics ϵ_{ij} are identically zero for all city pairs, then our modified specification becomes the usual regression model where $E(U) = 0$ and $E(UU') = \sigma_u^2 I$ hold.

It can be verified that the inverse of the variance-covariance matrix can be expressed as:

$$\Omega^{-1} = [I_{nm} - kM]/\sigma_\nu^2 \qquad (5.3)$$

where $k = \delta/(1 + m\delta) = \sigma_\epsilon^2/[\sigma_\nu^2 + m\sigma_\epsilon^2]$. Therefore, the generalized least squares estimates can be written as

$$\tilde{\alpha} = (X'\Omega^{-1} X)^{-1}(X'\Omega^{-1} Y)$$

$$= [X'(I_{nm} - kM)X]^{-1} [X'(I_{nm} - kM)Y] \qquad (5.4)$$

It may be noted that the ordinary least-squares estimates approach the generalized least-squares estimates as m increases to infinity. This becomes clear by observing that $k = \delta/(1 + m\delta)$. The variance-covariance matrix of the estimates given in (5-4) can be derived from:

$$\text{cov}(\widetilde{\alpha}) = (X'\Omega^{-1}X)^{-1}$$

$$= \sigma_v^2 [X'(I_{nm} - kM)X]^{-1}$$

$$= \left\{\sigma_u^2(1 - mk)/[1 - (m - 1)k]\right\}[X'(I_{nm} - kM)X]^{-1}$$

$$(5.5)$$

where $\sigma_u^2 = E(U_{ijk}^2)$ is the variance of the composite error term. It can be seen from (5-4) that, for each value of k, there is a corresponding set of generalized least-squares estimates. When $k = 0$, the generalized least-squares estimates are identical to the ordinary least-squares estimates. A natural criterion for the selection of the "best" set of generalized least-squares estimates among all possible sets of estimates is the principle of minimum generalized least-squares, which is obtained by minimizing $U'\Omega^{-1}U$.

To demonstrate the application of our modified specification of the error term, we have selected Equations (2-3) and (2-7) for examination.[10] These models have been estimated for the Northeast Corridor data by the generalized least-squares procedure as just described, in addition to the ordinary least-squares. The results of both procedures are summarized in Table 5. A value of 0.2 was employed for k since this gave the best results among all values tried. As shown in this table, the generalized least-squares estimates are indeed more efficient than the ordinary least-squares estimates. The t-values of the former are comparable or higher than those of the latter, particularly for the t-values associated with log C_{ijk}^r and log H_{ijk}^r. An exception is the case of variable log H_{ij}^b which has the "wrong" sign in Equation (2-7). There generalized least-squares results in an even smaller t-value, thus making the "wrong" coefficient even less significant. While no estimates of the "intrinsic characteristics" are provided by the ordinary least-squares procedure, such estimates for generalized least-squares may be derived by

---

[10]Equation (2-3) is among the best when we consider the results of the Hoel test based on the unbiased predictions of travel volume. Equation (2-7) is among the best when the Hoel test is based on the logarithmic forecasts.

Table 5

**Estimates From Ordinary Least-Squares
and Generalized Least Squares*.
Northeast Corridor Data**

Parameter	Equation (2-3)		Equation (2-7)	
	OLS(k = 0)	GLS(k =.2)	OLS(k = 0)	GLS(k = .2)
α_1	0.73	0.75	0.93	0.95
	(7.23)	(7.13)	(8.05)	(7.99)
α_2			-1.30	-1.32
			(-3.59)	(-3.56)
α_3	-1.72	-2.70		
	(-3.74)	(-7.41)		
α_4			0.43	0.21
			(0.94)	(0.44)
α_5	-0.46	-0.78		
	(-1.63)	(-3.82)		
α_6	0.95	0.72		
	(7.17)	(7.28)		
α_{11}	-3.28	-3.34		
	(-2.82)	(-2.82)		
α_{12}	-7.17	-13.74		
	(-0.71)	(-1.30)		
α_{13}			-16.84	-23.33
			(-4.92)	(-8.75)
α_{14}			-4.14	-6.62
			(-2.09)	(-4.54)
α_{15}			6.26	4.82
			(6.21)	(6.58)
$\sigma_v^{\,2}$	1.74	1.13	1.58	1.09

*Figures in parentheses are t-values corre-
sponding to the coefficient estimates.

averaging over the residuals of the same city pair for different modes.
These estimated intrinsic characteristics are given in Table 6. These
figures reveal a great deal about intrinsic travel generating ability of
city pairs. A figure greater than one implies that the city pair
generates more traffic than would be predicted on the basis of
population, income and travel attributes alone; a figure less than one
implies that the city pair generates less traffic than would be

Table 6

Estimated Values of Intrinsic Characteristics: $e^{\epsilon_{ij}}$

City Pair (ij)	Equation	
	(2-3)	(2-7)
Boston-Providence	5.487	2.849
Boston-New Haven	2.092	1.235
Boston-New York	1.432	1.413
Boston-Philadelphia	1.219	1.375
Boston-Wilmington	1.627	1.043
Boston-Baltimore	1.775	1.939
Boston-Washington	3.175	3.293
Providence-New York	1.302	1.533
Providence-Philadelphia	0.552	0.680
Providence-Baltimore	0.944	0.577
Providence-Washington	1.592	2.103
New Haven-New York	0.620	0.578
New Haven-Philadelphia	0.560	0.708
New Haven-Baltimore	0.806	0.715
New Haven-Washington	1.277	1.801
Bridgeport-Baltimore	0.399	0.441
Bridgeport-Washington	1.947	2.755
New York-Trenton	0.187	0.189
New York-Philadelphia	0.367	0.302
New York-Wilmington	0.491	0.650
New York-Baltimore	0.631	0.803
New York-Washington	1.216	1.508
Trenton-Philadelphia	1.697	1.089
Trenton-Wilmington	0.353	0.478
Trenton-Baltimore	0.409	0.546
Trenton-Washington	1.370	1.741
Philadelphia-Wilmington	1.913	0.962
Philadelphia-Baltimore	0.594	0.634
Philadelphia-Washington	1.036	1.356
Wilmington-Baltimore	0.483	0.478
Wilmington-Washington	1.604	2.543
Baltimore-Washington	7.593	3.919

predicted on the basis of those factors alone. Thus, for example, the Boston-Providence or Baltimore-Washington arcs generate very large volumes of travel. In fact, every arc involving Washington at the Southern end generates "excess" volume. Trenton, N. J., on the other hand is, on the whole, a traffic inhibitor. These conclusions are intuitively quite plausible.

Two additional tests, one informal and one formal, were performed in order to facilitate the choice between ordinary and generalized least-squares. The first of these consisted in finding the simple correlation between the actual travel volume on the one hand and the unbiased prediction for volume from, alternately, the ordinary and generalized least-squares procedures on the other hand. For Equation (2-3), these correlation coefficients are 0.06 for *OLS* and 0.83 for *GLS;* and for Equation (2-7), they are 0.14 for *OLS* and 0.88 for *GLS*. It is clear that the correlation coefficients for *OLS* are astonishingly low despite the fact that the multiple R^2 in logarithmic form is as high as 0.89 and 0.81 for Equations (2-3) and (2-7) respectively. Thus *GLS* seem vastly superior. Second, the Hoel test was used to compare the *OLS* and *GLS* predictions for Equation (2-3) and also for Equation (2-7). In the case of Equation (2-3), the *t*-values associated with the β coefficient, treating the *OLS* prediction as the null hypothesis, are 35.54 and, reversing the roles of f_1 and f_2, -10.45 respectively. In the case of Equation (2-7) these values are 35.86 and -5.50. In both cases the predictions from the *OLS* procedure are overwhelmingly rejected. Finally, Hoel's test was also employed to discriminate the unbiased *GLS* predictions of Equations (2-3) and (2-7). The results show that Equation (2-7) is preferable to Equation (2-3), because the *t*-values associated with the β coefficient are 10.46 when Equation (2-3) is treated as the null hypothesis, and -3.52 when Equation (2-7) is treated as the null hypothesis.

6. Conclusions

A variety of potential demand equations has been estimated, principally by two methods. One of these consisted of direct minimization of the sum of squares of residuals; the other minimizes the sum of squares of residuals after a logarithmic transformation. The two estimating methods correspond to additive and multiplicative specification of the error terms in the models respectively.

A combination of various types of *a priori* restrictions in the estimated parameter values successfully eliminated from further consideration all but five of the potential demand equations and all the estimates obtained by direct minimization of the sum of squares. The application of the Hoel test further narrowed the choice among competing formulations.

The remaining models were still not entirely satisfactory and led to the hypothesis that city pairs might be considered to have intrinsic characteristics which might cause travel along particular arcs to be different from what might be predicted on the basis of exogenous economic variables and modal attributes alone. This hypothesis implies a generalized least-squares estimating procedure which was carried out on two equations and yielded superior results. Both the coefficient estimates as well as those of the intrinsic characteristics of city pairs appear to be quite satisfactory.

References

[1] Blackburn, A. "A Test of A Generalized Gravity Model with Competition Terms," Chapter 4 in *Studies in Travel Demand,* Vol. III, MATHEMATICA, July, 1967.

[2] Goldfeld, S. M., R. E. Quandt, and H. F. Trotter. "Maximization by Quadratic Hill Climbing," *Econometrica,* 34 (1966), 541-551.

[3] Hoel, P. G. "On the Choice of Forecasting Formulas," *Journal of the American Statistical Association,* 42 (1947), 605-611.

[4] Howrey, E. P. "On the Choice of Forecasting Models for Air Travel," *Journal of Regional Science,* 9 (1969), 215-224.

[5] Marquardt, D. W. "Least-Squares Estimation of Nonlinear Parameters," DuPont du Nemours, March, 1966.

[6] Quandt, R. E. "The Construction of Travel Demand Models with Incomplete Data," *Papers — Sixth Annual Meeting* Transportation Research Forum, 1966.

[7] _____ . "Tests of the Abstract Mode Model," Chapter 2 in *Studies in Travel Demand,* Vol. II, MATHEMATICA, September, 1966.

[8] _____ and W. J. Baumol. "The Demand for Abstract Transport Modes: Theory and Measurement," *Journal of Regional Science,* 6 (1966), 13-26; also Chapter 4 in this volume.

[9] Wilks, S. S. *Mathematical Statistics.* New York: John Wiley and Sons, Inc., 1962.

[10] Young, K. H. "Testing the Adequacy of the Linear Abstract Mode Model," Chapter 1 in *Studies in Travel Demand,* Vol. III, MATHEMATICA, July 1967.

7

Estimation of Modal Splits

Richard E. Quandt

1. Introduction

It has been shown by Quandt (1966b) that a modal split model can be formulated in terms of the probability that a randomly selected person will travel by some mode or other along given arcs in a network.* Models of this type depend upon an explicit formulation of the utility function as a function of the various modes' attributes. The approach has thus been called the explicit abstract mode model.[1] Models of this type resemble each other particularly through the feature that they employ the notion of a generalized travel cost or (dis)utility function. Thus, an individual is assumed to choose the mode which causes him to incur the least (generalized) cost. They differ from each other in terms of (a) the particular functional forms chosen for the travel cost (disutility) function, (b) the assumptions concerning what variables are assumed to be random and (c) the form of the particular distribution functions hypothesized.[2]

The present paper is an attempt to apply the simple model described by Quandt (1966b) to a sample of travel data in sixteen California city pairs. Section 2 contains a brief recapitulation of the model itself. Section 3 discusses the results of estimating the model and Section 4 contrasts these findings with those of a simple regression model.

2. The Model

It will be assumed that the various modes can be characterized abstractly in terms of two attributes: H, the hours of travel time, and

Reprinted from *Transportation Research,* Vol. 2 (1968), pp. 41-50. Copyright © by the Pergamon Press. Used with permission.

*The author is indebted to L. Hoffman for performing much of the computer programming. This study was performed under Mathematica's contract with the Office of High Speed Ground Transportation, U.S. Department of Transportation, under Contract No. C-187-66.

[1] See Quandt (1966a).

[2] See Quandt (1966a, b).

C, the cost of the trip. Each individual is assumed to possess a disutility function $U = U(H,C)$. When a travel decision is to be made, the individual evaluates $U(H,C)$ for each mode and compares the resulting disutility figures with some threshold U_0.[3] If the disutilities of all modes exceed U_0, no travel occurs. If one or more modes have disutilities less than or equal to U_0, the individual selects the mode with lowest $U(H,C)$.

The mathematical details of the model depend upon how many modes are included in it. The California data pertain to travel by air, bus and car. The cost and journey time configuration for these modes is such that bus travel is dominated; i.e. the model, as developed for these modes, predicts that the probability of bus travel is zero.[4] Thus the three-mode model reduces to the two-mode model in the present case, and we shall therefore develop the details of the model only for the case in which two modes and two travel attributes exist.

Definitions. H_k and C_k represent the travel time and travel cost by mode k for some origin-destination pair which we leave unspecified at present. P_k represents the probability that a randomly selected person will travel by mode k along the route. P_0 denotes the probability that a person will not travel at all.

The assumptions of the model are:

A-1. Each individual has a disutility function of the form $U = \alpha H^\beta C^\gamma$, where $\alpha, \beta, \gamma \geqslant 0$.

A-2. Travel time and cost are measured in such units that for any origin-destination pair $H_1, H_2, C_1, C_2 > 1$.

A-3. $H_1 > H_2$ and $C_1 < C_2$. Only under this assumption can there be travel by both modes; if, for example, $H_1 > H_2$ and $C_1 > C_2$, then $P_1 = 0$.

A-4. α, β, γ are random variables, differing from individual to individual. We assume that α, β, γ are distributed independently according to the exponential distributions:

$$f(\alpha) = a_1 \exp(-a_1\, \alpha)$$
$$f(\beta) = a_2 \exp(-a_2\, \beta)$$
$$f(\gamma) = a_3 \exp(-a_3\, \gamma)$$

---

[3] The magnitude of U_0 may be variable from travel decision to travel decision and depend upon the urgency of the occasion.

[4] This is clearly unrealistic and a defect of the model in which only two attributes (cost and time) are considered. As a prediction, however, it is not bad for eleven out of the sixteen city pairs.

with the joint density being

$$f(\alpha,\beta,\gamma) = a_1 a_2 a_3 \exp(-a_1 \alpha - a_2 \beta - a_3 \gamma) \tag{2.1}$$

where a_1, a_2, a_3 are parameters to be estimated.

A-5. Since the travel decision is linearly homogeneous in U_0 and α, we can assume without loss of generality that U_0 is a constant. For simplicity we take $U_0 = 1$.[5]

Denoting by U_1 and U_2 the disutilities associated with modes 1 and 2, the probability that a randomly selected person will travel by mode 1 is given by

$$P_1 = \int \int \int a_1 a_2 a_3 \exp(-a_1 \alpha - a_2 \beta - a_3 \gamma) d\alpha d\beta d\gamma$$
$$U_1 \leqslant U_0 \tag{2.2}$$
$$U_1 \leqslant U_2$$

The region over which the density (2.1) is to be integrated is defined by the inequalities $U_1 \leqslant U_0$ and $U_1 \leqslant U_2$. These, in turn, imply, by assumptions A-1 and A-5, that

$$\alpha H_1{}^\beta C_1{}^\gamma \leqslant 1 \tag{2.3}$$

$$\alpha H_1{}^\beta C_1{}^\gamma \leqslant a H_2{}^\beta C_2{}^\gamma \tag{2.4}$$

From (2.4) we obtain

$$\beta \leqslant k\gamma \tag{2.5}$$

where

$$k = \frac{\log(C_2/C_1)}{\log(H_1/H_2)} \geqslant 0, \quad \text{by} \quad \text{A-3}$$

Taking logarithms, we obtain from (2.3)

$$\log \alpha + \beta \log H_1 + \gamma \log C_1 \leqslant 0 \tag{2.6}$$

The integrations in (2.2) are therefore over the convex region R_1 in Figure 7-1. Also, in order to obtain P_2 we have to integrate over R_2. These integrals are, respectively,

---

[5] It might be reasonable to assume that U_0 is a decreasing function of the traveler's income. For an explicit use of such an assumption see Blackburn (1966).

$$P_1 = -A_1 B_1 \sum_{j=0}^{\infty} (-1)^j \frac{a_1{}^j}{(j+1)!(B_1+1+j)}$$

$$+ A_2 \sum_{j=0}^{\infty} (-1)^j \frac{a_1{}^j(B_3-B_2)}{j!(B_2+1+j)(B_3+1+j)} \qquad (2.7)$$

and

$$P_2 = -A_3 B_4 \sum_{j=0}^{\infty} (-1)^j \frac{a_1{}^j}{(j+1)!(B_4+1+j)}$$

$$+ A_4 \sum_{j=0}^{\infty} (-1)^j \frac{a_1{}^j(B_5-B_6)}{j!(B_5+1+j)(B_6+1+j)} \qquad (2.8)$$

where the $A_i(i = 1, \ldots, 4)$ and $B_j(j = 1, \ldots, 6)$ depend upon the a's, the H's and the C's.[6]

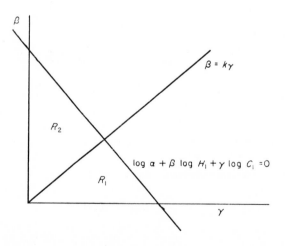

Figure 7-1

---

[6] For a derivation of these coefficients see Quandt (1966b, pp. 95, 96).

From P_1 and P_2 we can determine the modal split, i.e. the fraction of people who will travel by each of the two modes by calculating

$$Q_1 = P_1/(P_1 + P_2) \text{ and } Q_2 = P_2/(P_1 + P_2)$$

The model allows us to predict not only the modal split but also changes in the modal split resulting from some change in the underlying parameters, H_1, H_2, etc. In effect, changes in H_1, H_2, C_1, C_2 change the regions of integration in Figure 7-1. In addition, we can also predict the extent to which total travel demand will be influenced by such exogeneous changes. This prediction can be obtained either by an explicit calculation of $1 - P_0$ or simply by obtaining $P_1 + P_2$.

3. Estimation of the Model

Given observations on the number of travelers along various (ij) arcs of a network by each of k modes, one may compute modal split frequencies f_{ijk} defined as the fraction of travelers on the ijth arc who traveled by mode k.

Since there is no way of estimating P_{ij0} (the fraction of potential travelers on the ijth arc who stayed at home) the f_{ijk} will be used to estimate not the P_{ijk} but quantities Q_{ijk} defined by

$$Q_{ijk} = \frac{P_{ijk}}{\sum_{l \neq 0} P_{ifl}}$$

The Q_{ijk} are functions of the H's and C's (which are given) and of the a's (which are to be estimated). Estimation may be accomplished by selecting as the estimates those values of a_1, a_2, a_3 which minimize either of the two possible criterion functions

$$S_1 = \sum_{i,j,k} (Q_{ijk} - f_{ijk})^2 \tag{3.1}$$

or

$$S_2 = \sum_{i,j,k} \frac{(Q_{ijk} - f_{ijk})^2}{Q_{ijk}} \tag{3.2}$$

The former is equivalent to the sum of the squares of the errors. The latter is somewhat analogous to the χ^2 criterion of goodness of fit. Since each Q_{ijk} is expressed as a ratio of triple integrals, the estimation process is a non-trivial task. Evaluation of the integrals by (2.7) and (2.8) was found to be inappropriate since these equations represent infinite series with subsequent terms of opposite sign, and they converge very slowly. For this reason only two of the three integrations were done analytically; the third one was performed numerically.[7] The minimization was done by Newton's method with derivatives evaluated by perturbation of the coefficients.

Tables 1 and 2 display the basic results. They represent the results of minimization of S_1 and S_2 respectively. In each of these tables columns 1 and 5 contain the actually observed modal split for air and car travel respectively. Columns 2 and 6 contain the corresponding predicted values from the model. After a_1, a_2 and a_3 were estimated, the modal splits were recomputed, using the estimated values of the a's on the assumption that there was a uniform 25 per cent reduction in either (a) air journey time or (b) air fare or (c) car journey time or (d) car cost. The corresponding new modal splits for air travel [cases (a) and (b)] are displayed in columns 3 and 4 and for car travel [cases (c) and (d)] in columns 7 and 8.

A comparison of the two tables shows that the predictions of the model in Table 1 are worse for fourteen of the sixteen arcs in the network. Where the S_1 predictions are better, they are only marginally so. Thus minimization of S_2 seems preferable. Journey time and cost elasticities of demand can be computed from the computed changes in the modal split resulting from certain assumed changes in journey times and costs. These are not the usual elasticities but are *modal split elasticities.*[8] These modal split elasticities are given in Tables 3 and 4.

The only elasticities which exceed unity are the journey time elasticities of demand for air travel. The elasticities are different from arc to arc, and Tables 3 and 4 present minimum and maximum values as well as a crude mean value obtained by simple averaging of the individual figures. The elasticities with respect to journey time are

---

[7]This was performed by a seven-point quadrature known as the "Weddle rule". The extension of the model to three or perhaps even four attributes may be expected to raise the costs of analysis but probably not prohibitively. If the integrations are performed numerically, the major portion of the cost increase will consist of computational costs.

[8]The relation of modal split elasticities to the ordinary elasticities of demand is discussed in the Appendix. It should also be noted that these elasticities are arc elasticities.

Table 1

Actual and Predicted Modal Splits From Minimizing S_1

	Predicted air				Predicted car			
	Actual air	Standard	Reduce air H 25%	Reduce air C 25%	Actual car	Standard	Reduce car H 25%	Reduce car C 25%
Bakersfield-Los Angeles	0.002	0.120	0.181	0.132	0.998	0.880	0.959	0.930
Bakersfield-San Diego	0.012	0.134	0.162	0.139	0.988	0.866	0.919	0.915
Fresno-Los Angeles	0.026	0.135	0.169	0.142	0.974	0.865	0.925	0.915
Fresno-San Diego	0.232	0.095	0.116	0.094	0.968	0.905	0.954	0.940
Los Angeles-Sacramento	0.155	0.210	0.224	0.224	0.845	0.790	0.857	0.863
Los Angeles-San Diego	0.017	0.119	0.172	0.130	0.983	0.881	0.941	0.944
Los Angeles-San Francisco	0.209	0.228	0.237	0.242	0.791	0.772	0.830	0.848
Los Angeles-San Jose	0.056	0.232	0.246	0.251	0.944	0.768	0.834	0.848
Los Angeles-Santa Barbara	0.001	0.064	0.144	0.070	0.999	0.936	1.000	0.969
Los Angeles-Stockton	0.018	0.074	0.103	0.075	0.982	0.926	0.976	0.955
Sacramento-San Diego	0.258	0.137	0.149	0.139	0.742	0.863	0.915	0.912
Sacramento-San Francisco	0.003	0.063	0.129	0.068	0.997	0.938	1.000	1.000
Sacramento-San Jose	0.002	0.156	0.224	0.175	0.998	0.843	0.921	0.916
San Diego-San Francisco	0.327	0.229	0.231	0.241	0.673	0.770	0.831	0.848
San Diego-San Jose	0.020	0.217	0.224	0.231	0.980	0.783	0.850	0.860
San Diego-Santa Barbara	0.018	0.102	0.138	0.105	0.982	0.898	0.956	0.936

Table 2

**Actual and Predicted Modal Splits
From Minimizing S_2**

	Actual air	Predicted air			Actual car	Predicted car		
		Standard	Reduce air H 25%	Reduce air C 25%		Standard	Reduce car H 25%	Reduce car C 25%
Bakersfield-Los Angeles	0.002	0.113	0.180	0.130	0.998	0.887	0.962	0.931
Bakersfield-San Diego	0.012	0.126	0.161	0.138	0.988	0.874	0.921	0.915
Fresno-Los Angeles	0.026	0.126	0.168	0.141	0.974	0.874	0.927	0.916
Fresno-San Diego	0.232	0.087	0.116	0.093	0.768	0.913	0.955	0.941
Los Angeles-Sacramento	0.155	0.197	0.224	0.224	0.845	0.803	0.858	0.864
Los Angeles-San Diego	0.017	0.115	0.172	0.130	0.983	0.885	0.944	0.942
Los Angeles-San Francisco	0.209	0.215	0.237	0.242	0.791	0.785	0.831	0.849
Los Angeles-San Jose	0.056	0.218	0.246	0.251	0.944	0.782	0.835	0.849
Los Angeles-Santa Barbara	0.001	0.059	0.142	0.068	0.999	0.941	1.000	0.969
Los Angeles-Stockton	0.018	0.067	0.102	0.074	0.982	0.933	0.978	0.956
Sacramento-San Diego	0.258	0.127	0.148	0.138	0.742	0.873	0.916	0.913
Sacramento-San Francisco	0.003	0.061	0.130	0.067	0.997	0.939	1.000	1.000
Sacramento-San Jose	0.002	0.150	0.223	0.174	0.998	0.850	0.925	0.916
San Diego-San Francisco	0.327	0.215	0.232	0.241	0.673	0.785	0.831	0.848
San Diego-San Jose	0.020	0.203	0.224	0.232	0.980	0.797	0.850	0.860
San Diego-Santa Barbara	0.018	0.094	0.136	0.104	0.982	0.906	0.957	0.938

Table 3

**Estimated Modal Split Elasticities of
Demand from Minimizing S_1**

	Minimum value	Mean value	Maximum value
Demand for air travel			
Reduce air H by 25%	0.04	1.36	5.06
Reduce air C by 25%	0.02	0.24	0.48
Demand for car travel			
Reduce car H by 25%	0.21	0.29	0.36
Reduce car C by 25%	0.12	0.27	0.42

Table 4

**Estimated Modal Split Elasticities of
Demand from Minimizing S_2**

	Minimum value	Mean value	Maximum value
Demand for air travel			
Reduce air H by 25%	0.30	1.69	5.66
Reduce air C by 25%	0.32	0.49	0.62
Demand for car travel			
Reduce car H by 25%	0.18	0.24	0.36
Reduce car C by 25%	0.10	0.23	0.34

almost always greater than those with respect to cost. This finding is thoroughly consistent with earlier findings of Blackburn (1966). Moreover, if we consider the individual arcs to be ranked by the journey time elasticities computed from the present model as well as from Blackburn's model, we find that the rank correlation coefficient (Spearman's ρ) is 0.754, which is significant at the 0.01 level. The corresponding rank correlation for the cost elasticities is much lower, which is to be expected in view of the fact that the cost elasticities themselves are much smaller. In any event, these comparisons are not conclusive since the elasticities of the present model are modal split elasticities.

A final comparison of these elasticities may be made on the basis of the relation between modal split elasticities and ordinary elasticities as derived in the Appendix. Consider the regression model, fully analogous to those discussed in Quandt and Baumol (1966) of the form.[9]

$$T_{ijk} = \alpha_0 (P_i P_j)^{\alpha_1} (C_{ij}^{\ b})^{\alpha_2} (C_{ijk}^{\ r})^{\alpha_3} (H_{ij}^{\ b})^{\alpha_4} (H_{ijk}^{\ r})^{\alpha_5} (D_{ijk}^{\ r})^{\alpha_6} Y_{ij}^{\ \alpha_8}$$

where

T_{ijk}	=	travel volume on the ijth arc by mode k;
P_i, P_j	=	population at nodes i and j;
$C_{ij}^{\ b}$	=	best (cheapest) travel cost between i and j;
$C_{ijk}^{\ r}$	=	relative cost of mode k between i and j;
$H_{ij}^{\ b}$	=	best (fastest) travel time between i and j;
$H_{ijk}^{\ r}$	=	relative travel time by mode k between i and j;
$D_{ijk}^{\ r}$	=	relative departure frequency for mode k between i and j;
Y_{ij}	=	population weighted mean per capita income in nodes i and j.

Estimating this model from air and car travel data *alone* (for California) yields as estimates

$$\hat{\alpha}_2 = -0.31, \hat{\alpha}_3 = -2.41, \hat{\alpha}_4 = -1.61 \text{ and } \hat{\alpha}_5 = -2.78.$$

Since costs are higher but journey times lower for air travel on every arc, the ordinary elasticities of demand for air and car travel with respect to time and cost are as shown in Table 5. Substituting the estimated values of the α's and assuming that the ratio of car travel to air travel is nine (an assumption which is approximately but not uniformly correct), the application of the formula developed in the Appendix yields the following modal split elasticities as estimated from the regression model:

> Air elasticity with respect to air time = 2.50
> Air elasticity with respect to air cost = 2.17
> Car elasticity with respect to car time = 0.28
> Car elasticity with respect to car cost = 0.24

---

[9] Clearly we could have used any number of different formulations of the regression model and the results reported below would also have changed. The present formulation was selected for comparison because of its simplicity. For some similar approaches see also the extensive SARC report "Demand for intercity passenger travel in the Washington-Boston corridor", especially pp. V-9-V-12, V-44-V-46.

Table 5

Elasticities of Demand From the Regression Model

Elasticity of demand	With respect to			
	Air time	Car time	Air cost	Car cost
For air travel	α_4	0	α_3	$\alpha_2-\alpha_3$
For car travel	$\alpha_4-\alpha_5$	α_5	0	α_2

With the exception of the air elasticity with respect to cost, these figures compare quite favorably with the independently derived estimates in Tables 3 and 4. They also share the property of the earlier estimates that the air elasticities exceed the corresponding car elasticities. The results so far may be considered fairly encouraging although not conclusive.

4. Alternative Modal Split Models

Defining M_{ijk} as the fraction of travelers (or trips) on the ijth arc who employed the kth mode, one can easily formulate a regression approach to modal split forecasting. In analogy with the non-modal-split demand models discussed in Quandt and Baumol (1966), one might write

$$M_{ijk} = f(C_{ijk}{}^r, H_{ijk}{}^r \ldots)$$

and estimate the parameters of the function by least squares. Three alternative formulations of this type were considered and estimated. These are

$$M_{ijk} = \alpha_0 (C_{ijk}{}^r)^{\alpha_1} (H_{ijk}{}^r)^{\alpha_2} \tag{4.1}$$
$$M_{ijk} = \alpha_0 (C_{ijk}{}^r)^{\alpha_1} (H_{ijk}{}^r)^{\alpha_2} (C_{ij}{}^b)^{\alpha_3} (H_{ij}{}^b)^{\alpha_4} \tag{4.2}$$
$$M_{ijk} = \alpha_0 (C_{ijk}{}^r)^{\alpha_1} (H_{ijk}{}^r)^{\alpha_2} (C_{ij}{}^b)^{\alpha_3} (H_{ij}{}^b)^{\alpha_4} (D_{ijk}{}^r)^{\alpha_5} \tag{4.3}$$

Each of these models was estimated by using air and car travel data alone from the California sample, i.e. two modes for sixteen city pairs. The estimation was performed by least squares after taking logarithms on both sides of each estimating equation. The coefficient

Table 6

**Estimated Coefficients for Modal
Split Regressions**

Coefficient	Equation		
	(4.1)	(4.2)	(4.3)
$\log \alpha_0$	0.03	−0.58	−0.65
	(0.04)	(−0.77)	(−1.02)
α_1	−2.38	−3.23	−1.94
	(−4.72)	(−6.88)	(−3.50)
α_2	−0.30	−2.17	−2.49
	(−0.34)	(−2.49)	(−3.33)
α_3	—	1.76	1.79
	—	(2.40)	(2.89)
α_4	—	0.02	0.35
	—	(0.02)	(0.38)
α_5	—	—	0.90
	—	—	(3.35)
R^2	0.68	0.80	0.86
F	31.24	27.04	32.07

Figures in parentheses represent t-values.

estimates are shown in Table 6. The simplest of these formulations, equation (4.1), was included because it has almost the same number of parameters to be estimated as the probabilistic model of this article — specifically, the latter has three parameters, and equation (4.1) has four, namely α_0, α_1, α_2 and the error variance. The actual modal split for air travel and that predicted from the main model of this chapter, as well as from the regression models (4.1), (4.2) and (4.3), are displayed in Table 7. The ordinary predictions from the regression model were normalized so that the sum of the modal splits predicted is unity. It is noteworthy that even though every regression model estimates more parameters than the main model, this latter gives better predictions for five of the sixteen data points than do (4.1) and (4.2) and gives better predictions for four data points than does (4.3). This latter regression equation is also responsible for the single worst prediction.

Table 7

Modal Split for Air Forecasts
from Various Models

	Actual air %	Predicted from explicit model	Predicted from regression		
			(4.1)	(4.2)	(4.3)
Bakersfield–Los Angeles .	0.002	0.113	0.030	0.019	0.015
Bakersfield–San Diego	0.012	0.126	0.019	0.020	0.023
Fresno–Los Angeles	0.026	0.126	0.025	0.024	0.020
Fresno–San Diego	0.232	0.087	0.014	0.012	0.011
Los Angeles–Sacramento	0.155	0.197	0.052	0.115	0.067
Los Angeles–San Diego	0.017	0.115	0.022	0.014	0.035
Los Angeles–San Francisco	0.209	0.215	0.045	0.132	0.500
Los Angeles–San Jose	0.056	0.218	0.058	0.145	0.098
Los Angeles–Santa Barbara	0.001	0.059	0.024	0.010	0.009
Los Angeles–Stockton	0.018	0.067	0.020	0.013	0.004
Sacramento–San Diego	0.258	0.127	0.023	0.039	0.051
Sacramento–San Francisco	0.003	0.061	0.014	0.005	0.007
Sacramento–San Jose	0.002	0.150	0.033	0.024	0.006
San Diego–San Francisco	0.327	0.215	0.049	0.174	0.311
San Diego–San Jose	0.020	0.203	0.058	0.158	0.079
San Diego–Santa Barbara	0.018	0.094	0.017	0.011	0.011

A comparison of the predictive powers of two models can be obtained by a test which consists of estimating by least squares.[10]

$$y - f_2 = \alpha + \beta(f_1 - f_2)$$

where y are the actual values of the dependent variable, f_1 the values forecast by model 1 and f_2 those forecast by model 2. Here the values of f_2 will be provided by the forecasts from the main model and the values of f_1 will be, alternately, those from (4.1), (4.2) or (4.3). A significantly positive value of β would cause us to reject the f_2-values, i.e. the main model of this article. In point of fact, the three estimated β's are 0.08 (0.13), 1.01 (0.95), 0.39 (1.69), where the numbers in parentheses are the corresponding t-values. The main model cannot be rejected on the basis of these figures.

---

[10]See Young (1966).

5. *Conclusions*

The model outlined in Section 2 was successfully fitted and modal split elasticities as well as predictions were computed. The elasticities were compared with independently obtained estimates of the same quantities. This comparison showed that three of the relevant four figures were of comparable orders of magnitude. Similarity of the estimates is desirable since it suggests that both procedures are attempting to measure the same thing. The comparison is by no means conclusive, although it is rather suggestive. The predictions were compared with the predictions from several regression models for calculating modal split. Although the comparison favors the regression models slightly, it does not favor them conclusively or significantly from the statistical point of view, particularly when we take into account the fact that each regression model fitted more parameters than the basic model.

On the whole, this basic model has not performed too badly so far, particularly in view of the many limitations and shortcomings of our procedures. Some of the most notable of these are:

(1) The model has been tested only on the California sample which has many well-known weaknesses.[11]

(2) Only a two-attribute version of the model was fitted.

(3) Only air and automobile travel were considered.

(4) The regression models and elasticities used for comparative purposes all contain some element of arbitrariness.

(5) Only one kind of utility function and one kind of distribution function for the parameters of the utility function were employed.

(6) Not all numerical problems of evaluating integrals were fully resolved.

Further extensions of this approach seem therefore in order. The direction that additional research in this area should take is precisely toward relaxing the restrictive conditions enumerated above.

Appendix

Ordinary and modal split elasticities

Let T_1 and T_2 denote traffic volumes by modes 1 and 2 respectively and let p be a variable (such as the cost or journey time of the first mode) with respect to which demand elasticities are required.

---

[11] See Rose (1966).

The modal splits are defined by $M_1 = T_1/(T_1 + T_2)$ and $M_2 = 1 - M_1$. The *modal split elasticity* of the first mode with respects to p is then defined as

$$m_{1p} = \frac{\partial[T_1/(T_1 + T_2)]}{\partial p} \frac{p}{T_1/(T_1 + T_2)} \tag{A.1}$$

Performing the differentiation of the fraction in (A.1) we obtain

$$m_{1p} = \frac{\dfrac{\partial T_1}{\partial p}\dfrac{p}{T_1} - \dfrac{\partial T_2}{\partial p}\dfrac{p}{T_2}}{1 + \dfrac{T_1}{T_2}} = \frac{\eta_{1p} - \eta_{2p}}{1 + \dfrac{T_1}{T_2}} \tag{A.2}$$

where η_{1p} and η_{2p} are the elasticities of the demand for modes 1 and 2 with respect to variable p. Thus, for example, if p represents the price of mode 1 and if $T_1 = T_2$, then $m_{1p} = 0.5(\eta_{1p} - \eta_{2p})$, i.e. one-half of the difference between the own elasticity and the cross-elasticity.

References

Blackburn A. J. (1966). A nonlinear model of passenger demand. In *Studies in Travel Demand*, Vol. II, pp. 47-89. MATHEMATICA, Princeton, N.J.

Quandt R. E. (1966a). The construction of travel demand models with incomplete data. *Papers — Seventh Annual Meeting, Transportation Research Forum*, pp. 115-122.

Quandt R. E. and Baumol W. J. (1966). The demand for abstract transport modes: theory and measurement. *J. reg. Sci. 6*, 13-26; also Chapter 4 in this volume.

Rose M. (1966). Some problems and prospects in collecting data on travel demand. In *Studies in Travel Demand*, Vol. II, pp. 134-156. MATHEMATICA, Princeton, N.J.

Systems Analysis and Research Corporation. Demand for intercity passenger travel in the Washington-Boston corridor. Prepared for the U.S. Department of Commerce.

Young, K. H. (1966). Some considerations on the choice among forecasting formulas. In *Studies in Travel Demand*, Vol. II, pp. 114-132. MATHEMATICA, Princeton, N.J.

8

A Non-Linear Model of the Demand for Travel

Anthony J. Blackburn

1. Introduction

The model of this chapter attempts to describe the demand for intercity passenger transportation by all available modes.* Specification of the model, which is performed in Sections 2 and 3, can be decomposed into two stages. Firstly, the individual demand functions are derived from assumptions on the nature of consumers' choice between transportation alternatives. Secondly, the individual demands are combined by specifying the way tastes vary between individuals and by taking expectations.

The resulting market demand functions are mathematically quite complex, and this in turn leads to severe problems of estimation. The complexity of the model does, I believe, mirror to some extent the essential complexity of the market it attempts to explain, and simpler formulations may never be able to account completely for the observed variation of demands in this market. Nevertheless, the cost of the attempt to achieve greater realism is high. Estimation of the model, which is discussed in Section 4, is extremely difficult, and attempts to obtain better fits by sequential revision of assumptions and re-estimation is out of the question.

As a means of gaining perspective on this model, it is perhaps useful to contemplate the existence of a trade-off curve for transportation demand models, with computational dollars on one axis and conceptual realism on the other. This model, quite frankly, represents a fairly extreme point on the curve.

---

*This chapter is based on part of a study carried out at MATHEMATICA, Inc., for the U.S. Department of Commerce under contract number C-187-66. The author wishes to acknowledge indebtedness to Richard E. Quandt, Francis Sand, Kan Hua Young and Mark Rose for valuable comments and suggestions.

2. Behavioral Assumptions of the Model

All transportation demand models can be decomposed into terms which measure the mutual attractiveness of origins and destinations and terms which measure the effort of the impedance imposed by the transportation system. In attempting to describe the nature of individual choice we will be concerned primarily with the specification of impedance terms; in particular we will be concerned with representing the individual's choice between alternative modes and between alternative amounts of travel.

The central assumption of this section is that alternative modes of transportation are perfect substitutes for one another, in the sense that, if an individual prefers one mode over all others on one occasion, he will, other things being equal, prefer it on subsequent occasions. This assumption, though seemingly innocent, turns out to be quite restrictive. We now examine its implications.

In developing the model of individual choice between modes, it is necessary to extend the conventional model of consumer equilibrium to take into account the characteristics of the goods entering the market. The framework for expressing consumers' welfare as a function of the characteristics or 'attributes' of goods has been developed by Lancaster.[1] We now apply this treatment to the demand for alternative transportation modes.

At the beginning it is useful to restrict the analysis to a single origin-destination pair; the available goods are then simply the alternative modes of transportation between specified origin and destination. Consumers' equilibrium is assumed to be given by the maximum of a function of the consumption rates of n 'attributes,' such as travel time, safety, etc., and consumers' income after expenditures on travel have been deducted. The consumption level of each attribute is taken to depend linearly on the number of trips made by each mode. Notation is as follows:

$$\xi_i \ : \ \text{consumption of } i^{\text{th}} \text{ attribute,}$$
$$x_j \ : \ \text{demand for } j^{\text{th}} \text{ good (mode),}$$
$$p_j \ : \ \text{cost of trip by } j^{\text{th}} \text{ mode,}$$
$$y \ : \ \text{consumers' income.}$$

---

[1] K. J. Lancaster, "A New Approach to Consumer Theory," *Journal of Political Economy*, Vol. 74, April 1966, reprinted as Chapter 2 in the present volume. Although Lancaster's treatment of the demand for attributes is the first general formulation, transportation demand models have for a long time included "attributes" such as journey time, frequency, etc.

The dependence of the consumption of 'attributes' on the demand for goods is given by:

$$\xi_i = \sum_{j=1}^{m} \alpha_{ij}\, x_j \qquad\qquad i = 1,2,\ldots,n \qquad (2.1)$$

The coefficients of these relations are given technically; for example if the ith 'attribute' is travel time, a_{ij} denotes the travel time of a trip by the jth mode.

Consumers' equilibrium is then given by:

$$\text{Max } U(\xi_1,\ldots,\xi_n, y - \sum_{j=1}^{m} p_j x_j)$$

subject to

$$\xi_i = \sum_{j=1}^{m} \alpha_{ij} x_j \qquad\qquad i = 1,2,\ldots,n \qquad (2.2)$$

We now consider the implications of the assumption that modes are perfect substitutes for each other. Suppose the kth mode is to be preferred over all other available modes on a given trip. For this to be the case, the change in U resulting from one more journey by the kth mode must be greater than the change which results from one more journey by any other mode; if this were not the case, the kth mode would not be preferred. This condition can be written:

$$\sum_{i=1}^{n} U_i \alpha_{ik} - U_{n+1} p_k \geqslant \sum_{i=1}^{n} U_i \alpha_{ij} - U_{n+1} p_j \qquad j = 1,2,\ldots,m$$
$$(2.3)$$

where U_i is the partial derivative of U with respect to its ith argument. For convenience in notation we will let w_i denote the marginal rate of substitution in demand between money income and the ith attribute:

$$w_i = -\frac{U_i}{U_{n+1}} \qquad (2.4)$$

The condition (2.3) can then be written:

$$\sum_{i=1}^{n} w_i(\alpha_{ik} - \alpha_{ij}) + (p_k - p_j) \leqslant 0 \quad j = 1, 2, \ldots, m$$

$$(2.5)$$

If the kth mode *only* is to be demanded, in the manner of a perfect substitute, this condition must hold however many trips are made. It is clearly both necessary and sufficient for this to be the case, that *either* w_i be constant *or* that $\alpha_{ik} = \alpha_{ij}$.

In the context of travel demand, at least one of the 'attributes' must be the same for all modes. This is the attribute which defines the origin and destination of the journey and each trip, by whatever mode, will have the same impact on the consumption of this attribute. At the same time it is clearly unreasonable to require that the remaining attribute coefficients, denoting such things as journey time, be the same for all modes. The trade-off rates associated with these attributes must therefore be invariant with respect to the number of trips demanded.

We can now complete the derivation of the individual's demand for trips by each mode. Letting the origin-destination attribute be denoted by ξ_1 and setting α_{1j} equal unity for all modes, we will denote by C_k the sum of the travel cost of the kth mode and the attribute coefficients α_{ik} each weighted by their (constant) dollar trade-off rates:

$$C_k = p_k + \sum_{i=2}^{n} w_i \alpha_{ik} \qquad (2.6)$$

This we will call the generalized trip-cost of the kth mode. The condition for the kth mode to be preferred is then simply:

$$C_k \leqslant C_j \qquad j = 1, 2, \ldots, m \qquad (2.7)$$

Consumers' equilibrium is achieved by increasing the number of trips by the preferred mode until further trips yield no increment to economic welfare:

$$w_1(x_k) + C_k = 0 \qquad (2.8)$$

w_1 denotes the marginal rate of substitution between money and trips and will be an increasing function of x_k. Denoting the inverse function of $-w_1(x_k)$ by ψ, the individual demand for trips by the kth mode can be written:

$$
x_k = \begin{cases} \psi(C_k) & C_k \leqslant C_j \quad j = 1,2,\ldots,m \\ \\ 0 & \text{otherwise} \end{cases}
$$

$$
k = 1,2,\ldots,m \tag{2.9}
$$

This completes the *general* derivation of the individual's demand for trips by mode. The nature of the dependence of demand on trip-costs is shown, for the two mode cases in Figures 8-1 and 8-2. It is worth noting that both the discontinuities exhibited in Figures 8-1 and 8-2 *and* the linearity of the trip-cost function are derived from the requirement that transportation modes be perfect substitutes for one another. Final specification of the individual demand function must be carried out subject to these restrictions.

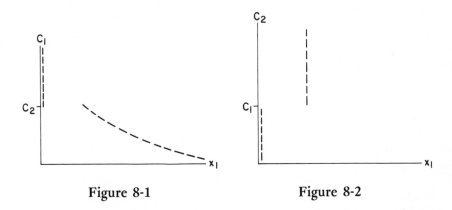

Figure 8-1   Figure 8-2

Two items remain before the individual demand function is fully specified; these are: the choice of ψ and the determination of which 'attributes' are to be included in the trip-cost function. We now deal with these in turn.

In specifying ψ it is necessary to determine the way in which demand is affected by both trip cost and those variables which measure the attractiveness of the trip ends. In this model demand is required to decline exponentially with trip cost and to have constant elasticity with respect to changes in both population and per capita income at the destination. In writing this out, we extend the notation to distinguish trips by origin and destination as well as mode:

x_{ijk} : individual's demand for trips from origin i to destination j by the kth mode
C_{ijk} : trip cost from i to j by the kth mode
P_j : population of j
Y_j : per capita income at j

The individual demand can now be written:

$$x_{ijk} = \begin{cases} \alpha_1 P_j^{\alpha_2} Y_j^{\alpha_3} e^{w_0 - \alpha_4 C_{ijk}} & C_{ijk} \leqslant C_{ijn} \\ & n = 1,2,\ldots,m \\ 0 & \text{otherwise.} \end{cases} \qquad (2.10)$$

The exponential formulation has been widely used in demand models and ensures that integrals of travel demand converge for all spatial distributions of individuals.[2] The use of population as a sole measure of attractiveness reflects the availability of data for estimation; clearly more elaborate measures of attractiveness are appropriate when the data permit their use.

The trip-cost function is required to be linear, and it is therefore only necessary to specify which 'attributes' are to be included in the function. Here again data availability operates as a serious constraint. Conceptually all those variables which characterize the differences between modes should be included, since all may potentially influence the individual's choice. In practice, this is clearly impossible. It is useful in this discussion to distinguish between those variables characterizing the mode which vary across both modes and origin-destination pairs, such as journey time, and those variables which vary only across modes, such as safety. In the latter case, since

---

[2] For a discussion of this see J. C. Tanner, "Factors Affecting the Amount of Travel," Department of Scientific and Industrial Research, Research Paper No. 5, London, 1961.

there are at most four available modes, it is clearly impossible to determine statistically the separate contribution of each variable to the individual's trip-cost. For this reason, these will all be subsumed in a single mode-specific variable, which measures, other things being equal, the cost to the individual of travelling on the mode in question. Of those attributes which vary both across modes and origin-destination pairs, line-haul time, access and egress time, and departure frequency are the most important. Separate inclusion of each of these would, however, lead to an unacceptable increase in the number of unknown parameters in this case, and it was therefore decided to combine them into a single term designed to measure journey time. Denoting journey time between i and j on the kth mode by t_{ijk}, and requiring the modal subscript to run from 2 to $m+1$, the trip cost function is now fully specified:

$$C_{ijk} = p_{ijk} + w_1 t_{ijk} + w_k \qquad k = 2,3, \ldots, m+1 \qquad (2.11)$$

w_k now denotes the kth mode-specific cost variable, and w_1 denotes the individual's trade-off rate between money and journey time. Equations (2.10) and (2.11) completely define the individual's demand for travel.

3. Aggregative Assumptions of the Model

The second stage in the formulation of this model covers the specification of the way in which the individual demands are to be combined to form the market demand for trips. It is clear from the nature of the individual demand equation, that unless the parameters of the individual demand functions are allowed to vary between individuals, only one mode will be used on each origin-destination pair. To put this in another way, we may remark that the observed variation in the travel demands of different individuals is properly a reflection of differences in their tastes and trade-offs.

In order to aggregate the individual demands it is therefore necessary to find a way of representing the variation in tastes across individuals. In this model, this variation is introduced by treating parameters of the individual demand functions as observations on a set of continuously distributed random variables. The individual demand, being then a function of random variables, is itself random, and the expected market demand is equal to the expected value of the individual demand times the number of individuals. Denoting the market demand for trips from i to j by mode k by X_{ijk}, and the population at i by P_i, we have:

$$E\{X_{ijk}\} = P_i E\{x_{ijk}\} \tag{3.1}$$

Substituting from (2.10), this becomes:

$$E\{X_{ijk}\} = P_i E\{\alpha_1 P_j{}^{\alpha_2} Y_j{}^{\alpha_3} \ e^{w_0 - \alpha_4 C_{ijk}} \mid C_{ijk} \leqslant C_{ijn}\}$$

$$\times Pr\{C_{ijk} \leqslant C_{ijn}\} \qquad n = 2,3,\ldots, m+1 \tag{3.2}$$

To evaluate this expression the joint distribution of the random elements is required. For convenience in notation, the trip-cost function (2.11), will be written in slightly different form:

$$C_{ijk} = p_{ijk} + \exp\{w_1\}\, t_{ijk} + w_k \qquad k = 2,\ldots, m+1 \tag{3.3}$$

The parameters w_i ($i = 0,\ldots, m+1$) are now treated as random variables, with joint multivariate normal probability distribution. Determination of the parameters of this distribution closes the model.

In the event that no restrictions were imposed on the distribution and supposing there to be four modes, there would then be twenty-seven unknown parameters of the distribution to be estimated; and this would lie clearly beyond the capabilities of the data. For this reason the mode-specific variables in the trip-cost function are treated as being independently distributed of each other, and of the other variables.

The coefficient of time in the trip-cost function is distributed log-normally, and in this way the possibility of negative trade-off rates, between money and time is avoided. In addition, since it is to be expected that higher income levels are associated with higher values of time, the mean of this variable is made to depend on income.[3]

The treatment of w_o as random reflects the variability in the

---

[3] In this context 'income' properly means personal income. Unfortunately, the data being aggregated, it was impossible to break journeys down by income group, and so per-capita income was used. This will tend to raise the variance of w_1.

demand for travel even between individuals faced with similar costs in terms of dollars, time and inconvenience. Furthermore, positive covariance between w_o and w_1 tends to offset the negative influence which high valuation of time exerts on demand. Finally, the mean of w_o is restricted to be zero, the effect of any change in this parameter being taken up in the constant term α_o.

These distributional assumptions can be conveniently presented in matrix form. Using four modes of transportation, there are six random variables in the model. The vector of these variables is denoted by $\widetilde{W}$, and its expectation is given by:

$$E\left\{\widetilde{W}\right\} = \begin{bmatrix} 0 \\ \alpha_5 + \alpha_6 Y_j \\ \alpha_7 \\ \alpha_8 \\ \alpha_9 \\ \alpha_{10} \end{bmatrix} \tag{3.4}$$

For convenience we will express the covariance matrix as the product of a square matrix and its transpose:

$$E\left\{(\widetilde{W} - E(\widetilde{W}))\,(\widetilde{W} - E(\widetilde{W}))'\right\} = AA'$$

where:

$$A = \begin{bmatrix} \alpha_{11} & 0 & 0 & 0 & 0 & 0 \\ \alpha_{12} & \alpha_{13} & 0 & 0 & 0 & 0 \\ 0 & 0 & \alpha_{14} & 0 & 0 & 0 \\ 0 & 0 & 0 & \alpha_{15} & 0 & 0 \\ 0 & 0 & 0 & 0 & \alpha_{16} & 0 \\ 0 & 0 & 0 & 0 & 0 & \alpha_{17} \end{bmatrix} \tag{3.5}$$

This completes the specification of the model. There are altogether seventeen unknown parameters in the model, all but four of which describe the variation of tastes across the population. The model itself involves a six dimensional expectation integral; the problems surrounding the evaluation of this integral and the estimation of the model are described in Section 5.

4. Data

The data used in estimating the parameters of the model[4] consisted of passenger volumes by air, automobile, bus and rail between twenty California city pairs in 1960, together with the associated fares, journey times, departure frequencies, estimates of population and per capita income. These data have a number of defects.

All passenger volumes by common carrier modes are terminal-to-terminal volumes, rather than genuine origin-to-destination volumes. It is likely, therefore, that some journeys are attributed in error to particular city-pairs. More serious is the unreliability of automobile volumes, since they are, characteristically, of much greater magnitude than volumes by common carrier modes and may therefore be expected to have a correspondingly larger influence on the final estimates of the parameters. After several attempts at estimation, four automobile volumes were discarded; their inclusion had led to poor predictions of demand for common carrier modes and several parameter estimates with unexpected signs. These volumes were:

(i)   Los Angeles − Santa Barbara
(ii)   Los Angeles − Bakersfield
(iii) Sacramento − San Francisco
(iv)   Sacramento − San Jose

While it is no doubt possible to conjecture particular reasons why these four observations should be inaccurate, they would not have been excluded if they had agreed well with the model. The

---

[4]The data on passenger volumes were gathered from different sources by the Stanford Research Institute in connection with a study for the Federal Aviation Agency. The sources were: CAB Domestic Origin and Destination Survey of Airline Passenger Traffic; Atchison, Topeka and Santa Fe Railway Co.; Southern Pacific Company; Western Greyhound Lines; California Division of Highways; and Parsons, Brinckerhoff, Quade and Douglass.

Data on 1960 fares, departure frequencies, line-haul and access times were collected by Mr. J. Goodman of Traffic Research Corporation. Population and income statistics for 1960 were taken from the U.S. Bureau of the Census, *County and City Data Book*, 1962.

automobile volume between Fresno and San Diego, being less than the bus volume, was also excluded as being inherently implausible. The total number of observations remaining was sixty, since, for some city pairs, no data were available for particular modes, either because service did not exist, or because observations had not been made.

In calculating the per-person costs of automobile journeys, the costs per vehicle were reduced by 38 per cent to allow for multiple occupancy. This correction factor was derived from Lansing's investigation of travel habits.[5] Lansing gives the percentage of trips made by groups of different sizes. The mean value of the reciprocal of the size of group, calculated from Lansing's figures, is 0.62. Mean access times to common carrier terminals were taken to lie exactly between the average peak and average off-peak access times. Journey times by automobile were corrected to allow thirty minutes for refreshment for every four hours of driving time.

5. Estimation

The parameters of the model were estimated by direct application of least-squares; choice both with regard to the numerical evaluation of the integral and the minimization procedure was required.[6] The evaluation of the probability integral was carried out by Monte-Carlo

---

[5] J. B. Lansing, *The Travel Market 1964-1965*, Survey Research Center, Institute for Social Research, University of Michigan, 1966.

[6] It turns out that, while neither the minimization of the error sum of squares nor the function evaluation present serious difficulties when taken by themselves, in conjunction they create special difficulties. The reasons for this are not difficult to understand. Since, evidently, the least-squares equations cannot be solved analytically, some kind of iterative procedure is required to minimize the error sum of squares. At the same time it will be clear that the accuracy of the function evaluation, involving as it does the numerical approximation of a six-dimensional integral, can be indefinitely increased by investing more and more machine time. Each time the error sum of squares is calculated, it is necessary to evaluate the function at each data point – sixty in the present instance – and if a high degree of accuracy is required, this may take a comparatively long time. The iterative nature of the minimization process, however, means that the error sum of squares may have to be calculated many times, and this may take a very long time. While these considerations suggest that some accuracy in the function evaluation should be sacrificed, there are limits to how far this can be carried. As the evaluation of the function becomes more and more approximate, the direction in which the parameters should be changed by the minimization procedure becomes progressively less certain, and while each function evaluation is much quicker, the number of such evaluations necessary to get to a solution is much larger.

methods.[7] Random variables were generated according to the appropriate multivariate normal distribution. If they fell within the limits of integration, the function giving the passenger's demand for journeys by a particular mode (provided that mode is preferred) was evaluated; if they did not fall within the limits of integration, the function was set to zero. The random variables were generated in the following way. Random variables generated uniformly between 0 and 1, by the method of Rotenberg,[8] were transformed into independent standardized normal variables by the method of Box and Muller.[9] Checks of sample variances, means, and first-order serial correlation were made on a sample of 10,000. These standardized normal variates were then transformed into multivariate normal variables by multiplying a 6 x 1 dimensional vector of these variables by a 6 x 6 triangular matrix. This is the A matrix of equation (3.5). Denoting the column vector of independent standardized variables by U and the column vector of multivariate normal variables by W, this transformation can be written:

$$W = AU + \mu \qquad (4.1)$$

where μ denotes the 6 x 1 dimensional vector of means. From this, the variance-covariance matrix of W, is given by:

$$E\{(W - \mu)(W - \mu)'\} = E\{AUU'A'\} = AA' \qquad (4.2)$$

In evaluating the function, five hundred sets of random numbers were used in the early stages of the minimization; this was increased to one thousand in the final stages. All results given here relate to predictions of the model using one thousand sets of random numbers to evaluate the function. Before leaving the discussion of the numerical approximation to the integral, it should be noted that, since the quadrature by Monte Carlo methods is performed by breaking up the integrand into a probability density and a function

[7]The alternative of performing successive Gaussian quadratures on the integrals was rejected as being too costly. Since there are six intergrals, an eight-point quadrature on each of them would require 86 evaluations of the intergrand.

[8] A. Rotenberg, "A New Pseudo-Random Number Generator," *Journal of the Association of Computing Machinery,* March 1960.

[9] G. E. P. Box and M. W. Muller, "A Note on the Generation of Random Normal Deviates," *Annals of Mathematical Statistics,* Vol. 29, 1958.

of random variables, the procedure is formally equivalent to a simulation. The evaluation of the function may be considered as having accomplished the hypothetical sampling of a thousand individuals to derive estimates of mean passenger demands.

The minimization procedure used is due to Marquardt.[10] While this is a well-tested algorithm, arriving at a solution was a lengthy affair; using one thousand sets of random numbers, each iteration required about five minutes of IBM 7094 time. The program was allowed to run for short periods of time, being restarted at the new values of the parameters. In many cases some of the parameters were held constant, and changes were made in the size of the displacement used in the approximations to the derivatives. A weak convergence test based on the rate of improvement, was applied to determine when the solution was satisfactory. Estimated parameter values are given in Table 1.

Table 1

Estimated Parameter Values

$$\alpha_1 = .488 \times 10^{-12} \qquad \alpha_2 = .116 \times 10^1 \qquad \alpha_3 = .128 \times 10^1$$

$$\alpha_4 = -.596 \times 10^{-1} \qquad \alpha_5 = .423 \times 10^0 \qquad \alpha_6 = .132 \times 10^{-3}$$

$$\alpha_7 = .211 \times 10^2 \qquad \alpha_8 = -.110 \times 10^2 \qquad \alpha_9 = .314 \times 10^1$$

$$\alpha_{10} = .342 \times 10^1 \qquad \alpha_{11} = -.295 \times 10^1 \qquad \alpha_{12} = -.107 \times 10^1$$

$$\alpha_{13} = .713 \times 10^0 \qquad \alpha_{14} = .134 \times 10^2 \qquad \alpha_{15} = .156 \times 10^2$$

$$\alpha_{16} = .109 \times 10^2 \qquad \alpha_{17} = .132 \times 10^2$$

The standard error of estimate was .0199 and the squared coefficient of multiple determination was .995; the high value of this coefficient can, to some extent, be explained by the large dispersion in the

---

[10]D. W. Marquardt, "An Algorithm for Least-Squares Estimation of Nonlinear Parameters," *Journal of the Society of Industrial and Applied Mathematics*, Vol II, No. 2, 1963.

observed values; the signs of the parameters are all as expected. Since all of these parameters, except the constant, have an economic interpretation, it is worth considering them in some detail:

1. α_2 — The model assumes the demand by residents of city i for journeys to city j to be proportional to $P_j^{\alpha_2}$, where P_j denotes the population of city j. Being close to unity, the model approximates the conventional gravity model formulation.

2. α_3, α_6 — These together account for the influence of income on passenger demand. The separate influence of income on a passenger's valuation of hourly time means that the income elasticity of demand will vary from mode to mode and city pair to city pair. The estimate of α_6 seems rather low, implying an income elasticity for the value of time of .33 for a per capita income of $2,500. This may be partly the result of using mean incomes for city pairs and thereby neglecting the problem of aggregating over individuals. It should also be remembered that although there are 60 passenger volumes, there are only 20 distinct per capita incomes, one for each city pair.

3. α_4 — The individual cost elasticity of demand for journeys is equal to total cost times α_4. The estimated value of this parameter implies a demand for journeys which is cost elastic for cost greater than about $20, and cost inelastic for cost less than this amount.

4. α_5, α_{12}, α_{13} — These, together with α_6, determine the distribution of the value of time across individuals. Estimated parameter values were used to determine both mean and median hourly time costs. The results are given in Table 2. The large divergence

Table 2

**Mean and Median $ Value of Time
by Income Level**

Per Capita Income (1960 Dollars)	Mean Value of Time (Dollars Per Hour)	Median Value of Time (Dollars Per Hour)
2,000	4.55	1.99
2,500	4.86	2.12
3,000	5.19	2.27
3,500	5.55	2.42

Standard Error of Value of Time (1960 dollars) = $4.68.

between mean and median illustrates the skewness of the distribution. While the mean values appear somewhat high, these are not the mean values of time for those who travel, but for the population as a whole. Those individuals who would pay twenty dollars to avoid an hour in transit do not travel.

5. The positive covariance, $\alpha_{11}\alpha_{12}$, between the valuation set on journey time and the random variable w_o is as expected. People who set a moderately high valuation on journey time do not necessarily travel less frequently. Conversely, those who travel frequently set a high value on reducing their time in transit.

6. α_7, α_8, α_9, α_{10} — These represent the mean values of the costs associated with travelling on a particular mode. The mean cost associated with travelling by air is by far the highest at $21.08; next comes rail at $3.42 and bus at $3.18; the mean cost associated with the use of an automobile is negative, – $10.98, reflecting perhaps the convenience of having an automobile at one's destination.

7. α_{14}, α_{15}, α_{16}, α_{17} — These denote the standard errors of the costs associated with travelling by a particular mode. It will be noted that they are all quite high, reflecting the wide divergence between individuals in their valuations of the convenience offered by different modes.

There is no general theory of confidence region estimation for the parameters of nonlinear relationships, but two heuristic approaches exist. The first depends on the accuracy of an approximate representation of the model, in the vicinity of the minimum, by the linear terms of a Taylor series expansion. If this approximation is accurate, tests of significance may be carried out as in the linear case. This approach was used to compute standard errors and confidence regions for the parameters of the model. In only six cases out of seventeen were the parameters found to be significant with this approach. This is not necessarily damaging because: (1) the model is very non-linear, (2) there are reasons for doubting the accuracy of the derivatives of the function with respect to the parameters, and (3) it cannot be assumed that the estimates of the parameters do correspond exactly to their solution values.

When the assumption of linearity breaks down, there is an alternative approach. At the least squares point the estimated error variance is given by:

$$\hat{\sigma}^2 = \hat{\phi}/(n - k)$$

where $\hat{\phi}$ denotes the error sum of squares at the solution, n denotes the number of observations and k denotes the number of parameters. Assuming that the specification of the nonlinear model is correct, the deviations of the parameters from their true values are due to random errors in the data. In this case, the expression:

$$\frac{(\phi - \hat{\phi})/k}{\hat{\phi}/(n - k)}$$

is distributed approximately as Fisher's F with k and $n - k$ degrees of freedom, so then with probability approximately $(1 - \alpha)$ we have:

$$\frac{(\phi - \hat{\phi})/k}{\hat{\phi}/(n - k)} \leqslant F_{1-\alpha}(k, n - k)$$

The critical value of ϕ corresponding to a probability of $(1 - \alpha)$ is then given by the solution of:

$$\phi_{critical} = \hat{\phi}\left[1 + \frac{k}{n - k} F_{1-\alpha}(k, n - k)\right]$$

To determine confidence limits, the parameters are then varied one at a time until ϕ assumes its critical value. These confidence limits were calculated by displacing the parameters by ten per cent in either direction and measuring the resultant error sum of squares. Using these two values, together with the value of the error sum of the squares at the solution, upper and lower one per cent confidence limits were determined by quadratic interpolation. In two cases the interpolation failed and in two cases, those of a_{14} and a_{16} the parameter estimates were found to be not significantly different from zero.

Since the predictions of the model are subject to random variation, by reason of the Monte Carlo integration, it was decided to evaluate the model using estimated values of the parameters with ten different samples of one thousand sets of random variables. Since the predicted demand for journeys by a particular mode is the sum of independent random variables, it was assumed to be normally distributed. Five per cent confidence limits for the predicted demand were then calculated for each data point, using an estimate of its standard error based on its variation in the ten successive samples. In 33 out of the 60 cases the hypothesis that the predicted value was different from the observed value was rejected. In the total sample of 10,000, the squared coefficient of multiple determination was 0.985.

6. Summary

The model presented in this chapter is in many ways conceptually satisfying. It is based upon an intuitively reasonable description of individual behavior, and it provides predictions of market demand which make sense in the context of changes in the operating characteristics of existing modes and the introduction of new modes. Whether or not these advantages offset the severe difficulties surrounding its estimation and refinement is for the reader to decide.

9

An Alternative Approach to Aggregation and Estimation in the Non-Linear Model

Anthony J. Blackburn

1. Introduction

The non-linear model of intercity passenger demand* presented in an earlier paper[1] led to quite severe difficulties in estimation. This chapter now describes modifications which are designed to remove some of the difficulties associated with the earlier model without, at the same time, undermining its conceptual basis.

The behavioral assumptions of the original model are preserved in their entirety in the new version, but the methods of aggregating individual demands and of estimating the model are now changed. In part those changes reflect the opportunities created by the availability of new, disaggregated data; in part they were stimulated by a growing belief that theoretical considerations had exercised too strong an influence in the original version. This is not to suggest that the model presented here is computationally trivial, but only that it represents what may appear to be a more reasonable compromise between theoretical appeal and computational difficulty.

2. Behavioral Assumptions

The behavioral assumptions of this model are unchanged from the earlier variant.[2] By treating transportation modes as perfect substitutes in demand, the individual's demand for trips by the kth mode is of the form:

$$x_k = \begin{cases} \psi(C_k) & C_k \leqslant C_n \quad n = 1,2,\ldots,m \\ 0 & \text{otherwise} \end{cases} \qquad (2.1)$$

*This chapter is based on part of a study carried out at MATHEMATICA, INC., for the U.S. Department of Transportation under Contract No. 3-0009. The author wishes to acknowledge the assistance he received from Michel Pinton, Mark Rose and Howard Weiss.

[1] See Chapter 8.

[2] For a detailed discussion of these and their theoretical implications see Chapter 8.

where

$$C_k = p_k + \sum_{j=1}^{n} w_j \alpha_{kj} \qquad (2.2)$$

Notation as follows:

x_k : individual's demand for trips by the kth mode
C_k : generalized trip cost of kth mode
p_k : dollar cost of a trip by the kth mode (fare)
w_j : marginal rate of substitution between money and the jth 'attribute'
α_{kj} : the level of the jth 'attribute' on the kth mode
m : number of available modes

The 'attributes' of a mode are those non-pecuniary variables which characterize a trip by that mode, such as journey time, safety and so on. The model therefore represents the individual's transportation choice in two stages; firstly, the choice between alternatives on the basis of their generalized trip-costs, denoted by C_k. Secondly, the choice between alternative amounts of travel on the basis of the trip-cost of the preferred mode. As shown in the earlier paper, the linearity of the trip-cost function is not a matter of computational convenience, but a direct consequence of the requirement that modes be perfect substitutes.[3]

To complete specification of the individual demand functions, it is necessary to select a functional form for ψ and to determine which 'attributes' are to be included in the trip-cost function. In both cases the assumptions made in the original model are preserved. Demand is required to decline exponentially with increases in the trip-cost of the preferred mode and to have constant elasticity with respect to population at the destination.[4] Introducing origin-destination subscripts for trip demand and trip-cost, and denoting population at j by P_j, (2.1) now becomes:

---

[3] See pp. 165-166.

[4] Per-capita income at the destination was also included, but dropped for lack of statistical significance.

$$x_{ijk} = \begin{cases} \alpha_1 P_j^{\alpha_2} e^{-\lambda C_{ijk}} & C_{ijk} \leqslant C_{ijn} \\ & n = 1, 2, \ldots, m \\ 0 & \text{otherwise} \end{cases} \quad (2.3)$$

As before, mode-specific constants are introduced into the trip-cost function to measure the influence of those attributes, such as safety and comfort, which vary across modes but not across origin-destination pairs, and whose separate influence cannot, for this reason, be statistically determined. In addition to these, we include journey time, which is made up of line-haul time plus mean access and egress time between common carrier terminals and final destinations.[5] Denoting the journey time of a trip by the kth mode between i and j by t_{ijk}, the fare by p_{ijk}, and allowing the modal subscript to run from 2 to $m+1$, the trip-cost function can be written:

$$C_{ijk} = p_{ijk} + w_1 t_{ijk} + w_k \quad k = 2, 3, \ldots, m+1 \quad (2.4)$$

Equations (2.3) and (2.4) now completely define the individual's demand for trips by mode and by origin-destination pair. We now consider how these individual demand functions are to be combined to yield a market demand function for travel.

3. Aggregative Assumptions of the Model

It is an implication of the behavioral assumptions of this model, that unless the parameters of the individual demand functions are allowed to vary between individuals, all individuals will choose the same mode of transportation on each origin-destination pair. Accordingly, as in the earlier variant, the parameters of the individual demand functions will be treated as observations on continuously distributed random variables. The expected market demand for trips is then given by the expected value of the individual demand function multiplied by the number of individuals. Denoting the population at

---

[5] An attempt was made to include the reciprocal of departure frequency as a separate 'attribute' designed to measure waiting time. It was not found to be significant.

i by P_i and the market demand for trips between i and j by mode k by X_{ijk}, we have:

$$E\{X_{ijk}\} = P_i E \{X_{ijk}\} \qquad (3.1)$$

This relationship, together with equations (2.3) and (2.4) will, once the joint distribution of the random elements of the individual demand function is specified, completely determine the market demand for trips. It is in the specification of this joint distribution that the model described in this paper differs from the earlier version.

The central difficulties which arose in the estimation of the original model stemmed directly from the existence of expectation integrals requiring numerical evaluation. While the numerical evaluation itself presented no special problems, the necessity to use an iterative method of estimation meant that the numerical evaluation had to be performed many times.[6] In order to avoid this problem the distributional assumptions are now changed in such a way that analytical expressions for the expectation integrals can be obtained. As the reader will notice, this simplification is not obtained without some sacrifice in the conceptual realism of the model.

The new distributional assumptions can be generally described as limiting the extent of purely random variation between individuals. The availability of individual trip data made it possible to use household income as an explanatory variable in the individual demand function and much of the required variation in the parameters of the individual demand function can therefore be achieved by allowing these parameters to depend directly on the individual's household income, which is then the primary source of variation. This approach was followed with respect to both w_1, the valuation of the time parameter in the trip-cost function, and to λ, the attenuation coefficient of equation (2.3).

In describing the dependence of these two parameters on household income, it is convenient to work within the framework of the data used in estimation. Since trips were classified by household income groups, individuals' household income is taken to be the average value of the group. Denoting by Y_r the mean income of households in the rth income group, and denoting the valuation of time coefficient for an individual in the rth income group by w_{1r} we have, assuming constant elasticity:

---

[6] For a discussion of this, see p. 173.

$$w_{1r} = \alpha_5 Y_r^{\alpha_6} \qquad (3.2)$$

The attenuation coefficient must also be allowed to vary between income groups. If this were not the case, the dependence of the individual's time-valuation on income would always lead the rich to travel less. For reasons which will become apparent later, it is necessary for λ to be bounded from above; this consideration led to rejection of a constant-elasticity dependence in favor of an exponential formulation. Denoting the attenuation coefficient of an individual in the rth income group by λ_r, we have:

$$\lambda_r = \alpha_3 e^{-\alpha_4 Y_r} \qquad (3.3)$$

The dependence of these parameters on income will, in most circumstances, ensure that individuals do not all choose to travel by the same mode. If there is no other source of variation between individuals, however, individuals in the same income group will all behave identically. To remove this feature, we now permit the mode-specific cost elements to vary randomly across individuals.

In doing this it is convenient to define a new set of variables, z_j, as follows:

$$z_k = e^{w_k \xi} \qquad k = 2, \ldots, m+1 \qquad (3.4)$$

By treating the z_k's as random variables, we now, by reason of (3.4), permit the mode-specific cost components w_k to vary across individuals. Denoting the probability density function of z_k by f_k, and requiring the z_k's to be distributed negative exponentially, we have:

$$f_k(z_k) = \frac{1}{\mu_k} e^{-z_k/\mu_k} \qquad k = 2, \ldots, m+1 \qquad (3.5)$$

The μ_k's are the unknown parameters of these distributions. We are now in a position to derive the expected demand for trips between i and j by the kth mode for an individual in the rth income group. Denoting this demand by x_{ijkr}, and the associated trip cost by C_{ijkr} we have from (2.3) and (2.4):

$$E\{x_{ijkr}\} = E\{\alpha_1 P_j^{\alpha_2} e^{-\lambda_r C_{ijkr}} \mid C_{ijkr} \leqslant C_{ijnr}\} \text{ Prob}\{C_{ijkr} \leqslant C_{ijnr}\}$$

$$n = 2, \ldots, m+1 \qquad (3.6)$$

The region of integration, given by the condition $C_{ijkr} \leqslant C_{ijnr}$, for $n = 2, 3, \ldots, m+1$, can now be expressed in terms of the z_n's; from (2.4) and (3.4) we have:

$$C_{ijkr} = p_{ijk} + w_{1r}t_{ijk} + (1/\xi) \log z_k \qquad (3.7)$$

and the condition for the kth mode to be preferred can therefore be written:

$$\log z_n \geqslant \log z_k + \xi\left((p_{ijk} - p_{ijn}) + w_{1r}(t_{ijk} - t_{ijn})\right)$$

$$n = 2, 3 \ldots m+1 \qquad (3.8)$$

or alternatively:

$$z_n \geqslant z_k \, e^{\xi}\left((p_{ijk} - p_{ijn}) + w_{1r}(t_{ijk} - t_{ijn})\right)$$

$$n = 2, 3 \ldots, m+1$$

$$(3.9)$$

For convenience of notation, we denote the exponential component by s_{kn}, the condition (3.9) now becoming simply:

$$z_n \geqslant z_k s_{kn} \qquad n = 2, 3, \ldots, m+1 \qquad (3.10)$$

We now denote by A_{ijkr} those terms in (3.6) which do not involve the z_n's:

$$A_{ijkr} = \alpha_1 P_j^{\alpha_2} e^{-\lambda_r(p_{ijk} + w_{1r}t_{ijk})} \qquad (3.11)$$

Equation (3.6) then becomes:

$$E\{x_{ijkr}\} = A_{ijkr} \int_0^\infty z_k^{-(\lambda_r/\xi)} \int_{z_k s_2}^\infty$$

$$\ldots \int_{z_k s_{k,m+1}}^\infty \prod_{n=2}^{m+1} \left(\frac{1}{\mu_n} e^{-\frac{z_n}{\mu_n}}\right) dz_2 \ldots dz_{m+1} \qquad (3.12)$$

Integrating over all $n \neq k$, and remembering that $s_{kk} = 1$, we have:

$$E\{x_{ijkr}\} = A_{ijkr} \int_0^\infty \frac{z_k}{\mu_k}^{-(\lambda_r/\xi)} e^{-\left(\sum_{n=2}^{m+1} \frac{s_{kn}}{\mu_n}\right)z_k} dz_k$$

(3.13)

and finally:

$$E\{x_{ijkr}\} = \frac{A_{ijkr}\Gamma\left(\frac{\lambda_r}{\xi}-1\right)}{\mu_k} \left(\sum_{n=2}^{m+1} \frac{s_{kn}}{\mu_n}\right)^{\frac{\lambda_r}{\xi}-1}$$

(3.14)

To simplify the resulting expressions we will introduce two new variables, μ_k^* and C_{ijkr}^* defined as follows:

$$\mu_k^* = \frac{1}{\xi}\log\mu_k \qquad k = 2,3,\ldots,m+1$$

$$C_{ijkr}^* = p_{ijk} + w_r t_{ijk} + \mu_k^* \qquad k = 2,3,\ldots,m+1$$

Returning to the original notation, and absorbing the gamma function in the constant term,[7] (3.14) becomes:

$$E\{x_{ijkr}\} = \alpha_1 P_j^{\alpha_2} e^{-\xi C_{ijkr}^*} \left(\sum_{n=2}^{m+1} e^{-\xi C_{ijnr}^*}\right)^{\frac{\lambda_r}{\xi}-1}$$

(3.15)

Several features of this equation are worth a mention. In the first place, in order that the model make sense, the expression $(\lambda_r/\xi - 1)$ must be non-positive; if this were not the case increases in the costs and journey times of competing modes would lead to reductions in travel demand. This consideration was responsible for requiring λ_r to be bounded from above.[8]

Secondly the expressions for modal splits and for total travel are both simple and appealing; total travel from i to j by all modes by persons in the rth income group is obtained by summing over k in (3.15) and applying (3.1). Denoting the sum by x_{ij*r} we have:

---

[7] Although this term will vary between income groups, there are simpler ways of allowing the constant to depend on income. It was therefore dropped.

[8] See page 185.

$$E\left\{x_{ij \cdot r}\right\} = \alpha_1 P_{ir}P_j^{\alpha_2} \left(\sum_{n=2}^{m+1} e^{-\xi C_{ijnr}^{*}} \right)^{\frac{\lambda_r}{\xi}} \qquad (3.16)$$

The expression for the modal split is even simpler; denoting the share of the total traffic in the rth income group which uses the kth mode by S_{ijkr}, this is given by:

$$S_{ijkr} = \left(\sum_{n=2}^{m+1} e^{\xi(C_{ijkr}^{*} - C_{ijnr}^{*})} \right)^{-1} \qquad (3.17)$$

Both these expressions will play important roles in the estimation of the model.

Complete specification of the model requires one additional step. In the expressions for both total travel and for modal splits it is clear that the absolute values of the mode specific terms μ_k^* are unimportant; in the expression for demand by all modes, the absolute values can be absorbed in the constant term and in the expression for modal splits only the differences between the μ_k^* are of importance. Some form of normalization is therefore required.

At the same time it is clear that the mode-specific costs associated with automobile travel will vary systematically with car ownership; since considerable variation in levels of auto ownership existed in the data used to estimate this model it was considered necessary to allow the auto-specific cost variable, call it μ_2^*, to vary with the level of auto ownership in the city of trip origin. Since the observed level of auto ownership measured the probability that any resident owned a car, the expected cost of using a car was made to depend linearly on auto ownership. Normalization, alluded to in the preceding paragraph, was carried out by requiring the intercept to be zero; i.e., no mode-specific costs would be associated with auto travel in the case of hundred percent auto ownership. Denoting by u_i the observed level of ownership in city i, measured as a decimal fraction, we have:

$$\mu_2^* = \alpha_8 (1 - u_i) \qquad (3.18)$$

This completes the specification of the model. For convenience in the discussion of estimation, we will consolidate the notation by defining new parameters as follows:

$$\alpha_7 = \xi$$
$$\alpha_9 = \mu_3{}^*$$
$$\alpha_{10} = \mu_4{}^*$$
$$\alpha_{11} = \mu_5{}^*$$

The model now provides the demand for trips in the four mode case broken down between income groups. Estimation of the eleven unknown parameters is the subject of the next sections.

4. Estimation

Estimation of the model described in the last section is complicated by the fact that the expressions for trip demand are nonlinear in the unknown parameters. These complications would be less serious if the available data had been well-suited to the calibration of the model, but, as will be described in this section, the sparsity of the available data made it necessary to use specially adapted techniques of inference.

Estimation of the model requires data of three district types; socio-economic data, impedance data and trip data. The socio-economic and impedance data, which are required at the analysis district level, presented no particular problems.[9] Major difficulties arose, however, with the trip data, which were originally collected for use by the Tri-State Commission in their study of transportation demand within the Tri-State region. In a study of some 57,000 households within the Tri-State region, each household was

---

[9] Population by analysis district and by income group for 1963 is required by the model. This was obtained as follows. Populations by analysis district for 1963 were obtained by linear interpolation between the 1960 *County and City Data Book* figures and the 1967 *Sales Management* figures. The only breakdown by income group available was the 1967 *Sales Management* data, and this was adjusted for 1963 by fitting time dependent log-normal distributions to the data. Six income groups were used: ($000's) 0-3, 3-5, 5-7.5, 7.5-10, 10-15, 15-. Auto occupancy was taken directly from the 1967 *Sales Management* figures. The impedance data, line-haul costs, times and frequencies together with access and egress costs and times, were provided by Peat, Marwick and Livingstone at the district level ·for 1960 and 1965. All costs were converted into 1960 dollars, and to make these data compatible with the 1963 trip data, linear interpolation between 1960 and 1965 values was performed. In a few cases access costs or times were missing, and these were then generated by regressing access costs on access times and conversely over the remaining data, and using the predicted value of the missing variable.

questioned about its travel behavior on a specified day, weekends and holidays being excluded. Although upwards of 65,000 journeys were recorded, these were predominantly short journeys of the shopping/commuting variety. When attention is directed towards the longer journeys, which are the principal interest of the study, the available number of journeys becomes very small. With origins and destinations disaggregated to the analysis district level, less than 1,500 trips remain with inter-district automobile journey times greater than one and one quarter hours. When these journeys are sorted according to origin/destination, mode of travel and income group of traveller, it is no surprise to find that most of those cells have no recorded travel at all, and of the rest the reported flows seldom exceed three journeys.

For these reasons it is clear that the variation between the number of trips recorded as one moves across origin-destination pairs, modes and income groups, is only to a small extent accounted for by variation in the socio-economic and impedance variables, the principal part of this variation being attributable to sampling error. The method of estimation used must therefore take this into account explicitly; that is to say, it must precisely follow the sampling procedure if it is to be able to extract that part of the variation in recorded trips which is properly attributable to the variation of the socio-economic and impedance variables; unless this is done it is likely that the standard errors of the estimated parameters will be unacceptably large.

The sampling procedure can be looked at in two ways, and both ways of looking at it lead to the same result, one directly and one asymptotically. In the first place one can regard the number of trips made by the sampled households between specified origins and destinations as a random process through time; observations made on this process over a fixed interval, like a specified weekday are therefore to be considered as observations on a Poisson process. Alternatively, one can consider that there is a fixed probability that any sample respondent will have made a trip on the day in question to a particular destination, in which case the observations can be treated as observations on a binomial variable. Taking the latter approach, however, and noting that the fixed probability of a trip is small, and that the expected number of trips given the sample size is also small, it is proper to make the Poisson approximation to the binomial; in either case therefore, the recorded trips can be regarded as observations on a set of random variables each with a Poisson distribution whose mean is given by the model described in Section 3.

These distributional considerations clearly suggest the use of maximum likelihood methods for estimating the model, these estimators possessing the desirable properties of asymptotic unbiasedness and efficiency. There is an additional reason, of a computational nature, for preferring this approach. Direct application of least squares to the model of Section 3, would require minimization of a function of eleven variables, and is likely to be quite difficult. By adopting maximum likelihood methods, however, it is possible to decompose estimation into 2 stages, each involving minimization of a function of a subset of the unknown parameters. This approach, it is hoped, reduced the computational requirements of estimation.

Decomposition of the estimation procedure into two stages is performed in the following way. During the first stage, attention is focussed only upon the individual's choice between modes, his choice between alternative amounts of travel being ignored. The expression for the share of the kth mode of travel between i and j by persons in the rth income group is given by (3.17) This expression for the split can also be interpreted as the probability that a trip, drawn at random on this origin-destination pair from the population of all such trips made by persons in the rth income group, is made on the kth mode. Denoting the number of such trips observed by N_{ijkr}, the likelihood of the sample, L_1, is simply:

$$L_1 = \prod_{ijkr} S_{ijkr}{}^{N_{ijkr}} \qquad (4.1)$$

Maximization of L_1 with respect to the unknown parameters yields estimates of seven of the eleven unknown parameters.

Second-stage estimation is performed using the Poisson assumption discussed above, together with the expression for travel by all modes (3.16).[10] If the data had been less sparse the case for applying the Poisson assumption during the second-stage of estimation would be less strong, equation (3.16) lending itself to log-linear regression once the modal choice parameters are estimated. As has already been mentioned, however, when the available trips were classified according to origin-destination pair and income group, less than ten

---

[10] See page 188.

percent of the cells have any recorded journeys. To reduce the computational problem still further, it was decided to eliminate from the data all those cells with zero observations, and to work instead with the likelihood of the sample, conditional on those with one or more journeys recorded. Denoting by h_i the percentage of households sampled in district i, and denoting by $\hat{X}_{ij*r}$, the number of journeys predicted by the model by all modes, then the expected number of trips recorded by all modes between i and j by persons in the rth group is $h_i\hat{X}_{ij*r}$. If N_{ij*r} denotes total recorded travel by all modes between i and j by persons in the rth income group, the conditional likelihood of the sample, L_2, is then given by:

$$
L_2 = \prod_{ijr} \frac{e^{-h_i\hat{X}_{ij*r}} \left(h_i\hat{X}_{ij*r}\right)^{N_{ij*r}}}{N_{ij*r}! \left(1 - e^{-h_i\hat{X}_{ij*r}}\right)}
\tag{4.2}
$$

Maximization of L_2 with respect to the remaining four parameters concludes estimation of the model.

5. First-Stage Estimates

In performing the first-stage of the estimation procedure a distinction was made between trips according to purpose, journeys with work recorded as the journey purpose being distinguished from other journeys. This separation of journeys was intended to permit determination of the extent to which journey purpose affected the individual's choice of mode. The parameter denoting the income elasticity of the individual's time-money tradeoff, α, was then estimated separately for each journey purpose.

Maximization of the likelihood function was performed using the conjugate gradient method of Powell.[11] By excluding all origin-destination pairs separated by less than 1.75 hours driving time, it was possible to eliminate the shorter commuter/shopping trips and to concentrate attention on the intercity demand. The number of trips was reduced in this way to 661. Even with this limitation estimation was lengthy; each observation requires the evaluation of three exponentials and evaluation of the likelihood function requires that

[11]Powell, M. J. D., "An Efficient Method for Finding the Minimum of a Function of Several Variables without Calculating Derivatives." *Computer Journal,* 7, (1964), pp. 155-162.

over a thousand exponential terms be computed. Repeated evaluation of the likelihood of the sample during maximization does, therefore, take time.

Maximization of the likelihood function was considered complete when all variables were changing by less than 10^{-3} of their absolute values, and the matrix of second partial derivatives of the likelihood function was checked for negative definiteness. This matrix was then inverted and its diagonal elements, which give the asymptotic variances of the parameter estimates, were used to check their statistical significance. These results are presented in Table 1.

Table 1

First Stage Parameter Estimates

	α_5	Work	α_6 Non-Work	Parameters α_7	α_8	α_9	α_{10}	α_{11}
Estimates	.055	0.56	0.53	0.127	16.32	10.75	14.17	27.20
Standard Errors	.066	0.11	*	0.054	6.39	4.32	6.55	6.39

*The non-work value of α_6 was estimated indirectly as a multiple of the work-value. The multiplicative constant was 0.95 and its standard error was 0.026.

With the exception of α_5 all estimates are significant at the 90% level and all of these but one at the 95% level. The non-work estimate of α_6 is significantly lower than the work estimate. The case of α_5 is rather puzzling since it is hard to see how α_6 can be significant if α_5 is not, by the nature of the function. The most likely explanation is that, since derivatives were taken by displacing parameters by 10^{-3} of their absolute value and since α_5 has the smallest absolute value and is of the order of 10^{-2}, a rounding error in the second derivative routine is responsible.

Two remaining aspects of the final parameter values are worthy of note. The differences between the mode-specific terms (expressed here as deviations from the auto-specific cost) are very similar to those found when the earlier variant,[12] was calibrated against California data. They are given here in Table 2 for purposes of contrast and are based on the assumption of 80% auto ownership; which may be reasonable for California.

Table 2

Differences between Mode-Specific Constants (Bus, Rail, Air, Subtracted from Auto)

	Auto vs. Bus	Auto vs. Rail	Auto vs. Air
Tri-State	10.75	14.17	27.19
California	10.90	11.14	28.80

Lastly mention should be made of the trade-offs between time and money; the dependence of this trade-off on passenger's household income is the instrument by which the market shares of the modes change with the growth of income; those trade-offs are given here in dollars:

Table 3

Trade-offs Between Time and Money ($ per hour)

Household Income ($000's p.a.)	Work	Non-Work
0-3	4.01	3.19
3-5	5.58	4.36
5-7.5	7.11	5.49
7.5-10	8.61	6.58
10-15	10.03	7.83
15-	13.73	10.24

---

[12] See "A Non-Linear Model of the Demand for Travel," Chapter 8.

6. Second Stage Estimates

As in the first stage of estimation, trips were again classified by journey purpose. Whereas in the first stage only one parameter was allowed to differ according to the purpose of the journey, in the second stage all parameters were allowed to vary according to purpose. This meant, therefore, that estimation could be carried out separately for work and non-work trips.

Maximum likelihood estimation, using the conditional Poisson probabilities discussed in Section 3, was performed, again making use of Powell's method. Because of the reduction in the number of exponential terms to be evaluated, a larger number of trips was used, only trips with inter-district origin-destination times of less than 1.25 hours being excluded.

The same convergence tests as in the first stage were applied to maximization of the Poisson likelihood function. The matrix of second-partials of the log-likelihood was again negative definite, and the diagonal elements of the inverse were used to provide the estimates of the sampling variances. The results are given in Table 4.

Table 4

Parameters	Estimates	
	Work	*Non-Work* *
$\log \alpha_1$	−12.52	−5.96
	(0.97)	
α_2	0.56	0.00
	(0.07)	
α_3	0.15	0.11
	(0.02)	
α_4	0.88×10^{-4}	0.12×10^{-3}
	(0.34×10^{-4})	

*These values were calculated indirectly as multiples of the corresponding work parameters; it is therefore not possible to supply standard errors. All multiplicative constants were significantly different from unity.

Two features of these results are worthy of comment; The first, which is encouraging concerns the expression $\dfrac{\alpha^3}{\alpha_7} e^{-\alpha_4 Y_r}$ which must lie between 0 and 1 for the model to make economic sense.[13] This condition is satisfied by the parameter estimates for both work and non-work trips at all income levels.

Less satisfactory are the estimates of α_2. The work estimate of α_2 is lower than most empirical studies suggest, the non-work estimate was found to be insignificantly different from zero, and was therefore deleted. This is clearly disappointing being both conceptually and empirically unacceptable. A number of explanations suggest themselves, but most likely the reason is to be found in the exclusion of other relevant socio-economic variables and/or the breakdown of the Poisson assumption. In the former case the necessity to limit the number of variables is to be found in the sparseness of the data; in the latter case, it is possible, since zero observations were excluded, that much of the variation in trips is accounted for by variations in the size of groups travelling together; in this case the travel decisions are not independent, and the Poisson assumption breaks down.[14]

Both these difficulties and the difficulties associated with finding maximum likelihood estimates, would be removed by the availability of more data. In this case, given the first-stage estimates, the second-stage could be carried out by ordinary linear regression. In such an event it would be possible to introduce additional socio-economic data and to avoid the potential dangers of the Poisson assumption.

7. Summary

Careful choice of aggregation methods in this chapter made it possible to preserve the behavioral assumptions of the earlier model, without at the same time, creating such severe numerical difficulties. To some extent, fruits of simplification were not realized. The limitations of the available data made it necessary to adopt rather strong distributional assumptions during the second stage of estimation, and the results suggest that these assumptions may not have been valid. Hopefully, the availability of new data will provide an opportunity to subject the model to more powerful tests.

---

[13] For discussion of this see page 187.

[14] This would go some way toward explaining the result if much of the non-work group travel was made to low density vacation resorts.

10 Value of Time, Choice of Mode, and the Subsidy Issue in Urban Transportation

Leon N. Moses and Harold F. Williamson, Jr.

The last two decades have clearly shown that increased automobile ownership and highway construction can facilitate profound redistributions of population and economic activity within metropolitan areas.* These changes are related in a fundamental way to many of the social and economic difficulties of our large, mature, central cities:[1] loss of middle and upper income groups to the suburbs, declining retail sales in downtown areas, erosion of the tax base, shift of manufacturing and service establishments to suburban areas, decline of mass transit service and patronage, and increased traffic congestion. There is a great deal of support for the view that there has been too much highway construction and that the time has come to help public transportation. Such assistance is expected to improve the economic future of central cities.

Congress has responded to the difficulties of such cities as Boston, New York, and Chicago, and to the above sentiment by passing a bill (Public Law 87-70, 87th Cong., S. 1922, June 30, 1961) that provides funds, both loan and grant, for demonstration projects. The purpose of these projects is to determine the effect of fare reductions and service improvements on public transportation patronage. This bill is probably a first step in what will eventually be a large-scale assistance program.[2] It is essential that some basic thinking be done as to its objectives, cost, and likely success. Indeed, all parts of our emerging urban program require similar examination, since their cost

Reprinted from the *Journal of Political Economy*, Vol. LXXI, 1963, pp. 247-264. Copyright © by the University of Chicago Press. Used with permission.

*The authors wish to express their gratitude to Professors J. Rothenberg and R. H. Strotz for a number of valuable suggestions.

[1] The term "central city" refers to the large, dominant city of a metropolitan area that usually includes a number of smaller, politically independent communities.

[2] A number of bills in this area have recently been introduced in the Senate and the House of Representatives. One such bill is the "Urban Mass Transportation Act of 1963" introduced by Senator Williams and others (S.6).

could easily dwarf the agricultural, maritime, and airline subsidies combined.

This paper explores some of the issues involved in a program of assistance to public transportation. Many of them have already been analyzed in connection with studies of the benefits from highway investment. Therefore, this paper reviews techniques that have been used in a particular variety of highway benefit studies. The objective of these studies is to estimate the value of travel-time savings achieved by improving an old road or building a new one.[3] The theoretical structure underlying these studies will be scrutinized, exclusive attention being given to work trips. From many points of view such trips are the most important component of passenger travel in urban areas.

Estimates of the value of travel time are not always based on formal techniques. Thus, a recent publication contains the following statement: "The dollar value of time saving may vary considerably and no precise method of evaluation has yet been determined. A value of time for passenger cars of $1.55 per hour . . . is used herein as representative of current opinion for a logical and practical value."[4] No explanation is given for why $1.55 is more logical and practical than any other figure. On a more formal basis, two techniques have most commonly been used to estimate that part of total highway benefits accounted for by savings in travel time.[5] One of them ignores the problem of consumer choice between alternative modes. This method, which we will call the income or productivity approach, values travel time according to the worth of time in work. The second method rests on there being a choice between modes (or between alternative routes for the same mode) with different time and money outlay characteristics. With this method, called here the pure cost approach, travel-time savings are valued according to

---

[3] Other highway studies deal with economic impact. They attempt to measure the stimulus highways provide to economic growth. For an appraisal of such studies see H. D. Mohring and M. Harwitz, *Highway Benefits: An Analytical Framework* (Evanston, Ill.: Transportation Center and Northwestern University Press, 1962).

[4] Committee on Planning and Design Policies, American Association of State Highway Officials, *Informational Report by* [the Committee] *on Road User Benefit Analyses for Highway Improvements* (Washington: American Association of State Highway Officials, 1960), p. 126.

[5] A third approach has been suggested by F. Hoffman in an unpublished paper, "Route Choice and Valuation of Travel Time" (RAND Corporation, June 25, 1958).

money cost differentials between the modes. In the first part of this paper, these two techniques will be examined and a third developed that combines them. In the second part, a price structure that would divert automobile commuters to other modes will be estimated by means of this third approach and some available data. Both the analysis and the empirical work will be presented first under the assumption that workers are free to choose the combination of income and leisure that is optimal for them, and then under the assumption that there is a standard number of hours to which they must conform.

The diversion issue is central to much of the argument that is taking place on the need to subsidize public transportation as a way of reducing automobile congestion in central cities. The extent to which such diversion might improve the economic future of these cities is a disputed point on which the present paper takes no position.

1. The Three Approaches

Of the two traditional approaches referred to above, the income approach generally implies a single mode. Aggregate time savings due to a highway investment are estimated and multiplied by the wage rate. At one time it was customary for highway planners to use the legal minimum wage as a way of countering the claim that highway investment was being justified on the basis of exaggerated estimates of benefits. We will ignore this aspect of the approach and concentrate instead on its basic logic: the valuation of travel-time savings by their worth in work. A report from the Secretary of Commerce took the following position on this method: "Time saving contributes to a tangible reduction in the cost of transportation only to the extent users are able to make productive, i.e., gainful, use of the time saved. The productivity concept is, however, so defective as to be unrealistic in the face of demands by motorists and other travelers for reductions in time of travel."[6] Since the approach

---

[6] United States Secretary of Commerce, *Final Report of the Highway Cost Allocation Study,* letter from [the Secretary] transmitting [*Final Report*] pursuant to Sec. 210 of the Highway Revenue Act of 1956 as amended by Sec. 2 of the Act approved August 28, 1958, January 23, 1961 (87th Cong., 1st sess. [Washington: Government Printing Office, 1961]), p. 205.

developed in this paper embraces the productivity concept, a review of its logic is essential and is presented in this part.

The pure cost approach has been used mainly in studies that derive the value of time from information on consumer's choice between alternative (auto) routes with different time and money outlay characteristics.[7] These studies have not distinguished among trips made for different purposes. In addition, most of them have attempted to value such things as safety and general convenience, as well as time savings. However, so far as the latter are concerned, their method is to attach a value equal to the amount trip-takers have been willing to pay in the form of higher gasoline costs, tolls, and so on, to take a faster route. This logic can also be applied when the choice is between different modes.

Figure 10-1 presents the basic techniques for analyzing the two traditional approaches and for presenting the third approach used in this paper. Leisure time is measured on the horizontal axis and income on the vertical axis. The figure pertains to a number of individuals each of whom views travel and work time as equally onerous. Each of them faces a wage rate equal to the negative of the slope of line AB and has a stock of time equal to OA. The income line, AB, shows the combinations of income and leisure each individual could have if commuting involved zero time and money outlay.

Various time and money cost combinations can be introduced by shifting the line AB; these will be considered in this section. If the mode in question involves no money cost but requires time in route, then AB can be shifted to the left to some parallel position, say CD, implying travel time equal to AC and an unchanged wage rate. CD

---

[7] For studies where this is the fundamental principle for determining the value of travel time see P. J. Claffey, "Characteristics of Passenger Car Travel on Toll Roads and Comparable Free Roads for Highway User Benefit Studies," *Public Roads: A Journal of Highway Research*, XXXI, No. 3 (June, 1961), 166-67 (the results of this study were included in United States Secretary of Commerce, *op. cit.*, p. 203); R. Vaswani, "Value of Automobile Transit Time in Highway Planning," *Proceedings, 37th Annual Meeting of the Highway Research Board* (January, 1958), pp. 58-71, esp. p. 62; G. P. St. Clair and N. Leider, "Evaluation of Unit Cost of Time and Strain-and-Discomfort Cost of Non-Uniform Driving," *Economic Analysis in Highway Programming, Location and Design* (Highway Research Board Special Report 56 [1960]), pp. 116-29, esp. pp. 118-19; M. E. Campbell, *Toll Bridge Influence on Highway Traffic Operation* (Bureau of Highway Traffic, Technical Report No. 2 [New Haven, Conn.: Eno Foundation for Highway Traffic Control, 1947]), pp. 36-44; M. H. West, "Economic Value of Time Savings in Traffic," *Proceedings, Institute of Traffic Engineers*, XVII (1946), 144-48.

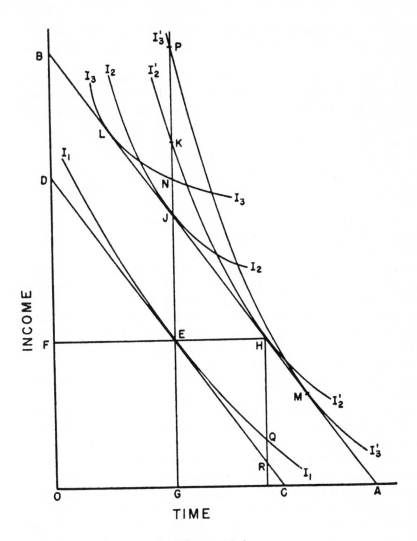

Figure 10-1

then represents the net income line for this particular mode. With freedom to choose hours, the individual who takes this mode may select any combination of leisure and income along *CD* or no income and all leisure — point *A*. Similarly, *CD* could represent the net income line of a mode that involved no travel time but entailed an expenditure equal to BD. Once again *CD* (which can now be said to represent the position of *AB* when it is shifted *down* a distance *BD*) represents the income and leisure choices for the individual on this mode.

Figure 10-1 can be viewed in a third fashion as representing the net income lines of two modes. The income line (*AB* in the above example) would be the same for each mode for a given individual faced with a choice between them. The net income line for each mode would be the parallel position of the income line after it had been shifted down and then left to take into account the money and time costs, respectively, of that mode. Thus, *AB* could represent the combinations of income and leisure available if the individual chose the first mode while *CD* would represent those available if the second were chosen. This approach to Figure 1 will be discussed more fully when the third, or income-cost, approach is analyzed.

The first technique to be examined will be the income or productivity approach. To discuss this approach, consider the first interpretation of Figure 10-1. *CD* represents the net income line when there is travel time *AC* but no money cost. As was noted above, with freedom to choose hours of work the individual may pick some point on *CD* or point *A*. As the figure is drawn, point *E* on indifference curve $I_1 I_1$ is a position of maximum satisfaction for each individual. It involves *AC* time spent in travel, *CG* in work, *OG* in leisure, and income equal to OF[8]. Suppose travel time is reduced by highway investment. In order to keep the figure from becoming too complicated, assume that travel time is reduced to zero. Each worker now selects a new point of equilibrium along *AB*. Those individuals for whom neither income nor leisure is an inferior good will choose a position along the line segment *HJ*. What value does the reduction in travel time have for them? In terms of satisfaction it is the difference between being on a higher or lower indifference curve, but a quantitative estimate of benefits cannot be based on levels of utility. Therefore, according to the basic methodology of the income approach, travel-time savings would be multiplied by the wage rate.

This procedure yields the measure *EJ* and the problem is to judge

---

[8]Here, and in the remainder of the paper, it is assumed that there always exists some combination of positive income and leisure which is preferred to the all-leisure point. Although the latter choice can be easily handled theoretically, its inclusion unnecessarily complicates the analysis. It can also be noted that even though point *A* might appear to be preferable to point *E* in Fig. 1, this is unlikely to be the case in reality. The distances on the horizontal axis are not to scale. *AC* should actually be about one-sixteenth or less the length of *CG*.

its validity as an estimate of benefits. We suggest two criteria for this purpose. The first will be called the income levy. It is the maximum amount the individual is prepared to pay to keep the reduction in travel time that he has just experienced. The second criterion will be called the income supplement and is defined as the amount it is necessary to pay a worker in his original position in order to make him as well off as the reduction in travel time would make him. As will be seen below, if the workers are free to choose an optimal combination of income and leisure, the two criteria are identical.[9]

Consider the case of the individual whose preference system is represented by the difference curves $I_1 I_1$ and $I_2 I_2$. This worker chooses to devote all of the savings in travel time to work. His demand for *leisure* is perfectly inelastic with respect to an AC reduction in travel time. Surely, EJ is a precise estimate of the two criteria defined above. It is the maximum amount the individual would be willing to pay for the privilege of having his travel time reduced by AC. Similarly, it is the amount that must be paid the worker in his original equilibrium position, E, to make him as well off as he is by the reduction in travel time.[10] However, the appropriateness of the income approach may be questioned with regard to workers who react differently.

The individual whose preference system is represented by $I_1 I_1$ and $I'_2 I'_2$ reacts in an opposite manner. His demand for *income* is perfectly inelastic with respect to a time saving of AC. He could have added EJ to his income but chose to consume all of the time saving (EH equal to AC) as leisure, suggesting that this increment to his

---

[9] The reader will note the similarity between these two criteria and the compensating variation and equivalent variation defined by J. R. Hicks (see *A Revision of Demand Theory* [London: Oxford University Press 1956], p. 80).

[10] This holds true for all cases only if the worker receives this payment when and if he makes the work trip. If, for example, he receives the supplement EJ no matter what he does, he might not have a new equilibrium at J. Instead, he might choose not to work at all. He would then have leisure time equal to OA, income equal to EJ, and be at a point a distance of EJ above A. If this point (not shown) were in fact on a higher indifference curve than $I_2 I_2$, it would be preferred to J. The amount necessary to meet the second criteria, the income supplement, would then be less than EJ. Such a choice is unlikely, however, since the amount of EJ is rarely as much as one-tenth of GJ, his daily income. In addition, the compensation is not intended to enable him to reach a position unattainable through a reduction in travel time. Instead, it is a measure of the worth of the travel-time reduction to him when he is unable to have it. Therefore, the paper assumes throughout that a compensation granted or a toll charged to a traveler will be done on a *per trip basis* and only *when he actually makes the trip.*

leisure is worth more to him than the possible increment to his income. In this situation, the income method might be thought to yield biased estimates of the two measures of the value of travel time. For example, *EK*, greater than *EJ*, *would appear* to be the income supplement: the amount of income the individual would have to receive *in his original equilibrium position* in order to achieve as high a level of satisfaction as that permitted by the reduction in travel time, points *K* and *H* being on indifference curve $I'_2 I'_2$. This conclusion is incorrect, however, when individuals are free to choose the number of hours they work. If the above worker were given *EK* in his original equilibrium position, he would be on a higher budget line (not shown) through *K* and parallel to the others, and he would achieve equilibrium on a higher indifference curve (not shown) than $I'_2 I'_2$. On the other hand, if he received *EJ*, he would move along budget line *AB* to *H*. Thus, with the right to recontract — and this is what is entailed in freedom to choose hours of work — *EJ* is a precise estimate of the value of the income supplement even if the demand for income is perfectly inelastic with respect to changes in travel time. Similarly, the right to recontract means that *EJ* is a precise estimate of the income levy.[11] The same reasoning establishes the validity of *EJ* as an estimate of the value of travel time for those workers who find their new equilibrium between *H* and *J*. It is also valid even if leisure or income is an inferior good with respect to changes in the stock of time.[12]

A number of objections can be raised to the above analysis. First, the existence of alternative modes and money costs of travel have been ignored. These will be examined when the other two approaches are considered. Second, the influence that changes in travel time have on the entire system of prices, factor as well as goods and services, over a metropolitan area has not been taken into

---

[11] In other words, *HQ*, less than *EJ*, would appear to be the income levy: the maximum amount the individual would be willing to pay at *H* to keep the reduction in travel time. With the right to recontract, this conclusion would be incorrect. If an individual were only charged *HQ*, he would be on a higher budget line than *CD* and would achieve equilibrium on a higher indifference curve than $I_1 I_1$. Instead he must be charged *HR* equal to *EJ*. This places him on budget line *CD* along which he reaches point *E*.

[12] The movement from *E* on indifference curve $I_1 I_1$ to *L* on $I_3 I_3$ illustrates the former case whereas the movement from *E* to *M* on $I'_3 I'_3$ illustrates the latter. The use of the term "inferior" is justified since we are assuming that work and travel time involve equal disutility.

account.[13] This influence is extremely important. It bears directly on the changes that have been taking place in the distribution of population and economic activity within metropolitan areas. Unfortunately, it is much too complex to be dealt with in the present paper. Therefore, we assume that each individual's job, as well as the location of this job and his residence, are given. Third, it has been assumed that individuals are free to choose the number of hours they wish to work. Perhaps there is a standard number of hours to which workers must conform so that they are not in equilibrium either before or after a reduction in travel time.[14] Restrictions on work time and, therefore, on the number of work trips and travel time, can affect the size and direction of bias in estimates of the value of travel time obtained by the income approach. Let us now deal with the effect of such restrictions on the income approach.

In Figure 10-2 lines *AB* and *CD* can still be interpreted respectively as the income line and the net income line when only travel time is involved. The figure contains two new lines, *GJ* and *HF*. The intersection of each of them with the horizontal axis represents the standard number of hours. In other words, a worker on line *CD* can only have leisure time equal to *OG* since he *must* spend *CG* in work and *AC* in travel. Similarly, a worker on line *AB* has *OH* leisure: he has no travel time but must spend *AH* (equal to *CG*) in work. With travel time *AC*, the worker must be at *E*, which is not a position of equilibrium. Indifference curve $I_1 I_1$ intersects the budget line at *E* from below. In other words, given the wage rate, the stock of time, and required travel time, this individual — let us refer to him as an income preferrer — would be prepared to sacrifice some of his leisure time in order to increase his income. He is at *E* because he cannot obtain additional work in his primary employment or in a second job. A reduction in travel time equal to *AC* shifts this worker to *F* on $I_2 I_2$: while he would prefer additional income, leisure does

---

[13]On this subject see W. Alonso, "A Model of the Urban Land Market: Locations and Densities of Dwelling and Businesses" (Ph.D. Thesis, Department of Regional Science, University of Pennsylvania, 1960). Also see R. Muth, "Economic Change and Rural-Urban Land Conversion," *Econometrica*, XXIX, No. 1 (January, 1961), 1-23.

[14]The wage and hour implications of a standard number of hours to which workers must conform have been explored by L. N. Moses in "Income, Leisure, and Wage Pressure," *Economic Journal*, LXXII (June, 1962), 320-34. L. Wingo appears to have been the first author to recognize that the existence of a standard number of hours should be taken into account in valuing travel time (*Transportation and Urban Land* [Washington: Resources for the Future, 1961]).

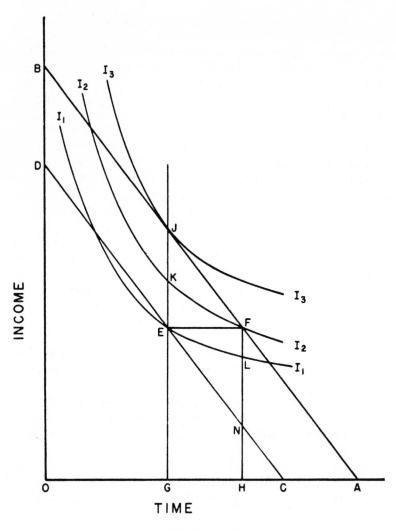

Figure 10-2

have positive marginal utility for him. However, F still involves the standard number of hours and is not a position of equilibrium. As the indifference curves have been drawn, the worker would be best off if he could devote all of the travel-time savings to work, that is, if he could reach J on indifference curve I_3I_3.[15] In such instances,

[15]The reader may object to the analysis on the grounds that travel-time savings can be used for overtime work in an individual's primary employment or in a second job. The complications caused by such activities are not sufficiently important to develop them here. If a worker has these options, then, except for minor difference, our earlier reasoning applies.

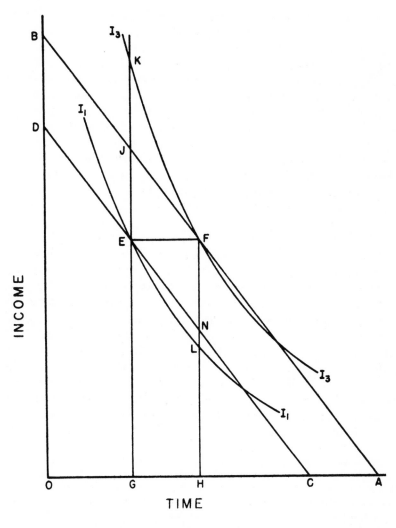

Figure 10-3

estimates of the value of travel time savings based on their worth in work have an upward bias. The income supplement this individual would have to receive at *E* in order to be as well off as the reduction in travel time makes him is less than the value of this time in work: *EK* is less than *EJ*. Similarly, the amount the individual would be willing to pay at *F* to keep the reduction in time (the income levy) is less than *EJ*: *FL* is less than *FN*.

Figure 10-3 deals with a different kind of individual, designated as a leisure preferrer. This figure is the same as Figure 10-2 except for the shape of the indifference curves. Given the wage rate, the stock of time, and the required travel time, a worker with these indifference curves would like to work fewer than the standard number of hours (CG) and have more leisure. This condition is indicated by the fact that indifference curve I_1I_1 intersects the budget line at E from above. Everything else constant, the reduction in travel time moves this individual to F on I_3I_3, increasing his leisure time and level of satisfaction. However, he is still in a position of disequilibrium and would prefer to have even more leisure. The income approach does not give an exact estimate in this case either and most usually understates the value of travel-time savings. With it we obtain EJ, which is less than EK, the income supplement. Similarly, we obtain FN with the income approach, which is less than FL, the income levy.[16] Our conclusions on the income technique can now be summarized.

We have been dealing with occupations in which travel is a fixed input.[17] Two basic situations were depicted. In the first, individuals were free to vary their work time and were in equilibrium before and after the reduction in travel time. It was shown that the income method of valuing travel-time savings is correct regardless of preference systems. The second set of cases arose because a standard number of hours was introduced and the assumption made that workers conform to it exactly. Here it was shown that the income method can have either an upward or downward bias. It overstates benefits for those individuals who would like to work more than the standard number of hours. It understates the value of travel-time savings for individuals who would like to work less than the standard number of hours.

---

[16]FN would be greater than or equal to FL if I_1I_1 sloped back sharply and crossed FH above or at N. This seems unlikely. It implies that the commuter would like to work fewer hours than those required (CG) but more than the present requirement, less the time savings (CH). Time savings are actually not as large a portion of the total stock of time (rarely over three per cent) as Fig. 10-3 suggests; that is, GJ and HF are actually quite close together. The authors believe that the worker would choose to reduce the time worked by more than the savings in travel time if he could do so.

[17]Thus, whether a secretary works for one or eight hours on any given day she must still spend the same amount of travel time and money. In other occupations travel is a variable input. The income of a door-to-door salesman depends on how many house calls he makes and, therefore, on how much time and money he spends in travel. In general, it may be said that we are ignoring problems that arise from the fact that occupations have different travel characteristics, and that the proportion of income earned as a result of the work trip varies between individuals. The analytical techniques developed in the paper can readily be adapted to cope with these problems.

It is tempting to step outside the realm of theory and judge whether those studies that have employed the income method have understated or overstated the value of travel-time savings and, therefore, some of the benefits of highway investment. In cases where the existence of alternative modes can realistically be ignored, it seems likely that they have understated benefits. The authors base this judgment on a belief that most individuals would choose to take travel-time savings in the form of leisure even if they could devote them to their regular income producing activity.

To examine the pure cost approach, consider Figures 10-1, 10-2, and 10-3 in light of the third interpretation that can be placed upon them. In this interpretation, *AB* and *CD* each represent the net income line of a particular mode (or route) that involves both time *and* money costs. The pure cost approach confines itself to these two characteristics of the choice of mode, ignoring the wage rate of the individual. This approach is usually applied to choices where individuals are willing to pay more on one mode or route than on others since that mode is faster. The higher cost of the faster mode is then used to value the time saving. Thus, the value per unit time is the ratio of the extra amount paid to the time saved when that mode is used. This must surely be equal to or less than the true value, since there may be some higher price that the commuter would be willing to pay to take the faster mode, given the price of a trip by the slower mode. In contrast, we are seeking in this paper to determine a measure of the net benefit to the consumer and thus must determine the price at which he would be indifferent between the two modes. The income and pure cost approaches are not satisfactory since the income approach relies solely on the wage rate and the time saving, while the pure cost approach uses only the time and cost characteristics of the modes.

The income-cost approach, which is the technique developed in this paper, therefore involves the wage rate as well as the time and cost techniques of the modes or routes. This approach can be considered in terms of Figure 10-1 when *AB* is taken to be the net income line for one mode — say, automobile — and *CD* is taken to be the income line for another — say, mass transit. If workers are free to choose an optimum combination of income and leisure and if variations in disutility of travel over time and by mode are ignored, all individuals who face the above budget lines would travel by auto (*AB*). *AB* is above *CD* and is tangent to a higher indifference curve no matter which preference system between income and leisure the individual may have.[18] *It is important to make clear, however, that this result depends upon the slope of the various budget lines: upon the wage rate as well as the time and money characteristics of the modes.* If we consider another group with a much different wage rate, *CD* might lie above *AB*. Mass transit would then be the superior mode choice for that group.

This logic can be seen in terms of simple algebra. The equation for the individual's net income line for the first mode (*AB* in Figure 10-1) gives income, Y_1, as a function of any given level of leisure, $\bar{L}$, as

$$Y_1 = w(s - \bar{L} - t_1) - c_1$$

where the variables are defined as follows:

w = worker's wage rate per unit of time
s = worker's stock of time (*OA* in Fig. 1)
t_1 = travel time by the first mode
c_1 = money cost by this mode.

If we define similar variables for the second mode, the equation for its net income line (*CD* in this case) will be

$$Y_2 = w(s - \bar{L} - t_2) - c_2.$$

The difference in net income between the two modes, Z, is thus

$$Z = Y_1 - Y_2 = w(t_2 - t_1) + (c_2 - c_1).$$

Under the conditions postulated, Z is constant at all levels of leisure, that is, the vertical distance between the net income lines is constant. In terms of Figure 10-1, Z is thus *BD*.

If workers are free to pick any combination of income and leisure and if the effect of disutility is ignored, Z indicates which mode they will take and what the diversion price will be. Thus, a worker will take the first mode if Z is positive, the second mode if it is negative,

---

[18]Mode choices have been specified as "all or nothing" choices for the sake of clarity. The analysis is equally suitable if modes can be combined. Each possible combination then becomes a choice whose time, cost, and disutility characteristics must be considered along with those of the primary modes.

and be indifferent between them if it is zero.[19] In addition, Z is the amount by which a commuter must either be compensated for taking the "wrong" mode or the minimum charge that must be imposed in order to make him switch from the "right" one. That is, if the worker were charged an additional amount equal to Z when he used his preferred mode, or paid an amount equal to Z when he used the alternative mode, the two net income lines would coincide and he would be indifferent between them.

These conclusions about Z are altered, however, when a restriction on hours is imposed — just as were the conclusions about the income approach.[20] The situation is similar (but not identical) to that which appears in Figures 10-2 and 10-3. Each choice point is now the intersection of the vertical line that represents the standard number of hours plus the time in transit on that mode with that mode's net income line which incorporates the time and cost on that mode. In the two-mode case under consideration, the choice points would be similar to points E and F in Figures 10-2 and 10-3 but would not be in the same juxtaposition (unless the two modes had the same cost). Thus, for example, points K and F in Figure 10-2 could be the alternatives facing an individual choosing one of two modes if the second mode's net income line were not CD but a parallel line (not shown) through K. Such a net income line as that through K would represent a mode with the same time in route as CD (since the hours line, GJ, applies to both) but which cost less since K is above E.

An examination of Figure 10-2 in this light shows that the introduction of a standard number of hours means that Z is unlikely to have the characteristics mentioned above. If K and F were in fact the choice points, then Z would be calculated to be JK. Given that AB is the first mode, JK would be a positive value; but it would not indicate mode choice nor be a measure of the diversion price. Being positive, this Z value would indicate a choice of the first mode (AB); yet the individual is indifferent between them since both choice

---

[19] For an alternate approach to the prediction of mode choice, see the recent, interesting work by Stanley L. Warner: *Stochastic Choice of Mode in Urban Travel: A Study in Binary Choice* (Evanston, Ill.: Transportation Center and Northwestern University Press, 1962).

[20] The restriction on hours is both a minimum and a maximum. In other words, there is not only a standard to which leisure preferrers must conform, but it is also assumed that income preferrers cannot work more than this number of hours. If through such devices as malingering, unpaid leave, overtime work, moonlighting, etc., both groups actually work an optimum number of hours, then the analysis above is appropriate.

points lie on indifference curve $I_2 I_2$. In addition, the diversion price indicated by the Z measure is JK, while actually the diversion price is zero.

It is thus impossible to measure the diversion price when there is a restriction on hours in the choice of mode case, just as it was in the earlier example, since we do not know the preference systems of the individuals concerned. The methods of analysis presented in this paper do allow us, however, to determine the nature of the bias involved in using the Z measure of the diversion price, given the mode choice and an assumption about the nature of the preference system of the individual involved.

This can be seen by examining the choice with the characteristics found most often in the empirical work presented in the next section — choice when the automobile is faster than public transportation but more expensive and the value of Z, when auto is the first mode, is positive. Since there is so much concern over automobile congestion for reasons mentioned in the introduction, the analysis here will concentrate on those whose present choice of mode is the automobile. The results are similar to those found in the income approach, since the situations are analogous. The income-cost approach underestimates the income supplement and the income levy measures for the leisure preferrer and overestimates them for the income preferrer.[21] The use of Z as a measure of the diversion price still has validity, however, for the leisure preferrer. Since it is impossible to measure the difference in utility exactly, it is desirable to err on the side of underestimating when approximating diversion prices. The values obtained can then be said to be the minimum prices necessary for diverting passengers from one mode to another.

The effect of disutility of travel time has been ignored in the analysis in this section. Let us now treat it explicitly and assume that disutility increases with travel time and varies between modes. The effect is that an individual, faced with the times and costs associated with a choice of mode, is likely to view one of the modes more favorably than the other. If this is true, then Z will no longer be an exact measure of the diversion price with freedom to choose hours of work. Assume, for example, that the automobile has a time and cost advantage as indicated by the sign of Z but involves greater disutility.

---

[21] Just as was the case with the income approach, there may be exceptions to these conclusions if the preference systems have unusual and unlikely shapes (see, for example, p. 17).

The commuter might then choose the alternate mode, say, public transit, if the greater disutility associated with the automobile outweighs its time and cost advantages. It would then be impossible to determine the diversion price since it might take only a small reduction in the cost of the automobile trip to make the monetary advantage sufficient to outweigh the greater disutility. A similar problem would arise if the automobile's monetary advantage were great enough initially to outweigh its greater disutility. A worker would then choose the automobile, but it would be impossible to estimate his diversion price. A small, non-calculable rise in the cost of an automobile trip might cause him to switch because the time and cost advantage no longer outweighed the greater disutility.

On the other hand, if the automobile involves less disutility for those who typically use this mode, as is commonly believed, taking disutility into account will strengthen the likelihood that Z will be an underestimate of the diversion price for the automobile driver in the restriction on hours case. For an individual to be diverted from the automobile, he must be compensated not only for the cost and time advantages foregone but also for the greater disutility incurred. Z is therefore even more assuredly an underestimate of the diversion price for leisure preferrers and more likely to be so for income preferrers.

The above analysis of the income-cost approach concentrated on the most common case — automobile faster but more expensive. There are three less common types of cases that cover the other possible combinations of time and money costs for the two modes. The technique used to analyze the first also applies to the other three. Space limitations preclude us from any analysis of them, especially as no definite conclusions can be reached about two of these cases — automobile slower and more expensive, automobile slower but cheaper. The results of the third — automobile faster and cheaper — are the same as those for the case studied: Z as a measure of the diversion price is an underestimate for the leisure preferrer but not for the income preferrer if the same assumptions are made.

2. Empirical Investigation of Diversion Prices

This section presents the results of an empirical investigation based on the theoretical arguments of Part I. The results are presented in the hope that they will reveal the kinds of price changes that would be required to induce shifts from automobile commuting to public transportation, if such a policy is deemed necessary.[22]

The data used for this work were the results of interviews of a sample of commuters from the Chicago area conducted by the Cook County Highway Department. Each commuter was questioned about his income and the time and cost characteristics of his preferred mode and the mode he considered his best alternative.[23] With this information it was possible for the authors to compute Z for each member of the sample. As was noted above, however, the application of our technique was limited to a subsample of this group, those for whom the automobile was the preferred mode.

Table 1 presents a tabulation of the Z values. It was constructed by dividing the commuters into subgroups according to the mode which they indicated was their best alternative. Cumulative frequency distributions of the Z's were calculated for each subgroup and are presented in columns (2)-(6). For example, column (2) shows that 83 per cent of those indicating bus-streetcar as their best alternative had Z values less than $1.00. In addition, a cumulative frequency distribution was calculated for the whole group and is presented in column (1). This column shows that 77 per cent of those using the automobile have Z values less than $1.00.

Under the assumptions presented in Part I, including freedom to choose hours and ignoring disutility, this table also shows what percentage of a given group will be diverted if automobile trip prices are raised by the amount in the "$Z¢$" column. Thus a $0.60 increase in the cost per trip of automobile commuting would induce 59 per cent of those respondents with bus-streetcar as their second choice to shift to this mode. Similarly, one can determine by how much the price of automobile commuting must be increased to divert to el-subway 50 per cent of the workers indicating that this was their second choice. The answer is found by looking down the "El-Subway" column to 50 per cent (actually 51) and then over to the Z column. The price of auto work trips would have to be increased by $0.70 per trip or $1.40 per day to accomplish such a diversion. The figures in the "All Modes" column also show diversion prices except that all of the alternatives are considered as one. For example, this

---

[22]Some authors, for example, argue for increases in the costs of auto trips on the grounds of efficiency pricing: see Mohring and Harwitz, *op. cit.,* pp. 75-87, and A. Walters, "The Theory and Measurement of Private and Social Cost of Highway Congestion," *Econometrics,* XXIX, No. 4 (October, 1961), 676-99.

[23]The nature of the sample, the data gathered, and other matters pertaining to the calculation of the Z's can be obtained from the authors.

Table 1

Distribution of Values of Z by Mode
(Per Cent)

Zȼ	Alternative Mode					
	All Modes (1)	Bus-Streetcar (2)	El-Subway (3)	Railway (4)	Walk (5)	Other (6)
10	7	6	9	9	26	2
20	14	13	18	17	37	6
30	23	24	21	21	68	6
40	33	37	24	28	79	11
50	43	47	37	36	79	20
60	54	59	46	51	89	28
70	63	67	51	60	89	42
80	68	73	57	64	100	47
90	73	79	61	64	....	51
100	77	83	64	64	....	54
110	80	86	69	68	....	59
120	82	87	69	70	....	63
130	84	89	70	72	....	68
140	85	91	70	74	....	72
150	88	93	72	79	....	77
160	89	94	73	79	....	77
170	89	94	75	83	....	78
180	90	94	78	83	....	81
190	91	95	78	87	....	83
200	92	95	78	89	....	84
210	92	95	79	89	....	84
220	92	96	79	89	....	85
230	94	96	81	91	....	88
240	94	96	81	91	....	88
250	94	97	81	91	....	89
260	95	97	85	91	....	89
270	96	98	87	96	....	91
280	96	98	87	96	....	91
290	96	98	88	96	....	91
300	97	99	91	96	....	91
310	97	99	91	96	....	91
320	97	99	91	96	....	93
330	97	99	91	96	....	93
340	97	99	91	96	....	93
350	97	99	91	96	....	93
360	98	100	91	96	....	93
370	98	....	91	98	....	93
380	98	....	93	98	....	93
390	98	....	93	98	....	94
400	98	....	93	98	....	94

column shows that 77 per cent of automobile commuters would be diverted to some alternative mode if the price of automobile commuting were increased by $1.00 per trip or $2.00 per day. The difference between the "All Modes" column and the other columns can also be appreciated if the reader will think in terms of a discriminating and non-discriminating monopolist. The latter would work only with the "All Modes" column while the former might choose to separate commuters into subgroups on the basis of next best mode and price differently to each of the groups.

Table 2 contains the same data as Table 1 but concentrates on the effect of lowering the price of the alternative mode rather than raising the cost of automobile transportation. A "reduced" or diversion price was calculated for each commuter by subtracting the value of his Z from the present cost of his alternative mode. Each column is the cumulative frequency distribution of these reduced prices for those specifying this alternative mode.[24] Column (2) shows, for example, that 52 per cent of the commuters specifying that el-subway was their best alternative had reduced prices greater than a − $0.50 per trip.

Ignoring disutility and assuming freedom to choose hours of work, this table also shows what percentage of each group will be diverted from automobile transport when such a reduction in price is made. Thus, column (1) shows that 13 per cent of the auto commuters who listed bus-streetcar as their second choice would be diverted to this mode if its price were zero. *It is evident from the table that negative prices would be necessary on all modes of public transportation to divert at least 50 per cent of those currently making the work trip by car.* For example, individuals who view el-subway as second best would have to be paid between $0.40 and $0.50 per trip to divert between 48 and 52 per cent of them. If our results are at all reasonable, the possibility of significantly reducing auto congestion

---

[24]It will be noted that Table 2 does not contain an "All Modes" column. It is left out because of the way the diversion issue is approached in Table 2, and because of the incomplete nature of the data in the sample. Commuters were only asked for the cost and time characteristics of their next best mode. They were not asked to rank all modes. This means that if the cost of traveling by each alternate mode were reduced to some common figure − this being the logic of an all-modes column − a commuter might choose some third mode before being diverted to his second choice. An example may clarify the point. In terms of time and possibly other quality attributes, an individual might view suburban railroad as most desired, auto second, and bus third. However, the cost characteristics of the modes are such that he actually ranks auto first, bus second, and rail third, that is, rail is very expensive. Now if all modes were reduced to some common price, this individual might shift to rail before shifting to bus. However, our information precludes such diversion because commuters were only asked about the time and cost characteristics of their preferred and second choices.

Table 2

**Per Cent Diverted by Mode for
Given Alternate-Mode Trip Prices**

	Alternate Mode				
price (¢)	Bus-Streetcar (1)	El-Subway (2)	Railway (3)	Walk (4)	Other (5)
90	. . . .	. . . .	. . . .	. . . .	. . . .
80	. . . .	. . . .	2	. . . .	. . . .
70	. . . .	. . . .	4	. . . .	. . . .
60	. . . .	. . . .	4	. . . .	. . . .
50	. . . .	. . . .	9	. . . .	. . . .
40	. . . .	. . . .	13	. . . .	. . . .
30	*	. . . .	15	. . . .	1
20	*	. . . .	15	. . . .	1
10	6	9	28	. . . .	4
0	13	18	32	. . . .	8
-10	24	23	45	26	13
-20	37	26	53	37	20
-30	47	38	64	68	30
-40	59	48	68	79	38
-50	68	52	68	79	51
-60	73	58	68	89	54
-70	78	65	68	89	58
-80	82	68	70	100	63
-90	85	71	72	. . . .	67
-100	87	71	74	. . . .	71
-110	89	72	74	. . . .	72
-120	90	72	83	. . . .	75
-130	92	75	83	. . . .	80
-140	93	77	85	. . . .	80
-150	94	78	85	. . . .	82
-160	94	80	87	. . . .	84
-170	94	80	87	. . . .	84
-180	94	80	91	. . . .	86
-190	95	82	91	. . . .	87
-200	95	82	94	. . . .	89
-210	96	82	94	. . . .	90
-220	96	82	94	. . . .	90
-230	96	82	94	. . . .	91
-240	97	88	96	. . . .	92
-250	97	88	96	. . . .	92
-260	97	88	96	. . . .	92
-270	98	89	96	. . . .	92
-280	98	92	96	. . . .	94
-290	98	92	96	. . . .	94
-300	98	92	96	. . . .	94

*Less than 0.5 per cent.

by reasonable reductions in the price of public transportation appears slight.

The boldest price reduction experiments of which the authors are aware are those proposed under grants from the federal government. In these demonstration projects, the reduction of some public transportation fares to zero was contemplated. Our results suggest that if such an experiment were carried out in Chicago, less than one fifth of the auto commuters would be diverted (13 per cent to bus-streetcar and 18 per cent to el-subway).

In addition, there are strong reasons for suspecting that the diversion percentages in the two tables are overestimates. First, if disutility is introduced and if, as is commonly believed, the auto involves less disutility for those who typically take this mode, the analysis in Part I showed that Z becomes even more of an underestimate of the diversion price, that is, even fewer people will be diverted. Second, our diversion prices are based on the assumption of one commuter to each car. The Chicago Area Transportation Study and the American Association of State Highway Officials state that on the average there are 1.5-1.8 persons per car.[25] If passengers do not share the cost of a trip, Z is the same for the car as for the driver. However, if expenses are shared, the necessary diversion price must be increased by an amount equal to the sum of the Z's for all other persons in the car. Finally, we have not taken into account the effect of diversion on travel time. Any price change that diverted some trip-takers to public transportation would reduce congestion and, therefore, the time required to make the trip by car for all other drivers.

Table 3 illustrates the effect of restriction on hours. It contains Z values for a subsample of the commuters in Table 1, those who faced the choice situation most common for this group: automobile preferred, faster, more expensive, and with a positive Z. We are unable to tell, of course, which of these commuters are leisure or income preferrers and whether they are subject to a restriction on hours. The percentages in Table 3 are valid minimum estimates only if it can be assumed that all or most people are leisure preferrers, and that they must work a standard number of hours. If these assumptions hold, column (2) of Table 3 indicates, for example, that to divert 75 per cent of those who specified that bus-streetcar was their best alternative, the price of an automobile trip must be raised *at least* $1.00. If one believed, instead, that most people are income preferrers, then the data in Table 3 are not valid when there is a restriction on hours. If one believes that there actually is no

---

[25] *Chicago Area Transportation Study: Final Report: Survey Findings,* I (December, 1959), 32; Committee on Planning and Design Policies, *op. cit.,* p. 126.

Table 3

**Distribution of Values of Z by Mode
(Per Cent)**

	Alternate Modes			
	All Modes	Bus-Streetcar	El-Subway	Other*
Zϙ	(1)	(2)	(3)	(4)
10	6	6	5	5
20	10	10	10	12
30	19	20	10	21
40	28	31	13	27
50	38	41	23	34
60	50	53	38	45
70	59	62	41	58
80	63	66	46	63
90	68	70	56	66
100	72	75	56	66
110	76	80	62	68
120	77	81	62	70
130	79	84	62	70
140	81	86	62	73
150	84	88	64	79
160	85	89	67	79
170	86	90	69	81
180	87	90	74	85
190	88	91	74	85
200	89	91	74	86
210	89	92	74	86
220	89	92	74	88
230	91	93	74	90
240	91	93	74	90
250	91	94	74	92
260	93	95	79	92
270	93	95	79	95
280	94	95	79	95
290	94	96	82	95
300	95	97	87	95
310	95	97	87	95
320	96	97	87	96
330	96	97	87	96
340	96	98	87	96
350	97	98	87	96
360	97	99	· 87	96
370	97	99	87	96
380	98	99	90	96
390	98	99	90	97
400	98	99	90	97

*Railroad and walking are included in this
column because of the small number of
these cases in this sample.

restriction on hours, the data presented in Tables 1 and 2 hold. The figures in Table 3 are even more likely to be underestimates for the reasons mentioned above with regard to the first two tables — disutility, more than one person per car, and so forth.

Conclusion

It is commonly believed that many of the problems of cities are due to the automobile, and that ways must be found to divert commuters to public transportation. Neither the belief nor the policy conclusion based on it has been at issue in this paper. Rather, we have developed a measure that we believe sheds light on the kinds of price changes that would be required to bring about diversion for the work trip. This measure is a function of the time and money costs of the mode choices available to a commuter and his wage rate. We were able to estimate actual diversion prices only for a group of commuters in the Chicago area, because Chicago is the only city for which appropriate data could be found. We believe the results obtained warrant collection of comparable data for other cities. It would also be worthwhile to determine what levels of investment would be required to reduce travel time by public transportation by various amounts. The cost of a diversion program based on price changes might then be compared with one based on improvements in this very significant aspect of quality of service.

11

The Value of Time Spent in Travelling: Some New Evidence

M. E. Beesley

1. Introduction

The valuation of time spent in travelling is important because, first, it has been prominent in studies of the value of investments in roads, a form of analysis recently extended to urban rail transport.* In the M.1 motorway study, for example, time savings accounted for 64 per cent of the measured gross benefits at the first year of operation, when the working time was valued at the lowest end of the range 2s. 0d. to 10s. 0d. an hour which was considered possible (1957 prices). At 10s. 0d. an hour, the proportion was 78 per cent.[1] In a study of the Victoria underground railway line, with savings in working time valued at 7s. 0d. an hour, and in non-working time (i.e. the vast bulk of the savings in this case) at 5s. 0d. an hour (1962 prices), time savings accounted for about 80 per cent. of total benefits at the first year of operation.[2]

Reprinted from *Economica,* Vol. 32, 1965, pp. 174-185. Copyright © by the London School of Economics and Political Science. Used with permission.

*The original stimulus for this work arose from discussion with Mr. A. J. Blackburn and Mr. C. D. Foster, whose influence is gratefully acknowledged. Mr. J. Murchland and Dr. J. F. Kain gave valuable advice on computation.

[1] T. M. Coburn, M. E. Beesley, and J. G. Reynolds, *The London-Birmingham Motorway: Traffic and Economics,* Technical Paper No. 46, Road Research Laboratory, D.S.I.R., 1959. Gross benefits, which included operation cost savings and accident savings, were £1.3 million when non-working time was valued at 2s. 0d., and £2.2 million when valued at 10s. 0d.

[2] C. D. Foster and M. E. Beesley, "Estimating the Social Benefit of Constructing an Underground Railway in London", *Journal of the Royal Statistical Society,* Series A. (General), vol. 126 (1963), Table 2 and *passim.* About 5 per cent of journey time is performed in working time on London's Underground. Other estimates of the values of non-working time have ranged from 0, as in the case of C. T. Brunner's pioneer studies of benefits from motorway investment, to 10s. 0d. an hour, as recently put forward by the Road Research Laboratory: *RN 4079,* Road Research Laboratory, D.S.I.R., 1961, p. 9.

Similarly, the recent Report of the Panel on Road Pricing estimated that the initial annual savings from a nation-wide system of metering vehicles in congested areas would be between £100 and £150 million a year.[3] Nearly 90 per cent. of these[4] come from time savings; of time savings, about 60 per cent. were time savings other than in working time. The evidence to be described later throws doubt on these assumptions about the valuation of non-working time.

Second, time spent in travelling is, by definition, time spent on a mode or modes of transport. The relative valuation of time by mode is crucial for predictions of numbers of travellers using each mode, and thus to their relative worth.[5] Valuation of time by modes is therefore also important in predictions concerning methods for rationing the use of existing transport investments. Thus, in England, the work of the Panel on Road Pricing indicated how important is the relative valuation of modes under different conditions for the likely effectiveness of new devices for charging vehicles. In America, Moses and Williamson have calculated, on the basis of assumed values for time spent in transit, the "diversion prices" necessary to shift specified numbers of car users to public transport.[6] It will be argued that the evidence to be put forward also throws some doubt on these estimates.

The particular kind of trip on which we have evidence is the journey to work in London. The preliminary explorations reported

---

[3] *Road Pricing: The Economic and Technical Possibilities.* Report of the Panel on Road Pricing, 1964.

[4] Covering working time saved, non-working time saved, and vehicles' capital and operating costs only.

[5] No large-scale attempt has been made yet, it seems, to set values upon time spent in varying conditions of travel. One might approach this task either by making observations in which time spent is used as an index of quality differences, taking the value of time in general as given, or by making observations like those this article will present — namely where time spent in specified conditions is, in effect, traded against money outlays. An example of the first approach is in the Victoria Line study where changes in comfort and convenience were investigated by observing choices made between slow, less-crowded, and fast, more-crowded, trains (see Foster and Beesley *loc. cit.* Appendix, pp. 60 ff.). This method is indirect in that the value taken for time must represent a disutility of travel which is independent of the quality differences that are measured. The second method, in attempting direct measurements, avoids this.

[6] Leon N. Moses and Harold F. Williamson, Jr., "Value of Time, Choice of Mode, and the Subsidy Issue in Urban Transportation," *Journal of Political Economy* vol. LXXI (1963); also Chapter 10 in this volume.

here attempt to set a value on the time spent by different (income) groups of people in travelling to work by public transport (viewed as an aggregate of bus and train service) and by privately-owned cars. The general method is first to infer an average value for disutility of time spent on public transport for groups choosing between public transport alternatives, and then, using this value as the value for the public transport alternative when similar groups choose between public transport and cars, to infer an average value for car time. The sort of biases this method may introduce are best canvassed when the data and precise procedure have been described. It is, of course, in principle possible to derive analogous values from any situation in which there is a trade-off of time against cost involving a mode. Thus, when a person decides to buy a new house he may be said to be, amongst other things, trading disutilities of the journey against the location-rent paid.[7] Clearly, however, it is best to be as direct as possible in choosing data to test people's trade-offs.[8]

2. The Data

The data concern choices of travel to work made by civil servants working at the headquarters of the Ministry of Transport in August 1963. All were employed in Central London and most at the St. Christopher House complex on Southwark Street.

Of the 2,700 people involved, including those in offices in London other than St. Christopher House, some 1,450 replied to a questionnaire in which they were asked to state in detail their address now, whether their household owned a car or cars, their usual journey to work (defining time by eight modes, time spent walking and waiting, cost where public transport was used, and mileage where own — or other's — private transport was used); each leg of the journey, defined by a change of mode, if any, was separately described; and

[7] See J. F. Kain, "A Contribution to the Urban Transportation Debate: An Econometric Model of Urban Residential and Travel Behaviour," *Review of Economics and Statistics*, vol. XLVI (1964).

[8] The present approach is an exercise in establishing the price of a service; one is trying to find out what prices people are prepared to pay to minimize the disutility of travel. In this, incomes are taken as given. This hypothesis about behaviour is not the only possible one. In particular, one could argue that the exercise should be directed to the trade-off between income (from work) and leisure, as do Moses and Williamson, *loc. cit.* The justification and possible reconciliation of these hypotheses cannot be dealt with in the space available here, and are held over for explicit treatment elsewhere.

parking charges, if any, incurred en route were noted. Parallel information was asked for the alternative they would adopt if they did not come by the usual mode. Their choice of defining an alternative was not guided: any variation from the usual route would in principle have sufficed. Most seemed not to have thought of very minor alternatives. A few were obviously pressed to find an alternative, and 250 recorded "no possible alternative". The cost of season tickets was translated into pence per single journey; and car, or motor bicycle, mileage into costs per mile, by using *Commercial Motor* tables of running expenses for the different kinds of car, etc. Running expenses exclude amortization, and vary from 2 1/2d. a mile for 750 c.c. to 4 1/2d. a mile for 4,000 c.c. cars. This particular definition of car costs (made as a preliminary estimate only) will be kept in mind in what follows.

The important factor, income, is a proxy: the average of the salary scales of the respondents' grade. Since there are at least ten important grades, with known scales, this is perhaps as good an approximation as is usually met with in studies of trip behaviour.

3. Preliminary Analysis

The important assumptions we make here are the following: (*a*) people choose their mode of travelling so as to minimize disutility of travel; (*b*) people of a given income class, as defined by grade, comprise a homogeneous aggregate: they have the same incomes; (*c*) marginal and average disutility of travel are equal for each person; (*d*) and the disutility of public transport travel is the same for those in a group who report a choice between public transport and car.

Our first task is to estimate the value set upon time for groups reporting choices between public transport alternatives; we then use the values to substitute into the choices made by the same income group who report choices between public transport and car. For this first analysis, we regard the public transport choices as representing a series of trials of different combinations of time and cost confronting persons of similar characteristics; we look for the value of time that best describes the set of observations. We make the heuristic assumption that people are indifferent to the proportions of travelling time, walking time and waiting time associated with each public transport choice, and that they are indifferent to the proportions of time spent on each kind of public transport, viz. bus, British Railway train, or Underground.[9]

With these assumptions we may sum up the choice of each person in terms of an inequality of this form:

$$a + b < x + y,$$

where $a + b$ refer to the preferred journey, with a equal to minutes spent to get to work, and b the cost (fares, parking, etc.), and $x + y$ are similar quantities for the rejected journey. We shall be concerned here principally with Clerical Officers (C.O.'s) and their equivalents and with Executive Officers (E.O.'s). The former received an average annual salary of £650, the latter one of £850.'

The first observation to be made about the whole set of choices for which complete data are available,[10] namely 1109, is that, even with the crude aggregated form of the choice equation, choices are rare in which *both a* and *b* are greater than *x* and *y,* or in which there is a tie on one element with a greater quantity for the other element. Second, as is to be expected with a public transport system like that of London where there is an explicit policy to equalize fares for similar distances on modes, the predominant pattern of choices is of the type:

$$a < x \text{ and } b \leqslant y.$$

From these choices no information can be gained for the first exercise. There remains, however, the third possibility, namely choices where $a > x$ and $b < y,$ or *vice versa.* These are cases in which a trade-off of time against cost appears to have been made, and furnish the basis of this exercise. Cases of the first type arise in 6.3 per cent. of all choices; cases of the second type in 66.2 per cent and cases of the third type in 27.5 per cent. Were time spent in transit

---

[9]The assumptions are not in themselves plausible; but this level of aggregation is justified here by the small sample, and by the possibility that differences in disutility as amongst different kinds of public transport are likely to be much smaller than such differences between public transport as a whole and cars. We hope to study later many other possible sources of differences in valuation, including the possibility that the home locations of people affect in some systematic manner their opportunity to make choices.

[10]This set excludes cases where bicycling or walking all the way is one element of choice and a number of incomplete returns.

not regarded as a disutility (and especially considering the level of aggregation of public transport choices, walking, etc. used here), one might well have expected a larger incidence of people who report what appear to be choices inconsistent with the hypothesis that people minimize disutility as we have defined it.[11] Reporting error must account for some of these inconsistent observations. Table 1 shows, as one might expect, that the incidence of apparently inconsistent choices is markedly higher with choices involving public transport and cars. (As we see later, some of this is removed when the public transport side of the choice is valued.) It seems that we may usefully proceed on the assumption that time in transit *is* regarded as a disutility, and with the aggregated public transport data.

We call the 27.5 per cent. "traders", i.e. traders of time against cost, or *vice versa*. "Traders" are most frequent in public transport alone among C.O.'s and E.O.'s. Our hope is that a study of the 65 choices for C.O.'s and, very tentatively because of the few observations, of the 21 choices for E.O.'s, will yield some "measure of central tendency" of the value of time in public transport. Now, each individual inequality yields either a maximum or a minimum value of time under our assumptions. If the choice happens to yield a gain of p time for a loss of q pence for the journey, there will be a set of values of time (in pence per minute) which would be consistent with our hypothesis of minimizing disutility, equal to or greater than q/p, i.e. from q/p as a minimum value to infinity. Where the choice happens to yield a gain of q pence for a loss of p time, there will be

---

[11] Nine combinations of time and cost could be observed, as follows:

Preferred transit		Rejected transit	
time	cost	time	cost
a	b	x	y

The following values are possible:

(1) $a > x$	(2) $b > y$
(3) $a = x$	(4) $b = y$
(5) $a < x$	(6) $b < y$

The combinations *a priori* not in accordance with the idea that time is a disutility (group A) are (1) + (2); (1) + (4); and (3) + (2).

Possible "traders" (group B) (see text below) are (1) + (6); and (5) + (2).

The rest (group C) are (5) + (4); (5) + (6); (3) + (6); and (3) + (4).

Disregarding (3) + (4) as *a priori* very infrequent (exact equality on both), a random distribution of choices would give an expectation of 37.5 per cent, groups A and C, and 25 per cent, group B.

Table 1

Incidence of "Inconsistent" Choices

| | Choices Involving | | | | |
| | Public Transport Only | | Cars (incl. Motorcycles) | | Total |
Grade	Inconsistent*	Consistent	Inconsistent	Consistent	
Clerical Assistant	2	68	2	4	76
Clerical Officer	18	217	8	63	306
Executive Officer	2	109	10	76	197
Higher Ex. Off.	3	48	3	44	98
Engineers	1	34	2	78	115
Other higher grades at St. Christopher House	4	58	6	70	138
Officers not at St. Christopher House	5	110	3	61	179
Totals	35	644	34	396	1109

*"Inconsistent" choices are those where the preferred journey both takes more time *and* costs more than the rejected journey; or where the preferred journey takes more time when cost is the same; or where the time is the same and the cost greater.

similarly a set of values greater than 0, less than or equal to q/p, i.e. from 0 to q/p as a maximum. For example, regarding the whole set of observations for C.O.'s as a set of trials, we would in a truly homogeneous group, expect a value for time which is consistent with all the observations. All observed minima would fall just below or be equal to this value: all maxima would be equal to or be above this value. We could, if we wished, look at an observed minimum as a rejected maximum, and conversely. All observations could then be regarded as trials for a division between acceptance and rejection. We do not, of course, observe a perfect division. Figure 11-1 records the trade-offs of time against cost for E.O.'s.

This idea of acceptance or rejection does, however, suggest a method for deriving the measure of central tendency. We seek that value of time which minimizes the misclassification of observations.

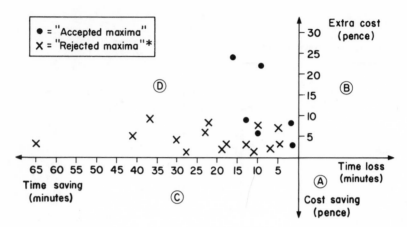

*The "rejected maxima" are values transformed from quadrant A, which would contain minimum values. Were all choices to be recorded on the diagram, quadrant B would contain the "inconsistent" choices, if any, and quadrant C the "predominant" choices.

Figure 11-1

(A value of time is represented by a line passing from a point in the quadrant through the origin of the graph.) Such a method can be more or less sophisticated. For the present it seems advisable to use the simplest form, viz., a straightforward minimization of the *number* of misclassifications, allowing, of course, for the fact that the numbers of observations of accepted maxima or rejected maxima, respectively, vary.[12] (We might for example have sought instead to minimize the measured deviance of misclassified observations from the trial value, or the square of that deviance, thus applying a form of least squares regression with constant terms disallowed. This kind of technique will be more appropriate for the further exploration of the data.) Our confidence in the value derived will depend on the proportion misclassified at that value. (Were the choices random, one would expect 50 per cent. misclassified at any value of time.) For C.O.'s the value conforming to the simple criterion is .40d. per minute; at that value 27 per cent. of observations are misclassified. For E.O.'s the corresponding value is

---

[12] Formally, we obtain the value of t which minimizes $\Sigma (n/m) ai + bj$, where ai = number of values $> t$, bj = number of values $< t$, m = sample size a and n = sample size b.

.63d. per minute, at which value 25 per cent. are misclassified. Both these misclassification levels are perhaps encouragingly low, considering the aggregation in the components of time.[13] The corresponding values per hour are: C.O.'s 2s. 0d., E.O.'s approximately 3s. 2d. These accord with expectation in that E.O.'s salaries are higher; their corresponding salaries (counting a working year of 2,000 hours) are: C.O.'s 6s. 6d. per hour, and E.O.'s 9s. 0d. per hour.

We must enquire whether these estimates are affected seriously by peculiarities in the data, in the sense either that the "traders" have special characteristics or that the extreme non-conforming values within the "trader" group, ignored in our treatment, should not be ignored. As to the first possibility, the "trader" group is found not to be obviously atypical in such characteristics as the relative proportions of walking and waiting times, the length of journeys, and the relative frequency of individuals who had lately changed their residence. More diligent searching might, however, disclose the presence of special characteristics, or special combinations of factors worthy of systematic analysis. As to the second possibility, a study of the extreme nonconforming values in the C.O. set reveals the interesting information that five out of six are women, compared with one quarter in the "trader" group as a whole. It is perhaps understandable that some women should appear at the extremes. Women generally tend to be rather lower down within a given grade than men, and therefore may tend to value time at less than the average for the grade; but, on the other hand some women are married and form part of a dual-income household and consequently have a high valuation of time both because of relatively high household income and also because time is usually a particularly valuable commodity for a working woman with a family. Such possibilities could be more systematically explored with additional data.

---

[13] Some variance in valuation for a given income level must be expected: classification error may arise from the fact that some C.O.'s may be "cash preferers" and others "time preferers", because salaries may not be an individual's only soucce of income and because the number of dependents varies.

"Cash preferers" are not necessarily those who accept the cash gain and reject the time gain. Whether they do so depends upon the terms of the trade-off — if the time loss is too high, "cash preferers" will still reject cash gains. But there is some presumption that the cash acceptors will contain cash preferers. It would obviously be useful to try to devise an independent test of this — e.g. taking account of the varying number of children of school age, etc.

Assuming we have a reasonable valuation of the time spent by C.O.'s and E.O.'s on public transport, we may enquire into the implied valuation of time spent in private cars, as revealed by the data for choices involving car against public transport. For this purpose we substitute the value obtained for public transport time in these choices, and proceed as before to seek the value giving the minimum misclassification. With this procedure, *all* such choices (and not only "trader" choices) can, of course, be used: where cars are preferred a maximum value for car time emerges; where public transport is preferred, a minimum.

The procedure gives the following results: C.O.'s value car time at .40d. per minute, the same as for public transport: E.O.'s value it at .73d., considerably higher than for public transport. The misclassification errors are lower than before. For C.O.'s the value is 19 per cent. on 57 observations; for E.O.'s it is 22 per cent. on 61 observations. Considering that this procedure obviously in general widens the possibilities of error,[14] this low degree of misclassification error is rather surprising.[15] Here again, many more data are needed to establish why the substitution apparently works so well.

The figures for the E.O.'s in particular are as one might expect on balance — the disutility of travel in cars (done as here, at peak times) is higher than that on public transport. The results depend crucially, of course, on the value set on car costs: were they to be rated more highly than in these calculations, the estimated valuation of time would be lower. We follow the conventional practice in computing them at running costs only: as yet there is no evidence indicating clearly that this should be changed. Other evidence suggests that the disutility of car travel in London increases with length of journey: on the average E.O.'s have somewhat longer journeys than C.O.'s.

One other, hypothetical, exercise can be performed with the data. The process of calculating the value of public-transport times and substituting these in public transport/car choices is not feasible for the information obtained from higher civil servants (who earned over £2,200 a year), though it would have been useful to have obtained some notion of their corresponding valuations because their reported

---

[14] For example, C.O.'s with cars may be better off than the average; car driving conditions vary widely; the valuation of car running-costs used may not conform to people's perception of those costs; and so on.

[15] Though, as noted earlier, "irrational" choices are higher where cars are involved. The number is reduced by splitting the choice into components.

choices lie mainly between public transport and car. Making use of the device of minimizing misclassifications, however, we can infer the (positive) values for public transport time and car time which give the minimum misclassification for public transport/car choices. To do this, we test for trial values of public transport time, substituting values in the reported choices; these give implicit car time values in each choice. We select the trial value that gives the lowest number of misclassifications. With trial values of 1.0, 1.5, 2.0, 2.5, and 3.0d. per minute for public transport time, the range of values giving least misclassifications for car choices is 2.0 to 2.5d. This compares with the average salary (on the same basis as before) of 4.8d. per minute. The value of time spent in cars in that range is somewhat higher than for public transport — about 5 per cent. higher.

4. Some Interim Conclusions

Though the study is at an early stage, it is of interest to draw out some of its implications, on the assumption that the survey respondents, for given salary levels, are typical of other commuters in their attitudes to, and behaviour in, the journey to work. The need to deal with the data at a more disaggregated level, and other steps useful to improve the analysis, have already been pointed out. It must also be admitted that there are inherent difficulties in devising tests which would enable one to reject, on the basis of the kind of data with which we are dealing, different hypotheses about behaviour from that considered here. For example, one alternative hypothesis might be that people minimize journey time irrespective of cost — or do so as long as cost differences do not exceed some absolute amount. One difficulty in testing this is that, because of the way the data were generated, we observe relatively few instances in which large cost savings were available. For the lower income groups, we have enough examples of people accepting a cash saving to be fairly sure that for them such hypotheses are implausible: but for the highest income group we do not. The chief reason for the latter may well be that most choices in this group lie between rail and car, and car travel is usually quicker where differences occur. In order safely to reject the alternative explanations, therefore, additional data will be necessary. Nevertheless, some interim conclusions and observations seem justified.

(a) From the London Traffic Survey we know that nearly half of all trips by people in the London area are made for the purpose of going to or from work, and that these trips are longer than the average of all trips. For this considerable proportion of all journeys, it seems from our data that time spent on public transport is valued in a way which varies with income. For workers earning at about the average wage level (our C.O.'s and E.O.'s) the value is about one-third of their average wage (C.O.'s 31 per cent., and E.O.'s 37 per cent.). More highly paid people (our highest grades) place a higher value proportionally — between 42 per cent. and 50 per cent. Time spent in car travel is valued a little, but only a little, more highly.[16]

(b) The present work indicates nothing directly about non-commuting trips. We may still retain the hypothesis that trips made in working time are valued at some rate near to an hourly wage rate: presumably here the predominant consideration is that it is in the interest of employers of labour to ensure that time they pay for is used fully, and they are able to rearrange work schedules and the number of workers they hire accordingly. We may also retain the idea that time spent on particularly irksome journeys may be valued highly: on very pleasant journeys much less. Some of these variances at least could be investigated by extending the kind of analysis we have presented.[17]

---

[16] In this connection it is significant that a recent American study, which of previous studies is the most nearly analogous to the present work in that it attempted to assess values of time by car by cross-section analysis of 14 pairs of toll roads and free roads in the U.S., concluded that time was valued at 1.4 dollars an hour, which, it may be calculated, is about one-third of the average wage of U.S. car owners in 1959. See P. J. Claffey, "Characteristics of Travel on Toll Roads and Comparable Free Roads for Highway User Benefit Studies", Highway Research Board Bulletin No. 306, 1961.

The method used was to find that value of time most consistently accounting for the observed proportions of motorists choosing free or toll road facilities in the different cases. An attempt was made to eliminate quality differentials by computing the number of significant speed alterations on the alternatives. The author is not satisfied with the results, feeling that they have been underestimated. The number of observations of pairs of trips is very small — effectively only ten pairs were used. The study is, however, a marked improvement on previous studies which were confined to single toll versus free road choices, and did not allow for quality differentials. These studies, of course, encounter great difficulties in standardizing for income levels, time and kind of trip — indeed no serious attempt has been made to control these factors.

[17] Similarly, the valuation of time in the other main categories of trip-making — for shopping and recreational needs — might be estimated by a development of the technique. In this connection it is particularly regrettable that the London Traffic Survey failed to emulate its American forbears to the extent of asking respondents about alternative choices of trip-making: details of trips to work are very easily collected; details of other trips much less easily for they probably involve household interviews.

(c) If the values for time found by us are nearer the truth than values based directly on average wages and salaries, past cost-benefit studies have to be re-evaluated. Discussion here is confined to the most relevant type of study, namely, of urban transport investment. In our paper on the Victoria Line,[18] Foster and I estimated that the present value, at 6 per cent., of net benefits from the investment was £70 million, with a capital outlay of £38.8 million, giving a "surplus" of £31 million. When the new values for time are substituted, net benefits are of the order of £52 million, with a "surplus" of £14 million.[19] Subsequent studies (as yet unpublished) of other investments in railways in London, calculated in a manner, and with values for time, similar to that adopted in the Victoria Line paper, have shown varying, but lower, surpluses, than did the Victoria Line. The new values for time are bound to reduce the benefits of these investments. To the extent that these exercises are useful as broadly indicating whether such investments are worth while, the conclusion must be that they justify very little extension of underground lines. Since the new values for car time are little higher than those for public transport time, the justification for road investments of urban motorway standard in the centre, say, of London, which already are rather precarious,[20] is made almost equally difficult. There is some comfort in these findings for those who are suspicious of the effect on the quality of urban living of large new transport investments; but it is, of course, too soon for their opponents to despair. First, there is a distinct possibility that investigations so far have not considered the "best" possible investments, because those that have been studied have been determined by engineering and commercial rules of thumb. The conventional wisdom in this area of policy is probably biased by undue preoccupation with peak demands: we have not found evidence in our data that people behave as if peak travelling were the purgatory it is usually assumed to be. Second, some potential benefits, such as the reduction of accidents and noise, have tended to be left out of account because of the difficulties of measurement. They merit more systematic study. Third, and

---

[18] Foster and Beesley, *loc cit.*, Table 2, p. 49.

[19] This recalculation is only approximate. One complication is that, where time was used as an index of benefit, as in valuing comfort and convenience, we cannot apply the new values of time without adjustment, because these themselves contain an average amount of discomfort, etc., in public transport travel.

[20] See, for example, M. E. Beesley, A. J. Blackburn, and C. D. Foster, "Urban Transport Models and Motorway Investment", *Economica*, vol. XXX (1963).

probably most important, we need to consider in far more detail the effects of time-saving improvements on the demand for and supply of jobs. A major effect of time saving is to introduce workers and employers to a larger labour market. Both a satisfactory model to deal with this effect and the necessary data to explore it have yet to be devised.

(d) Ideas about charging for vehicles in congested areas may have to be modified in two principal ways. (i) The benefits to be derived from the introduction of such a system will be lower than has hitherto been estimated. Relative to the investments discussed above, charging systems remain a good prospect, however, even when the estimates are adjusted. (ii) "Diversion prices" necessary to induce car travellers to shift to alternative public means of transport may be lower than those implied by estimates which have been constructed by adding fares or car operating costs to time valued at average hourly wages or salaries.[21]

However, the calculations we have made are not designed to tell us much about the important determinants of the outcome of such schemes — for example, the substitution of local trips for trips to town, the frequency of bus services in affecting demand for travel by bus, the significance of restricted parking space, the effect of trip length, family car demands, and so on. Here again an appropriate model to test conditions of substitution of modes is needed. All we know so far is that differing time on modes relative to other factors may be less important than has previously been thought.

---

[21] Compare Moses and Williamson, *loc. cit.* p. 262: "Negative prices would be necessary on all modes of public transportation to divert at least 50 per cent. of those currently making the work-trip by car." This major conclusion can be challenged on at least two grounds. First, if in fact the time element has to be divided by 3, the percentage would probably fall drastically — the limited detail given in the article does not allow us to estimate this. Second, it is not clear why one should be concerned with percentages as large as 50; one would have thought that a much lower percentage shift to public transport would have markedly beneficial results, for example, in de-congesting roads.

12

Choice of Travel Mode for the Journey to Work: Some Findings

D. A. Quarmby

1. Introduction

The worst urban traffic congestion usually occurs during the periods of travel to and from work, although there is some evidence that in London "peak" conditions are spreading throughout the day. The situation is worse in the typical nineteenth century core-oriented cities, such as those in northern industrial areas. While this pattern of urban form persists — and with current town planning philosophies there is good reason to think it will, although probably more shopping will be done in the suburbs — heavy morning and evening flows of commuters to and from the centres of towns will continue. Congestion exists partly because many car owners find it more convenient to travel to work by car than by public transport, even in congested conditions. As car ownership increases, an increasing proportion of present "captive riders" on public transport will have the choice of car or public transport. While public transport vehicles share the same road as private vehicles, the shift of commuters from public transport to private car will increase congestion and will delay both types of vehicles. But this shift will happen as long as commuters continue to find a *relative* advantage in driving their own cars. It seems likely that, under present policies, this relative advantage will persist even as conditions worsen.

It has been estimated that in Leeds (where this study was made), to maintain approximately the same *numbers* of commuters travelling by car as now, the *proportion* of car owners using their cars to drive to work would have to be reduced from about 70 per cent now to about 20 per cent in 40 years' time.[1] Given continuing

Reprinted from the *Journal of Transport Economics and Policy*, Vol. 1, No. 3, 1967, pp. 1-42. Copyright © by the London School of Economics and Political Science. Used with permission.

[1] D. A. Quarmby, *Transport Planning and the Choice of Travel Mode: Summary Report* (Department of Management Studies, Leeds University, December 1966).

congestion, some reduction would come about by "natural" processes, *i.e.* by the sort of "feedback" process which somehow ensures that total breakdown of traffic is a rare occurrence. But the conditions under which these natural processes operate are very costly, particularly in time lost by congestion, and it may well be that specific policy action — increasing either the disincentives of car usage or the attractiveness of public transport — could achieve the same result at less cost.

Various *ad hoc* measures have been proposed from time to time. Buchanan mentioned four main alternatives: a system of permits or licences to control the entry of vehicles; a system of pricing the use of road space; parking policy; subsidising public transport.[2] The acceptability, and cost, of such measures would depend on how much of each or any would be required — this might be expressed in terms of a target percentage of *potential* car commuters diverted to public transport. Evaluation of possible measures is difficult because very little is known quantitatively about what influences people's choices of travel mode for the journey to work. This point is brought out in a timely, but not entirely coincidental, way in Dr. Sharp's article in the first issue of this journal,[3] an article which discusses the "supply" side of the general problem — *i.e.* the effect of a transfer of commuters on speeds and times of different vehicles.

The research to be described here is an attempt to develop and calibrate a model to explain, and subsequently predict, the choice of travel mode of car owners on their journey to work, in terms of factors which can be directly related to policy variables and in terms of a plausible hypothesis about people's behaviour. The research was carried out at Leeds University from 1964 to 1966, under a grant from Leeds City Transport Department, which felt the need for guidelines in thinking about the long-range development of public transport facilities. It was seen as important for a modal choice model to offer a means of estimating the proportion of car-owning commuters that would be diverted to any proposed new transport system.

Since comprehensive transportation study models are continually improving, one might argue that a model for predicting modal choice alone, out of the context of the other travel decisions people make

---

[2] *Traffic in Towns* (HMSO, 1963).

[3] C. H. Sharp, "The Choice between Cars and Buses on Urban Roads," *Journal of Transport Economics and Policy*, Vol. 1, No. 1 (January 1967), 104-111.

(as represented by generation, distribution and assignment sub-models), would not be particularly useful. If we were examining all trips, or trips in general in urban areas, this point would have some validity. But the journey to work is a special case, because people in work nearly all make two trips per day, and their numbers can be fairly closely and simply related to population, so that the generation sub-model is extremely simple. With predominantly core-oriented cities, like Leeds and Manchester, the destinations of journeys to work are determined, so that the distribution sub-model is by-passed. Nearly all such cities have a largely radial road system and a radial public transport system, so that the route assignment is usually determined. To a large extent this is an over-simplification; but it suggests that in examining this particular situation the problems of ignoring sub-models other than modal choice may only be of secondary importance. Although not seen as a primary task of the research, it is to be hoped that the modal choice model outlined here may form the basis for a new sub-model in the typical transportation study model: modal split is often considered the least satisfactory part of the package.

The quantifying, or calibration, of the model to be described here was carried out by the little known technique of discriminant analysis, which was first used on this type of problem by Warner[4] at Northwestern University and during the last few years has been taken up in a somewhat modified form for modal choice forecasting on the North East Corridor Project.[5] It is noteworthy that a number of projects have started in the U.K. in the last twelve months, some sponsored by public authorities, to investigate further the application of discriminant analysis and other techniques for modal choice in the urban journey to work.

It will be shown later that in this particular case a straightforward multiple regression approach yields equivalent results. For some researchers this approach may be more convenient, since multiple regression programs are available for most computing installations. But the discriminant analysis approach derives direct from the nature of the problem and from a plausible hypothesis of behaviour, and the

---

[4] S. L. Warner, *Stochastic Choice of Mode in Urban Travel: A Study in Binary Choice* (Evanston: Northwestern University Press, 1962).

[5] *Some Aspects of Discriminant Functions and Other Interurban Modal Split Models* (Washington, D.C.: Traffic Research Corporation to NECTP, National Bureau of Standards, October 1965).

prediction of probability of choice of mode can be seen to come direct from the form of the discriminant function. In this article the development of the model is followed through in discriminant analysis terms, and reference is made to the multiple regression equivalent where appropriate.

Before turning to the model, we examine the context of other work in this general field.

Context. Almost all previous work concerned with explaining modal choice, or levels of usage of different modes of travel, within urban areas has been carried out in the United States, and can be classified in three ways. Firstly, there is the type of study which relates the use of public transport throughout a city to such characteristics as size, density and age of the city, and to population characteristics such as income, car ownership, and so on. Secondly, there are models of mode choice developed by North American transportation consultants as part of their comprehensive travel forecasting procedures: typically the aim is to predict public transport and private car use for all trips made between any pair of the zones into which the urban area is divided. Factors such as relative travel times and costs for pairs of zones are often taken into account. Thirdly, some researchers have developed models to explain and predict individual choice of mode, taking account of individual travel and household characteristics.

Studies of the first type tend to be of little use for short or medium-term policy — for instance, for increasing use of public transport by improvements or by increasing the disincentives of car use. A study by Schnore[6] relates the use of public transport in different cities to factors such as size, density and age of the cities; a more comprehensive study by Adams[7] develops regression equations explaining city-wide use of public transport in terms of five independent variables — population over five years old, quality of service, income, land use distribution, and urbanised land area in square miles. A recent article by Beesley and Kain[8] has looked at the

---

[6] Leo F. Schnore, "The use of Public Transportation in Urban Areas," *Traffic Quarterly* (October 1962).

[7] Warren T. Adams, "Factors Influencing Mass-transit and Automobile Use in Urban Areas," *Public Roads*, Vol. 30 (1959), 256-260.

[8] M. E. Beesley and J. F. Kain, "Forecasting Car Ownership and Use," *Urban Studies*, Vol. 2, No. 2 (November 1965), 163-185.

use of public transport in Leeds in relation to the number of cars per 1,000 population and to urban population density. The article is primarily a discussion of car ownership, but considers the use of public transport as a simple function of population density and income.

Empirical relationships such as these embody no *a priori* causal hypothesis about people's travel behaviour. It is in fact highly likely that the quality of public transport service, the routeing and structure of services, and aspects of car travel such as the provision of freeways and parking facilities are closely associated with some of the independent variables mentioned above (size, density, urban land area, etc.). This is to be expected where there is, and has been, across the country some general implicit agreement on the development of transport facilities in urban areas. But if some new policy decision were adopted, such as the spending of large sums of money on public transport development (as by a recent decision in the United States), these implicit relationships between public transport service and highway facilities and the size, density, etc., of cities would change. Since it is reasonable to suppose that, in the first instance, the use of public transport depends on the former, more immediate, variables rather than on the latter, "global", variables, associations such as those measured by Schnore will no longer be valid. Where one is concerned only to explain the *status quo,* this does not matter; but where one is concerned to explain and predict what will happen in new circumstances, or to suggest ways of implementing change, it is important that all variables which are likely to change, or can be changed, be incorporated into a model which has some *a priori* causal basis — *i.e.* involves some plausible hypothesis about the behaviour of travellers.

Most of the comprehensive travel forecasting models (the "transportation study" models) currently in use by consultants for the analysis of travel within urban areas embody modal split as an integral part of the model.[9] It has long been disputed "where modal split should come" in these models — whether the sequence of trip generation, distribution, modal split or assignment is appropriate. This question matters not only from the viewpoint of estimating as closely as possible the behaviour of the individual, but because the

[9] It is not appropriate to digress into an exposition of the basic model here; there are many descriptions and discussions, among which the reader is referred to: Chicago Area Transportation Study, Final Report, Vol II (July 1955); and Detroit Metropolitan Area Traffic Study, Part 1 (July 1955).

position of the modal choice procedure in the forecasting model determines the method of analysis and prediction used. It is also important because it affects the validity of other studies of modal choice which are based to a greater extent on hypotheses of individual behaviour (see below), since these mainly concern the choice of mode *on the assumption* that the trip itself, its purpose and its destination have already been decided. This problem will not be taken up here; we confine ourselves to a discussion of the modal choice procedure most commonly advocated. This procedure comes after the distribution stage, and its development owes much to Traffic Research Corporation of Toronto.

The procedure, or model, is based on a family of "diversion curves". These curves enable one to predict what proportion of the trips made for a particular purpose between any pair of zones will be by public transport, given the ratio of travel times by public transport to private car (for that zone pair), the cost ratio, the service ratio (a measure of the walking and waiting times involved), and the economic status of the travellers.

Rather than attempting to use linear, logarithmic or other versions of the variables in a regression equation to explain the public transport share of trips, the approach has been to stratify by four ranges of cost ratio, five ranges of economic status, and four ranges of service ratio. Then, on the basis of existing transport study data, a curve relating "public transport share of trips" to overall travel time ratio is fitted for each of the eighty sub-classifications. One purpose of stratifying in this way is to facilitate the application of diversion curves to particular zone pairs: instead of having to make some awkward judgment about the prevailing service ratio or income in a given zone half a mile square, one only has to classify the zone in up to five ways. But there is a problem in using zones for the grouping of observations about travel time and service ratios, particularly since TRC found that modal choice is fairly sensitive to service ratios.[10] Furthermore, one would expect as much variation of travel time ratios, service ratios and perhaps cost ratios among individual observations *within* one zone as among the mean values of these variables *between different* pairs of zones. This is recognised by TRC[11] and is one of the strongest arguments against attempting to

[10] D. M. Hill and H. G. von Cube, *Notes on Studies of Factors Influencing People's Choice of Travel Modes* (Report prepared for the Metropolitan Toronto Planning Board, Traffic Research Corporation, Toronto, 1961).

[11] D. M. Hill and H. C. von Cube, *Development of a Model for Forecasting Travel Mode Choice in Urban Areas*, Highway Research Record No. 38, pp. 78-96.

use diversion curves and zonal analysis for predicting the use of
public transport for particular routes or corridors, or for investigating
policy changes on a "micro" basis. Nevertheless, the transportation
model as developed by TRC and others is undoubtedly the best
available for predicting travel within urban areas for aggregated
groups of zones, and it is based on reasonable hypotheses of
behaviour. The modal choice procedure has been tested by the
Bureau of Public Roads on Washington, D.C., data,[12] and has given
good results, particularly for journeys to work.

On the individual choice of mode, Warner's work[13] is interesting
and probably the most comprehensive. He uses multiple regression
and discriminant analysis techniques to obtain probability functions
which predict the probability that a traveller with given travel time,
cost and other characteristics will choose a particular mode for both
work and non-work trips to the Central Business District (CBD). He
uses information gathered by the Cook County Highway Department
from interviews in an outer suburban area of Chicago concerning
trips to the Loop, Chicago's CBD. The distances travelled by
respondents all lay within a small range, since interviews were
conducted within a defined suburban area; certain important
variables, such as walking and waiting times, were omitted. But by
direct use of individual travel and household data Warner avoids the
zonal aggregation inherent in the procedures used by TRC and other
consultants. His method is also attractive because it relates travel
behaviour to explanatory variables which are as direct as any in their
presumed influence; one can consequently have more confidence in
predictions from this model than from many other models. Warner
did not develop the model beyond predictions based on individuals;
he did not, for instance, suggest a means for predicting modal choice
on an area or corridor basis. His methodology, however, forms a basis
for the work described in this paper.

The remaining work to be commented on is less sophisticated
statistically and mainly concerns the valuation of time spent
travelling, which will be discussed at length later on. Here we are
concerned with the contribution made by this work to the modal
split problem; the connection arises, of course, because the choice
between two modes of travel frequently involves a trade-off of time

---

[12] A. B. Sosslau, K. E. Heanue and A. J. Balek, "Evaluation of a New Modal Split Procedure,"
Public Roads, Vol. 33, No. 1 (April 1964).

[13] S. L. Warner, *Stochastic Choice of Mode in Urban Travel: A Study in Binary Choice*
(Evanston: Northwestern University Press, 1962).

against money — *i.e.* one mode is cheaper but takes longer than the other. Moses and Williamson[14] develop an economic model to predict people's choice of mode, based on indifference curves and rates of substitution between working time, travelling time and leisure time. It ignores some factors which might seem important, such as the demand for car use in the household, the use of the car *for* work, and the relative inconveniences of each mode expressed in walking and waiting times. Using the marginal wage rate to represent the value of time spent in travelling to work, they predict the fares (or negative fares) needed on public transport to cause different proportions of commuters to use it. These are calculated for the sample of commuters in the Cook County survey. But the predictions are not empirically based, since the value of time used is not derived from empirical analysis but is assumed from the theory.

Instead of assuming a value of time and using this to predict modal choice, Beesley[15] sets out to find what valuation of time best explains the observed choices of a sample of commuters working in the Ministry of Transport. His approach is to compare, within one mode, those people who chose a cost saving at the expense of extra time with those who chose a time saving at extra cost, and to find that trade-off between time and cost which explains the observed choices with the minimum discrepancy. Beesley is the first to admit that the results are only exploratory — the sample is extremely small, and it is argued below that the method cannot be relied on to give good results. Conceptually the method has much in common with that used by Warner. It is discussed at greater length below.

This review is not exhaustive; its purpose is to indicate some of the approaches to the modal choice problem. Two criteria have been consistently invoked in discussing previous work: first, that any theory of modal choice should be able to take account of planning or policy variables as influences on modal choice, and secondly, that any hypotheses implicit in such theories should be plausible in relation to individual travel behaviour.

In this article we develop a model similar to those of Warner and Beesley; we use Beesley's method of solution to show how one can

[14]Leon Moses and H. Williamson, "Value of Time, Choice of Mode, and the Subsidy Issue in Urban Transportation," *Journal of Political Economy*, Vol. 71 (1963); also chapter 10 in this volume.

[15]M. E. Beesley, "The Value of Time spent in Travelling: Some New Evidence," *Economica*, Vol. 32 (1965); also chapter 1 in this volume.

derive, from first principles, a discriminant analysis approach to the quantification of the model parameters, which subsequently yields a probability model similar to Warner's. We start with a discussion of the chosen variables and then turn to the data and results of the Leeds survey. The general form of the model and its technical analysis are to be found in Appendix A.

2. Choice of Variables

The model is expressed in terms of the disutility of alternative modes of travel; this disutility is measured in several "dimensions" (time, cost, etc.). Where Z is the relative disutility of one mode compared with the other, the form of the model as derived in Appendix A is

$$Z = \lambda_1 x_1 + \lambda_2 x_2 + \ldots \lambda_n x_n$$

and x_i, $i = 1$ to n are relative measures of these dimensions. The task of discriminant analysis is to find the best values of λ_i, $i = 1$ to n, to explain the observed choices of a sample of commuters.

The number of variables that can be put in to measure the relative attractiveness of different modes is not limited by the model itself: it is more likely to be limited by the information that can be conveniently obtained by questionnaire from a sample of users of the two modes. In deciding on a list of variables about which to obtain information from a sample of car-owning commuters, some using car and some using public transport, account was taken of previous work done in the area and of what had previously been found to be important. In TRC's study[16] five variables were found to be important:
  — ratio of overall travel times by each mode;
  — cost ratio;
  — excess travel time ratio (walking and waiting times);
  — economic status of traveller;
  — trip purpose.
Since we are concerned with one trip purpose only, the journey to work, this list reduces effectively to four variables.

---

[16]D. M. Hill and H. G. von Cube, *Notes on Studies of Factors Influencing People's Choice of Travel Modes* (Report prepared for the Metropolitan Toronto Planning Board, Traffic Research Corporation, Toronto, 1961).

Cost. It can be argued that there is a further interrelationship between the effects of cost and income, which is not self-evident from these findings. From the axiom that higher income travellers are better able to afford to pay a premium to satisfy their preferences than are low income travellers, it follows that if the cost of travelling by car is greater than by public transport the effect of higher income is to lessen the effect of cost as a deterrent to using car. This would suggest that as long as public transport is cheaper than car, the probability of going by car ought to be positively related to income.) (The same applies to public transport if it is more expensive.) If relative costs are very different, the effect will depend on the size of the traveller's income; if costs are more nearly the same, the effect will be less, and one may wonder whether it will be significant.

Costs have no meaning for a traveller except in the context of his income and what he can spend: one might therefore argue that relative costs should always be expressed as a function of income. The problem is, what function?

If relative costs are expressed as a ratio, there is no way of expressing income in a way that is dimensionally correct. Note, in passing, that this is an argument against using cost *ratios* at all. If relative costs were expressed as a difference, one form would be the ratio of cost difference to income. But this presupposes that the effect of cost is directly proportional to the traveller's income. Too little is known about people's preferences for us to say with any certainty what a better form might be. One might argue that more important demands on the household's income leave a smaller sum subject to decisions about expenditure on commuter travel, and this smaller sum is not directly proportional to income. But one might also advance the possibility that, if higher income commuters spend more money in total on commuting than lower income people, the marginal utility of extra increments of cost could be much more nearly the same. Then cost differences between modes could justifiably be entered as one variable, and one would expect that income expressed as another variable would turn out in the course of the analysis to be insignificant. It was decided to test both ways of handling costs and income and also a further one, in which cost by mode 1/income is one variable, and cost by mode 2/income is a second variable.

There is an argument for incorporating income as a straight variable anyway. This is that the effect of income levels is not only financial, since those with high incomes might feel they should conform to certain patterns of social behaviour which are seen as appropriate to that economic status, and not using public transport could be an important part of the pattern. If this is a significant effect, then, quite separately from the above arguments relating to the expression of cost effects, discriminant analysis would be expected to yield a positive weighting coefficient for income in an expression measuring the relative disutility of public transport. But where costs and income are expressed independently it might be difficult to separate the financial effect from the social effect in the weighting coefficient for income.

In the formulation in which "mode 1 cost/income" and "mode 2 cost/income" are expressed as separate variables, we should expect the weighting coefficients for these two factors to be the same, or insignificantly different, since money is the same commodity however it is spent. The cost of running a car is not, however, an immediately evident sum; and if significant differences do exist between these coefficients, they might well be due to an inappropriate figure for car mileage cost being used to calculate total car costs. This figure of car mileage cost is crucial and will have an important effect on the results, yet very little is known about how people actually do cost out the running of their cars. In a model which is trying to explain and predict people's behaviour, it may be hazardous to use an "engineering" figure for mileage cost without question, since people might well *perceive* running costs quite differently. It is their perceptions that are important in influencing what they do. It will be seen later that it is possible to experiment with different car costs and find that cost which gives the best discrimination, other things being equal. If the difference between the best discrimination so achieved and the discrimination for other car costs is significant, this will be as good a guide as any to how people implicitly cost out their cars.

To start with, it was decided to use fourpence a mile as the variable cost per mile for all cars. This figure was a compromise between the Commercial Motor figures and the Road Research Laboratory operating cost formulae. Unfortunately, data on different car sizes in the sample had not been gathered. Previous work suggests that there is a choice of ways of expressing relative costs (when income is expressed separately): cost ratio, as TRC and other consultants express it; log of cost ratio, implied by Warner's methodology; and a cost difference, which is perhaps the most intuitively reasonable. It was decided to test all three forms, as well as the different ways of combining income mentioned above.

Time. Not much evidence is needed to support the inclusion of travel time as an important factor. TRC's addition of *excess* travel time suggests that people may value walking and waiting time differently from "in-vehicle" time. Goldberg[17] reports that analysis of a survey in Paris showed transfer time was treated as double actual time, and waiting time as treble. There may therefore be a case for separating walking time from waiting time. But this would again cause an increase in the number of variables, and in the absence of any further evidence it was decided to collect together all off-vehicle time (walking, waiting and transfer). Some researchers (for instance, Wilson[18]) have also counted the time spent in a car looking for a parking space. There is no doubt that such time might well be frustrating and therefore have a higher implicit cost than the ordinary driving time, but it is both hazardous and difficult to estimate. It was not considered here.

Given that relative excess travel time is worth including, it remains to decide whether the whole journey should be further characterised by relative *overall* travel time or by relative *in-vehicle* time, *i.e.* overall travel time less excess travel time. The argument in favour of the latter is that excess travel time and in-vehicle time are fairly independent, while excess travel time is a constituent part of overall travel time and therefore not independent. But its dependence is acceptable if account is taken of it in prediction schemes. The main case for using overall travel time is that people usually see a journey primarily in these terms, rather than in terms of in-vehicle time. At the time of the design of the research there was no evidence for this, but an interesting retrospective justification of it was developed on the basis of the survey data.

Travel times, like costs, can be expressed in different ways. The main ones considered are: overall and excess travel time differences, ratios, and logs of ratios. No other ways were considered, as there is neither evidence nor intuitive argument to support any. Although there is, in terms of the relative disutility model, an *a priori* case in favour of differences, it is difficult to justify this method on a

---

[17] *Traffic in Towns* (HMSO, 1963).

[18] F. R. Wilson, "Traffic Assignment Modal Split," *Traffic Engineering and Control*, Vol. 7, No. 7 (November 1965).

separate intuitive basis. Take the three men, A, B, and C, whose travel times in minutes by car and public transport are as follows:

	A	B	C
Time by public transport	50	50	20
Time by car	25	40	10
Travel time ratio	2	1.25	2
Travel time difference	25	10	10

If it is the ratio of travel time that is important for people in deciding what to do, then the car is equally preferable for A and C, but less preferable for B, other things being equal. If differences are important, the car is equally preferable for C and B, but more so for A. Which is more likely to express how people actually make comparisons? Because TRC's modal split procedures (based on ratios) actually "work" it does not necessarily follow that this is the only valid approach. Yet if the assumptions about travel time differences inherent in the process of valuing time savings are valid, is it merely an artefact that ratios seem to work?

Evidence by Wabe in a recent paper[19] seems to suggest that people's valuation of time varies according to the length of work journey. His analysis does not, however, support the time ratio measure; that would require the value of time to be directly proportional to the total journey time, whereas he found that the variations in the value of time were wider than this. On the other hand, it might be argued that the apparent time-cost trade-off is too closely involved with the rent gradient and the price of household space, which he considers concurrently, to permit this conclusion.

It was decided to test the following alternative forms, the second of the fourth pair being included because of an anticipated oversensitivity of excess travel time ratio, yet allowing that the ratio of overall travel times (rather than differences) may be a good explanatory variable.

---

[19] J. S. Wabe, *Some Empirical Work on Commuter Journeys and Work-force Participation in the London Metropolitan Region* (Working Paper produced by the Institute of Economics and Statistics, Oxford University, 1965).

(1) overall travel time ratio; excess travel time ratio.
(2) overall travel time difference; excess travel time difference.
(3) log (overall travel time ratio); log (excess travel time ratio).
(4) overall travel time ratio; excess travel time difference.

Other Variables. There are no other quantifiable variables which express the characteristics of travel by each mode. Comfort, safety and reliability may indeed be important factors affecting use of public transport, but they cannot easily be quantified, and are more open to argument about differential perception than are any of the previous factors. Results obtained without consideration of comfort, safety and reliability will be valid only as long as these do not change. For instance, if buses were suddenly made more comfortable and attractive this model would not be able to explain or predict any resulting modal change.

It is interesting that other researchers have recently devised a way of handling the problem which might help to show the order of magnitude of these effects. This involves asking the sample to indicate by some means (for instance, on a five-point scale) how they feel about the comfort or reliability of a public transport service, or to ask attitude questions designed to elicit non-quantifiable feelings about bus travel and car travel such as might influence modal choice. Then the sample is sub-divided according to the answers given to one or more of these questions, and the discriminant analysis run on each sub-sample. Significant differences between weighting coefficients, or the constant term, will indicate the effects of different attitudes or feelings corresponding to the sub-divisions of the sample. This was not done for the work reported here.

It is as well to acknowledge at this stage a further factor which by an oversight was not taken account of, and which future research could well examine: the carrying of passengers in the commuter's car. Their existence might well make him less inclined to give up his car, particularly if he were receiving payment. But this latter practice, being illegal in this country, might prove difficult to find out about.

At a personal level, it may be that age is an important factor, particularly in determining how far people are prepared to walk. It was not considered sufficiently important to incorporate here; no other researchers have taken account of it in modal split work.

Since the chosen approach to modal split concerns only the choice between private car and public transport (either bus or train) for the journey to work, there are certain other factors which may incur disutility if one or other of these modes is used, but which would not be important if the choice between two public transport modes were being examined. Although some of the more academic work on modal split has considered factors relating to alternative uses for the car at home as a possible influence on modal choice, none of the operational planning models has done so. If the commuter drives his car to work, he deprives the rest of the family of the use of the car for the whole day. The importance of this depends partly on how many other driving licences there are in the family. An arbitrary measure was chosen for the disutility that a commuter would incur if he used his car to drive to work: *car demand ratio,* which is the ratio of the number of driving licences in the household to the number of cars in the household. This was not further analysed: it might be argued, for instance, that a wife with a driving licence has more "pull" than a son or daughter, but this difference was not thought sufficiently important.

In the U.K. we are at a stage where the proportion of the working population which uses cars for the work journey is still small compared to the United States (even though, in relation to the size and scale of British city streets, it seems a large absolute number). Consequently it is to be expected that those who need or have occasion to use their cars *for* work will form a *higher* proportion of Britain's car commuters than of U.S. car commuters. However, there was felt to be a distinction between the commuter who had an overriding need to use his car for work (traveller, service man, etc.) and one who had occasional need to use his car for work but could, if necessary, organise his working day according to whether or not he had brought his car in. For the latter the sensitivity of modal choice to general conditions of travel would be much more like that of the man who never had occasion to use his car for work than that of the man who had an overriding need to do so. In these circumstances, the (occasional) use of car for work could be seen as another factor — not an overriding one — influencing his choice of mode. If he had an occasional use for his car during work, then the relative disutility of travel by bus would be somewhat higher. Thus, if this factor is given some arbitrary positive score, *a priori* we should expect the discriminant analysis to yield a positive weighting factor in an expression for relative disutility of bus travel.

It was also felt that, other things being equal, the commuter with a firm's car would feel more constrained to drive to work in it, irrespective of whether or not he used it *for* work, than if he owned it himself.

The following seven factors, and the versions of them described above, formed the basis for the early runs of the discriminant analysis. Subsequent versions of factors, and sub-groupings of them, suggested themselves on the basis of the early runs, and are described, together with their results, later on.

Relative overall travel time;
Relative excess travel time;
Relative cost ⎱
Income ⎰ combined in different ways;
Car demand ratio;
Use of car for work;
Ownership of car by firm.

3. Data and Results

For the model, information is needed from users of both car and public transport who have choices (*i.e.* they must be car owners) about times and cost of travel by both the chosen and the alternative modes, and about personal and household information — income, number of driving licences and cars in the household, ownership of the (relevant) car, and whether there is a non-overriding need to have the car available at work. An inexpensive method is to carry out the survey at people's places of work, particularly since we are studying only the journey to work (as Beesley did at the Ministry of Transport).

The sampling could be a problem here: if one large workplace is chosen, or a number of workplaces which are very close together, there may be a predominance of one, or a few, particular distances from parking place to workplace, or of one or a few distances from bus stop (or station) to workplace. To obviate this, care was taken in choosing the firms for this survey to achieve a spread in terms of their nearness to the core of the central business district of Leeds, and in terms of available parking facilities. A few of the 40 firms and organisations which co-operated provided free or low-price contract parking for their employees, but most did not. It was also possible to achieve a spread in terms of nearness to the main rail and bus termini. Thus the firms were chosen not at random, but to achieve a representative distribution of walking distances with the central business district (CBD). Within firms, it could be assumed that the other variables were randomly distributed, and not biassed with regard to the totality of car-owning commercial and office employees in the CBD. Further, there is no reason to suppose that the distribution of incomes among car-owners within the 40 firms approached was not representative of the distribution of car-owners' incomes within the whole CBD.

In each firm, after personal visits to its head, a liaison man was appointed. He was responsible for ascertaining the number of car owners in the firm, and for circulating the questionnaires; when completed, these were returned direct in reply-paid envelopes. The instructions were that those people who used their cars necessarily in the course of their jobs were to be excluded (as having no feasible choice of mode); and married women whose husbands owned cars were excluded, except where there were second cars of which they had exclusive use.

Of the 993 questionnaires sent out, a whole block of 152 were found to have been mislaid by one of the organisations and never distributed. It was confirmed that no bias would be introduced by excluding these from the calculation of response. Of the remaining 841, a total of 688 were returned, giving a response rate of 81.8 percent. Of these, 18 were excluded because the firm in question sent them out to suburban sub-offices and 31 because their chosen modes were as *passengers* in other people's cars, and we were not examining this particular choice. Of the remaining 639, there were 542 who had a choice between car and bus, and 97 between car and train.

Direct questions on income have been known to reduce significantly the response obtained on surveys.[20] This was possibly due to the way in which the question was phrased in many surveys — it is an important and sometimes embarrassing question for a respondent. The question we asked was:

"We would like some indication of your income, as this is an important piece of information for the research. However, many

---

[20]F. R. Wilson records some difficulty in his workplace surveys; this was tackled by issuing a further similar questionnaire with the income question omitted. The subsequent response was about 60 percent. See "Traffic Assignment Modal Splits," *Traffic Engineering and Control*, Vol. 7, No. 7 (November 1965), p. 456.

people are understandably reluctant to give this, so please do not feel obliged to if you prefer not to.

"If you *are* willing to give this information, would you please indicate in which of the ranges below your gross annual income lies?

> less than £600
> £600 to £900
> £900 to £1,200
> £1,200 to £1,500
> £1,500 to £1,800
> £1,800 to £2,400
> over £2,400"

In fact over 96 per cent of those returning questionnaires (82 per cent of the total) did answer it.

It is perhaps worth mentioning how the time questions were phrased. We had had some unfortunate experiences on previous surveys from asking questions like "When do you *usually* leave your home in the morning?" In the present case, all questions referred to what the respondent *actually* did on the morning of the day he answered the questionnaire (using the chosen mode of that day) and what he would have done on that morning if for some reason he had come by the other mode. Account was taken of the possibility of an untypical choice on the day in question by asking whether what he had done today was what he "normally" did. If not, a further question was asked, the answer to which would decide whether he should be transferred to the group of users of the other mode for analysis purposes. For instance, if a man came by bus though he did not use the bus normally, he would be transferred to the car mode if his car had gone in to be serviced on that day. If his wife needed the car on that day, however, then he would remain a bus user, since the fact of his wife's potential use would be taken account of by the number of driving licences in the family, which enters the analysis explicitly.

Simple Checks on the Data. In coding the questionnaires for punching, care was taken to check all the cost information. Minor discrepancies were ignored, but gross errors in, for instance, bus and train fares were corrected, on the grounds that when the traveller next used that mode he would find out exactly how much it cost him, and he might alter his relative usage of that mode.

There is a more fundamental problem in people's reporting of time. The first issue is people's perceptions of the time of walking and waiting. It can be argued that, if a person reports 5 minutes where it is actually 3, it *feels* like 5 minutes to him, and whatever decisions he makes will be made on the basis of that perception. Against this it can be argued that, where the perception refers to the mode not being used, the next use of that mode might cause him to revise his estimate. Even requiring people to think about the time taken might cause them to estimate it more accurately when they next travel, and the answer given then might be different. In order to explore this problem, linear regressions were carried out for a sub-sample of respondents of the reported walking times on corresponding distances as measured on a map — for walking time from home to bus stop, and for walking time from car parking place to workplace. It was striking that extremely good correlations were achieved in each case (0.942 and 0.906 respectively); the regression line suggested that in each case a good rule of thumb was a minute for a hundred yards and a minute over. During coding, trivial discrepancies with the regression estimate were in every case ignored; for gross discrepancies, a time midway between the reported time and the regression estimate was taken, to prevent emotionally exaggerated reports (which are perhaps not quite the basis for a decision) having an over-important effect.

Waiting times for buses can be approached in a similar way. This is rather more awkward: although a good estimate of mean waiting time is half the average interval between buses where intervals are 10 minutes or less and the service is regular, considerable variations from the scheduled intervals do occur during the peak in Leeds. A decision rule was adopted that reported waiting times were to be corrected only where the mode was the alternative, and only where an estimate was more than three times the scheduled interval: it was then reduced by half.

A further problem concerns people's estimates of (clock) times for the beginning and end of the whole journey, from which the overall travel time is calculated. This is particularly so for the journey by the alternative mode. It is not the problem of the time by a clock so much as one of a respondent's conscious or unconscious over-estimate of the time that the alternative mode would take, by which he can feel justified in having chosen the mode he did. Yet there is a distinction between over-estimation as an unconscious way of characterising some inconvenience or unattractiveness of the alternative mode, and over-estimation as a conscious rationalisation. To incorporate the former is valid, since it is part of the man's perceptions of the alternative mode, affecting his choice. But unconscious overestimates may be altered if the alternative mode is actually used. As the two types of over-estimate cannot normally be differentiated, it was decided to accept all times for coding as stated, and to determine subsequently whether there was any significant difference between the way bus users perceive journey times by car and bus and the way car users perceive them.

This subsequent analysis consisted of attempting to fit different types of relationships between speed, time and distance, by means of simple linear regression, for each mode and within the group of users of each mode. Any differences in the perception of — say — bus travel by bus users and by car users would emerge as significant differences between the regression parameters obtained by regressing — say — average bus speed on log (distance) for bus users, and then again for car users. The three types of relationships tested were: time on distance, time on log (distance), and average speed on log (distance); each was done twice, once for overall travel time, once for net in-vehicle time (overall travel time less excess travel time), and each of these was done for each mode and each group of mode users, making a total of 24 regressions.

All but three of the correlation coefficients lay between 0.60 and 0.82. There was little to choose between the three types of relationships as far as the goodness of correlation was concerned, although the speed *v.* log (distance) relationship was marginally the best. It was interesting that the regressions based on net in-vehicle time were not significantly better than those based on overall travel time. This is perhaps surprising, since different travellers have more in common in the conditions of speed and congestion in the traffic than in walking and waiting times at each end of the journey. It suggests that people *perceive* the overall travel time of their journey to some extent independently of variations in the amount of walking and waiting time.

In all three types of relationships, there was remarkable agreement between car users and bus users on the speed and time of car travel — in all cases the differences between regression coefficients are not significant. But bus travel in the perception of car users is about 20 per cent slower than in that of bus users, and the implied difference between the regression coefficients is significant at the 5 per cent level. Of this 20 per cent difference, it seems that about half is attributable to a difference in the walking and waiting times: bus users either know their time tables better or live (or work) nearer bus stops. But half the difference occurs on "in-vehicle" time, implying that there is a genuine difference in perception between car users and bus users of about 10 per cent in the actual speed of bus travel.

Analysis. With a basic model of the form

$$z = \lambda_1 x_1 + \lambda_2 x_2 + \ldots + \lambda_n x_n$$

where z is the relative disutility of the public transport mode, λ_i are weighting coefficients, and x_i are (relative) measures of factors, such as time and cost, the task of the analysis was to provide answers to the following questions:

Which type of formulation (ratios, differences, etc., of time and cost) provides the best explanation of the observed modal choices – *i.e.* which measure of relativeness most appropriately represents people's comparisons of two modes?

What can be said about how people cost the running of their cars?

What is the relative importance of the various factors in affecting choice of mode?

How well can the discriminant function explain the choice of mode, in terms of the "best" set of factors discovered?

What other relationships are there between factors, such as might affect the validity of predictions?

What can be said about how people value time?

Are there significant differences in the results obtained between car-bus and car-train choices?

Measures of Relativeness. The first piece of analysis was designed to compare the ratios method of expressing relative times and costs (as used by transportation study consultants), logs of ratios (Warner), and differences (Beesley, Moses and Williamson, etc.). (Note that no substantial case is argued by any writer in favour of one method over another.) The discriminant analysis programs were run on the car-bus sample of 542 with overall travel times, excess travel times, and costs expressed in these three different ways (set 1, set 2, set 3, respectively):

Set 1	*Set 2*	*Set 3*
Overall travel time ratio	Log (overall travel time ratio)	Overall travel time difference
Excess travel ratio	Log (excess travel time ratio)	Excess travel time difference
Cost ratio	Log (cost ratio)	Cost difference

In all three cases a further four factors were included: income, car demand ratio, use of car for work, and ownership of car by firm.

The cost for car travel was half the daily parking charge plus one-way mileage at 4d. a mile.

The multiple correlation coefficients in each case were:

Car-bus data

Set 1	46.2%
Set 2	50.2%
Set 3	52.3%

Set 1 and Set 3 were also run on the car-train sample, with these results:

Car-train data

Set 1	56.0%
Set 3	57.6%

It seems that the "differences" formulation of factors was the best of the three tried. This was further confirmed by the results of two additional sets, in which the costs of each mode, divided by income, were entered as separate factors:

Set 4	*Set 5*
Overall travel time ratio	Overall travel time difference
Excess travel time ratio	Excess travel time difference
Public transport cost/income	Public transport cost/income
Car cost/income	Car cost/income
Car demand ratio	Car demand ratio
Use of car for work	Use of car for work
Ownership of car by firm	Ownership of car by firm

The multiple correlation coefficients were:

Car-bus data

	Set 4	47.3%
	Set 5	52.3%

Car-train data

	Set 4	57.1%
	Set 5	58.0%

On the theory that misclassification of travellers can be measured about a notional threshold halfway between the means, a further indication of discrimination within the sample itself is a measure of the proportions misclassified, weighted for the different numbers of the car and bus-using populations. These were:

Car-bus data

	Set 1	26.9%
	Set 2	24.0%
	Set 3	23.6%

As a result of this it was decided to use differences for all the further analyses.[21]

---

[21] The important question is whether the differences between correlation coefficients for the different sets of factors are significant or not. As mentioned in Appendix A on the model, Fisher's transformation may be used to investigate whether differences between correlation coefficients are significant: at 52 per cent, the 95 per cent confidence interval appears to be about ±6 per cent. It is not clear whether this is applicable here; the alternative "jack-knife" technique was also used, running one set of factors (set 3) on 90 per cent of the data ten times, leaving out a different 10 per cent each time. The estimated variance of R comes out as 1.403 at 52 per cent, giving a standard error of 1.185, or 1.19. On this basis, differences greater than about 2.3 per cent are significant at the 5 per cent level. We would conclude, then, that the difference between set 3 and set 2 was almost significant, and that between set 2 and set 1 was certainly significant. For the car-train data, set 3 is better than set 1, but the difference is only significant at the 10 per cent level. As between set 4 and set 5, the differences for the car-bus data are conclusive, but again those for the car-train data are less so.

If the jack-knife estimate of the standard error of R is acceptable, one can say that use of ratios is definitely inferior to the other two methods, and that differences seem preferable to logs of ratios (although the evidence is not entirely conclusive) at a 5 per cent level of significance. The remainder of the analysis uses differences alone; little more work was done using logs of ratios, as the computing time available was limited.

Car Mileage Costs. There were certain results from the above set of runs which suggested that 4d. a mile was not an appropriate figure for the calculation of car mileage costs. It has been remarked before that, since a model of this type is seeking to explain people's decision-making behaviour, it is important to recognise that perceptions, on which decisions are based, may be different from reality. This is specially important where the reality is not evident, as with the cost of running a car.

In Set 4 and Set 5, it was noted that the coefficients for car cost/income and bus cost/income were very different:

Car-bus data

	Bus cost/income (λ_3)	Car cost/income (λ_4)	λ_3/λ_4
Set 4	0.1519	−0.0628	2.42
(*t*-value)	(4.14)	(3.90)	
i.e., λ/standard error of λ			
Set 5	0.1522	−0.0471	3.23
(*t*-value)	(4.03)	(2.83)	

Since there is no reason, *a priori,* why the two types of cost should have such very different coefficients, these results suggest, even though the *t*-values are not very high, that the figure for car mileage cost of 4d a mile, while approximating to the engineering cost, is not how people actually perceive car running costs. The fact that λ_4 is substantially less than λ_3 suggests that the car cost is overstated. But since parking charges enter the total cost calculation one cannot infer that car mileage cost is overestimated by any one of the four ratios of λ_3 to λ_4. It was decided, therefore, to design a new set of runs of the discriminant programs, experimenting with different car mileage costs, and the results are described below.

It is to be noted particularly that Set 4 gave as good a discrimination as Set 3, the best of the previous three tried, and that for the car-train data Set 4 is somewhat better than Set 3. In the car-bus case this suggests that the possible "constraints" in Set 4 of treating costs as a proportion of income must be complemented by some other constraint in Set 3, which can only be that of combining two costs into a cost difference (at 4d. a mile) instead of leaving them separate.

In the search for a value of car mileage cost that seems to best represent people's perceptions, the various factor sets were each run several times with different car mileage costs. Discrimination should be at its maximum when the "constraint" of using a cost difference, instead of treating car and bus costs as separate factors, was at a minimum: this would be when the figure inserted for car mileage cost most nearly corresponded with the mean value imputed by commuters in the sample. For those factor sets where bus or train costs and car costs are already separate, one would not expect the use of the "optimum" car mileage cost to make such a large difference to the discrimination achieved, since there is no constraint of using differences whose effect is thereby reduced. It was expected that the optimum car mileage cost would be less, rather than more, than 4d. a mile: consequently, up to 6 different car costs, ranging from 1d. to 3 1/2d. by 1/2d. intervals, were tried.

The correlation coefficients obtained for Set 3 were:

Car-bus data

Car costs per mile	R
1d.	52.5%
1½d.	53.0%
2d.	53.2%
2½d.	53.1%
3d.	52.9%
3½d.	52.6%
4d.	52.3% (as before)

A maximum occurs within the range, at 2d. a mile; but the differences between the correlation coefficients are not, by the previous criterion, particularly significant.

In Set 4 the differences between correlation coefficients were even smaller, as expected, and the ratio of the two cost coefficients, on the car-bus data, was about unity at 1 1/2d. a mile:

Car-bus data

Car costs per mile	λ_3 / λ_4
1d.	0.827
1½d.	1.079
2d.	1.338
2½d.	1.601
3d.	1.869
4d.	2.421 (as before)

The standard errors of λ_3 and λ_4 are not sufficiently low for us to conclude that 1 1/2d. is definitely the best value, although the coefficients themselves are clearly significant (from their *t*-values). For Set 2 optimum car mileage cost was 2d. a mile, but the difference between the correlation coefficients for car costs of 2d. and 2 1/2d. was only 0.1 per cent. On the car-train data the following results were achieved:

Car-train data

Set 3		Set 4	
Car costs per mile	*R*	*Car costs per mile*	λ_3/λ_4
1d.	55.1%	1d.	0.422
1½d.	56.0%	1½d.	0.621
2d.	57.0%	2d.	0.816
2½d.	57.7%	2½d.	1.011
3d.	57.8%	3d.	1.208
3½d.	57.7%	3½d.	1.402
4d.	57.6%	4d.	1.596

Maxima occur at 3d. a mile and 2 1/2d. a mile respectively.

Thus for the car-bus sample of 542 the differences are not significant, although nearly the same optimum mileage cost is given by two quite different methods of organising the factors. To continue the analysis one must choose some figure, and, while its validity is open to question, the figure of 2d. a mile was chosen as the most likely estimate for the car-bus data. From the car-train sample of 97 one might prefer 2 1/2d. per mile: there may well be a real difference here, since the mean income of the car-train sample was exactly £200 more than the mean income of the car-bus sample (£1,602 as against £1,402), and, on the argument that wealthier people tend to run more expensive and more thirsty cars, the mileage costs may indeed be perceived to be more in the car-train sample. There may, however, be no real difference between the true values. The smaller car-train sample merits less weight to results obtained from it, although the correlation is markedly better.

Perhaps the strongest case for accepting these figures is that 2d. to 2 1/2d. a mile was almost exactly the petrol cost of cars averaging 25-35 m.p.g., and this might represent the perceived cost for most motorists. It is regrettable that the original questionnaire did not ask people how much they thought their cars cost per mile to run or what kinds of cars they had; this would have enabled perceived costs to be related to actual costs for different sizes of car.

Further Exploration of Set 3. To continue the analysis using Set 3 at 2d. a mile, the full results were:

Car-bus data. Sample size 542 (376 car users, 166 bus users). R = 53.2%

Relative disutility of bus travel (= z)		$t = \lambda/s.e.(\lambda)$
0.0556	(overall travel time difference in minutes)	4.52
+0.0966	(excess travel time difference in minutes)	4.58
+0.0911	(cost difference, with 2d. a mile car cost)	4.38
−0.535	(income in £ p.a., divided by 1,000)	2.51
−0.333	(car demand ratio: $\dfrac{\text{driving licenses in households}}{\text{number of cars in households}}$)	1.48
+0.620	(use of car for work, either 3 or 0)	6.54
+0.323	(ownership of car by firm, either 1 or 0)	0.56
Constant term: 0.461		

From this, the first three factors and the sixth are clearly significant; car demand ratio and ownership of car by firm are not significant. The *t*-value for the income coefficient is 2.51, which suggests its effect is significant, but its magnitude is in some doubt. Its sign is the only implausible one: it suggests that increasing income will cause the relative disutility of bus travel to fall — *i.e.* will increase the likelihood of travelling by bus. This result is probably due to the very small difference between the mean incomes for the two modes: £1,395 for car users and £1,416 for bus users (compare also the mean incomes in the car-train sample: £1,677 for car users, and £1,441 for train users). Both these findings, the insignificant income coefficient and the small difference between incomes, can probably be explained as follows. In the original analysis, performed with mileage cost at 4d. a mile, the mean cost differences (bus cost less car cost) were −12.80d. for car users and −14.23d. for bus users. But at the optimising car mileage cost of 2d. a mile the mean cost differences are −1.04d. for car users and −3.75d. for bus users. It is argued above in the section on Choice of Variables that — social effects apart — income will only have a significant effect on modal choice if the costs of travel by the two modes are very different. It seems therefore that the insignificant income coefficient is plausible if car mileage is costed at 2d. a mile or thereabouts. This result thus adds more weight to the conclusions favouring 2d. a mile as an optimum. Putting the argument differently, it seems that, since we already have evidence that 2d. a mile is the appropriate figure, and with this figure there is little to choose between the modes on a cost basis, the fact that income appears to have an insignificant effect suggests that the "social" effect of income cannot be important either, particularly as the coefficient has a negative sign.

The cost difference coefficient is itself significant, however; it seems that, while there are differences in cost between one mode and the other, and these differences are different between car users and between bus users, they are not large enough for a person's income level to have much effect on how he decides to satisfy his preferences, at the margin at least.

There is, however, one possible explanation of this finding which need not imply that income is unimportant. Since bus fares increase almost uniformly with distance, and car mileage cost is reckoned on a linear basis, one might expect the cost difference to increase as distance to the CBD increased (more or less, since there are parking charges to take account of as well). If incomes increased with distance out from the CBD (a plausible hypothesis, given the form of Leeds), income would be associated with cost difference, and any dependence of the effect of cost difference on income in the discriminant analysis would be hidden by this pre-existing association. The correlation matrix for Set 3, however, shows the following:

Correlation between cost difference and income:

for car users: 0.0169
for bus users: 0.0068

In both cases the correlation is insignificant. But the cost differences themselves are so small that slight variations in the reporting of one cost or the other might render the correlation insignificant when in reality some association does exist. Now, there is some evidence for an association between income and distance. Correlations were carried out between income and log (distance travelled to CBD) for car users and bus users:

For car-bus sample: correlation for car users: 0.192   sample 376
easily significant at 1% level

correlation for bus users: 0.132   sample 166
not significant at 5% level

One might therefore suppose that income has a longer-term effect on modal choice, through its effect on where people live.

However, once the choice of place of residence has been made, income appears to have an insignificant effect. Nevertheless, such cost differences as do exist in individual cases do influence choice of mode — but these differences do not seem large enough for different income levels to affect how far people can satisfy their preferences. Warner[22] also reaches the conclusion that, once the decision has been made to buy a car and to live in a certain district, income has little effect on modal choice. None of this indicates what would happen were the cost of travelling to change radically; in addition to the alterations in real income, people's residential decisions would no longer be in equilibrium with the costs of travel, and some of the assumptions behind our analysis would no longer be valid.

As regards the other factors, since excess travel time is itself a component of overall travel time, it is valued at $(0.0966 + 0.0556)/0.0556$, i.e. about 2 1/2 to 3 times overall travel time. This means that walking and waiting time is valued at about 2 1/2 to 3 times the time spent in a vehicle. Goldberg in Paris[23] found that people treated transfer time as though it were double actual time, and waiting time as though it were treble. Our findings seem roughly consistent with this.

Since the overall travel time difference and cost difference coefficients represent a relative trade-off between these two factors, the imputed value of time, based on Set 3 at 2d. a mile, is $0.0556/0.0911$ pence per minute, i.e. 3s. 1d. per hour. With a mean income of £1,400 per annum, and a working year of 2,000 hours, this value of time is 21.4 per cent of the wage rate. The value of time will be discussed more extensively later. (See Appendix B for a discussion of the statistical significance of the results.)

To see how much of the discrimination is accounted for by fewer than the original seven factors, further runs were made of the discriminant program with one, two and then three of the four significant factors, with results as follows:

Car-bus data at 2d. a mile

	R
Overall travel time difference alone	38.1%
Ditto and cost difference	42.5%
Value of time 4s. 7d. per hour, or 33.0% of the wage rate	
Both, and excess travel time difference	46.9%
Value of time 2s. 10d. per hour, or 20.6% of the wage rate	

---

[22] S. L. Warner, *Stochastic Choice of Mode in Urban Travel: A Study in Binary Choice* (Evanston: Northwestern University Press, 1962).

[23] Goldberg, *A Comparison of Transport Plans for a Linear City* (paper presented to the International Conference on Operations Research and the Social Sciences, organised by the Operational Research Society, in Cambridge, 1964).

We can assume that the "use of car for work" factor is almost entirely responsible for raising the discrimination to 53.2 per cent in Set 3.

Additional Car-train Results. Analysis of the separate car-train sample using Set 3 yielded somewhat similar levels of significance:

Car-train data. Sample size 97 (68 car users, 29 train users). $R = 57.7\%$

Relative disutility of train travel (= z)		$t = \lambda/s.e.(\lambda)$
0.0607	(overall travel time difference)	3.69
+0.0793	(excess travel time difference)	2.72
+0.0739	(cost difference at 2½d. a mile)	3.15
−0.087	(income in £ p.a., divided by 1,000)	0.25
+0.093	(car demand ratio)	0.22
+0.248	(use of car for work, 3 or 0)	1.36
+0.843	(ownership of car by firm)	1.39
Constant term: 1.285		

The first three factors are clearly significant, the fourth and fifth clearly not, while the last two are not significant at the 5 per cent level. This accords reasonably well with the car-bus findings, although the insignificant income coefficient is a little more difficult to explain here, since with car mileage costs at 2 1/2d. a mile the mean cost differences are rather larger (– 8.59d. for car users, –12.76d. for train users). The mean income of train users is £236 less than that of the car users, which is consistent with larger cost differences; but the insignificant coefficient cannot have come about because of a small difference between mean incomes, as one might argue in the car-bus case. Note also that the "use of car for work" factor is insignificant. Some of all this may be explained by certain important differences between the car-bus and car-train samples. The mean distance travelled by the former was 5.84 miles, by the latter 11.32 miles. Most of the former live within the Leeds boundary; most of the latter live in the rural hinterland of the city, or in dormitory towns like Harrogate, Ilkley, Garforth, etc. If a person lives in Leeds, it is difficult for him *not* to be reasonably near a bus route. Outside the city, however, there are comparatively few bus routes (and these are slow), or railway routes (these are quite fast), and the choice of residential location may well depend on whether the commuter is likely to want to use the rail service. This in turn may depend on whether he is wealthy enough to travel by car a longish distance each day, or whether he needs his car for work, or on other factors; thus the fact that "use of car for work" is not explicitly significant here does not preclude the possibility of its having influenced residential location in the first place, affecting current overall and excess travel times. The same might be true for income. It is not surprising, therefore, to find in the correlation matrices for the car-train sample that income and the use of car for work are both correlated at the 1 per cent level with overall travel time difference.

The value of time is 4s. 1d. per hour, which with an average income of £1,600 p.a. is 25.6 per cent of the wage rate. Walking and waiting times are estimated at $(0.0793 + 0.0607)/0.0607$, or about 2.31 in-vehicle times. This compares with 2 1/2 to 3 times for the car-bus sample. Since the car-train sample typically has higher excess travel time than the car-bus sample, and since the higher excess travel times for train journeys are due entirely to longer walking times (waiting times for trains rarely exceeded 5 minutes), one might conclude that walking time is worth less than waiting time.

Further Results. It was suggested during discussion of the results that no allowance had been made for the possibility that people valued time differently by different modes, since the time variables had always been *differences* of overall and excess travel times. There may indeed have been a "constraint" here similar to that of a cost difference at 4d. a mile. A new set of runs was prepared, in which the overall travel time difference was represented as (bus overall travel time $- a$ x car overall travel time), and the cost difference as (bus cost $-$ car parking cost $-$ mileage cost at b pence per mile), where a took values from 0.2 to 1.5 and b took values from 1.5d. to 4.0d. per mile. The table below shows the subset of values of a and b around which maximum R was obtained, using the following factors:

bus overall travel time $- a$ X car overall travel time
excess travel time difference
bus cost $-$ car cost using b pence per mile
use of car for work
income
car demand ratio

	$b =$	2.5	3.0	3.5	4.0
$a = 0.2$		53.771	53.909	53.863	53.720
0.4		53.878	53.955	53.863	53.696
0.6		53.835	53.806	53.640	53.432

No other local maxima occurred in the range of a's and b's tried. A maximum occurs where $a = 0.4$, $b = 3.0$, *i.e.* where car time is worth 0.4 of bus time and mileage cost is 3d. per mile. But the differences between adjacent correlation coefficients are extremely small, as before, and do not permit a radical change on this evidence alone in the form of the best discriminant function. The values of time obtained from the results for $a = 0.4$ and $b = 3.0$ were: value of bus time 4s. 10d. per hour (33.7 per cent of the wage rate), and value of car time 1s. 10d. per hour (13.5 per cent of the wage rate). The average of these is 3s. 3d. or 23.6 per cent of the wage rate, which corresponds well with previous estimates. The implication of the two different values is that people are prepared to spend rather more to save a given amount of time on a bus than to save the same amount of time in a car — which is plausible.

An alternative approach is to enter bus time, car time, car mileage and (bus cost — car parking cost) as separate variables along with the remaining variables found by previous analysis to be significant. In this run, the components of excess travel time were disaggregated as well. The results may be written:

$z = 0.0787$ (bus time $- 0.327$ car time)
 $+0.0924$ (bus cost $-$ car parking cost $-$ car mileage at 3.21d per mile)
 $+0.579$ (use of car for work)
 $+ 0.0526$ (bus walking time $+ 2.53$ bus waiting time $- 2.23$ car walking time)

Thus the direct estimates of a and b are 0.327 and 3.21d per mile. Values of time are: for bus, 4s. 3d. per hour (30.5% of the wage rate); and for car, 1s. 4d. per hour (9.4% of wage rate). The average is 2s. 10d. of 20.0% of the wage rate.

These results would seem to suggest that bus times and car times really are differently valued; but splitting up times and costs in this way introduces a severe multicollinearity between certain of the variables. We must conclude, therefore, that, while there is some evidence that bus time has a larger value than car time (which is plausible), it is not possible to assign to each mode values that are different *and* reliable. The subsequent discussion on prediction and planning must, therefore, assume the same value for each mode, as implied in the original Set 3 formulation.

Values of Travelling Time. Summarising the estimates of value of time, so far, we have:

Car-bus data

		Per hour	% of wage rate
(i)	from Set 3 at 2d. a mile	3s. 1d.	21.4
(ii)	from the set of factors: overall travel time difference cost difference at 2d. a mile	4s. 7d.	33.0
(iii)	from the set of factors: overall travel time difference excess travel time difference cost difference at 2d. a mile	2s. 10d.	20.6
(iv)	from the results in the last section, with car time worth 0.4 bus time, and 3d. a mile car cost:		
	car time	1s. 10d.	13.5
	bus time	4s. 10d.	33.7
	average	3s. 3d.	23.6
(v)	from the results with times and costs disaggregated into separate factors as above:		
	car time	1s. 4d.	9.4
	bus time	4s. 3d.	30.5
	average	2s. 10d.	20.0
(vi)	from set 4 at 2d. a mile	n.a.	24.9

Car-train data

(i)	from Set 3 at 2½d. a mile	4s. 1d.	25.6
(ii)	from Set 3 at 2d. a mile	3s. 8d.	23.0
(iii)	from Set 4 at 2½d. a mile	n.a.	34.3

It is also worth reporting that, at an early stage of analysis, the car-bus sample was split into four income ranges (number in each range in brackets):

Range 1:	less than £900	(93)	mean income	£715
Range 2:	£900 - £1200	(149)	mean income	£1050
Range 3:	£1200 - £1800	(186)	mean income	£1480
Range 4:	over £1800	(114)	mean income	£2300

Discriminant analysis was run on each sub-sample, using factors "overall travel time difference" and "cost difference" alone, with mileage costs varying from 1d. to 4d. a mile in each case, and additionally with the other significant factors. The following optimum costs and resulting values of time were obtained with two factors:

Car-bus data

| | *optimum car mileage cost* | *R* | *t-value* λ_1 | *t-value* λ_2 | Value of time | |
					per hour	*as per cent of mean income*
Range 1	2d.	38.1%	2.46	2.53	2s. 4d.	32.6
Range 2	2d.	48.3%	5.15	3.72	3s. 1d.	29.4
Range 3	2½d.	42.9%	5.54	1.59	8s. 4d.	55.9
Range 4	about 2.8d. (take 3d.)	42.1%	4.38	2.44	7s. 3d.	31.5

Maximum discrimination occurs at car mileage costs which increase as incomes increase — which is plausible, since one might expect people with higher incomes to run more thirsty cars. Except in range 3, where the *t*-value for the second coefficient is lower than in the other ranges and thus casts doubt on the estimated value of time, the values of time are nearly a constant proportion (one third) of income. Part of the purpose of running the analysis on these two variables alone was to provide a comparison with Beesley's results on Ministry of Transport employees; there is close correspondence with his finding that the value of time is about one-third of the wage rate, as also with our earlier results when excess travel time and the use of car for work were omitted. Now the 7-variable analysis of Set 3 showed that these two factors are also significant in influencing modal choice. Thus, where analysis does not explicitly include these factors, they will still have a *hidden* effect through the factors that are used. Consequently, for deriving a value of travelling time we should have more confidence in results based on an analysis which includes all the significant factors explicitly.

The results from running the analysis on each sub-sample *with* excess travel time and use of car for work (the other significant factors) gave values of time as follows:

	optimum car mileage cost	R	t-value λ_1	t-value λ_2	Value of time	
					per hour	as per cent of mean income
Range 1	1.8d.	49.6%	2.44	2.85	1s. 9d.	24.0
Range 2	2.1d.	51.1%	2.97	3.17	2s. 7d.	24.6
Range 3	2.1d.	54.3%	2.71	1.31	5s. 2d.	34.4
Range 4	2.5d.	61.7%	3.07	2.35	4s. 10d.	21.1

The effect of taking explicit account of the other significant factors can be clearly seen. The resulting trade-offs between travelling time and cost lie in the same range (20 − 25% of wage rate) as that using the whole sample, and this percentage is roughly constant over a broad range of incomes. (Note that, as with the two-variable analysis, the value of time for Range 3 is unreliable).

Our general conclusions about the value of time are: firstly, it lies in the range 20 − 25% of the commuter's income; secondly, this proportion is roughly constant over a wide range of incomes; thirdly, there is insufficient evidence to conclude that bus times and car times have significantly different values.

Conclusions. Summarising this section, it has been shown that, as a measure of relativeness of time and cost, ratios are significantly inferior to logs of ratios and differences; and that differences are consistently better than logs of ratios, in both the car-bus and the car-train samples, but by an amount significant only at the 10 per cent level. Using differences, one may conclude that overall travel time difference, excess travel time difference, cost difference, and the possibility of use of car at work are all important in influencing modal choice; income is an insignificant factor, most probably because of the very small cost differences between modes (at 2d. a mile car cost), as also manifested by a small difference between mean incomes for both sets of mode users. It was also found that walking and waiting times are worth between two and three times in-vehicle times; that an average value of time on both modes lies between about 3s. and 3s. 6d. per hour, or between 21 per cent and 25 per cent of wage rates (or, leaving out two significant factors, about one-third of wage rates, corresponding closely with Beesley's results). The early analysis suggested that 2d. a mile was the car mileage cost which best fitted people's observed behaviour, but there was a large margin of error in this estimate. Subsequent analysis suggested that, if car time could be valued differently from bus time, the former was worth between 40 per cent and 50 per cent of the latter, and the car mileage cost was between 3d. and 3.5d. per mile. The car-train results were very similar to those from the car-bus sample; values of time were slightly higher, partly as a result of a questionable estimate of car mileage cost of 2 1/2d. a mile. The "use of car for work" factor was insignificant in the car-train sample, though it may have had a prior influence on residential location and thus influenced modal choice indirectly through travel times and costs.

It was found that conditions of homoscedasticity were not strictly met (see Appendix B); but there were no large intercorrelations between factors such as might upset the validity of predictions based on the discriminant function.

4. Prediction and Planning

The following discussion of prediction and planning employs the results from the Set 3 combination of factors, at a car mileage cost of 2d. a mile.

Prediction of modal choice is best regarded as assigning probability of choice of one mode, for a given value of the discriminant function, rather than as a deterministic classification into one mode or the other. The method is described in Appendix A. It gives us a way of estimating the proportion of car owners who will commute to the CBD of Leeds by car after different sets of public transport improvements or parking restrictions. It also provides a basis for estimating the car-using proportion among car owners living in the catchment area of a proposed public transport system. Changes in the behaviour of car-owning commuters to the CBD can be estimated by analysing the effect on the sample, on the assumption that the sample is representative of all car owners working in the CBD. It need hardly be emphasised that the quantitative estimates themselves are tentative; the results of further work in the area, already initiated, will help to confirm (or otherwise) the general method and results. There will always remain, however, the usual doubts about predictions using models with a multivariate statistical base, and only actual experiments on the ground can go some way towards dispelling them.

The effect of a policy change on an individual's probability of choosing a car depends on his existing z-value, and may also depend on his value of the relevant x-factor. Calculating the effect on the sample therefore requires the calculation of a new z-value and a new probability for each person in the sample. The new proportion of the sample likely to travel by car is then the mean of the probabilities of choice of car for everyone in the sample, where

$$p(z) = \frac{(n_2/n_1)e^{z+t}}{1 + (n_2/n_1)e^{z+t}}$$

expresses the possibility of choice of car for a given Z (and t is the constant term).

If one has confidence in the normality and homoscedasticity of the sample, an alternative method for treating changes in variables which are the same for everybody (*e.g.* absolute changes in cost) consists simply of calculating a new mean probability $\bar{p}'$, where

$$\bar{p}' = \frac{ke^{\delta z}}{1 + ke^{\delta z}}$$

and δz is the change in everyone's z-value resulting from the variable change. In our sample these two methods were found to give insignificantly different results in all cases where the second method could be applied.

The changes in percentage diversion in Leeds resulting from the policy changes detailed below are somewhat notional, however, since secondary effects would also occur and would usually reduce the effect of the change. For instance, if parking charges were increased and the car-using proportion fell to — say — 50 per cent, there would be less car traffic on the roads at peak periods, so that car travel would, on average, be slightly faster. The speed of bus travel would also increase, but probably not so much. Consequently there would be a "feedback" effect which would reduce the effect of the initial change, some of those who switched to bus coming back again to car with the improvement in conditions of car travel. The competition for parking places would be lower, too, so that some car walking times would probably be less. The final equilibrium effected by a change is difficult to predict without some knowledge of the "supply" side — the relationship between conditions of travel and the volumes of traffic approaching and entering the city at the relevant times — such as that proposed by Sharp.[24] A framework for the examination of the interaction of supply and demand in this context was recently proposed by the author.[25]

Policy change from present situation	% of cars owners using their cars	Change from present %	% diversion to public transport
No change	69	—	31
All bus fares up by 6d.	77	+8	23
Buses free	52	−17	48
All parking to cost 1s. per day more	57	−12	43
All parking to cost 3s. per day more	41	−28	59
Bus frequencies doubled	66	−3	34
All walking times from car parking place to workplaces increased by 5 mins.	61	−8	39
Cars 10 minutes faster	78	+9	22
Buses 10 minutes faster	60	−9	40

It is interesting to examine the possible combinations of changes in policy which, according to the model, could reduce the car-using proportion of car-owning commuters in Leeds to 20 per cent, the proportion required by the city's policy for the year 2010. For this purpose we are ignoring the secondary effects referred to above. This is not unreasonable, since the total *number* of car-using commuters will not be markedly different from what it is today. There will be an improved system of urban motorways, but with the growth of other miscellaneous traffic it is likely that general conditions of car travel would not be very different from today, *provided* that the diversion of 80 per cent to public transport is achieved.

In theory, one would expect this diversion to be achieved by any combination of changes in the following factors which together will

[24]C. H. Sharp, "The Choice between Cars and Buses on Urban Roads," *Journal of Transport Economics and Policy*, Vol. 1, No. 1 (January 1967), 104-111.

[25]D. A. Quarmby, "Relating Public Transport to Urban Planning," *Journal of the Institute of Transport*, Vol. 30, No. 12 (September 1964); and D. A. Quarmby, *A Model of Commuter Parking Behaviour* (Working Papers in Industrial Management No. 6, Department of Management Studies, Leeds University, July 1964).

reduce the general level of z-values (relative advantage of private over public transport) by the required amount:

Reductions in: time spent in the public transport vehicle;
walking and waiting time by public transport;
cost by public transport.

Increases in: time spent in the car;
walking time involved in the car journey;
cost of travel and parking by car.

It is estimated that, at 1966 incomes and prices, an 80 per cent diversion could be achieved by combining changes in one of the following ways:

(a) increasing all parking charges by 3s., and ensuring that all those bringing cars have to walk, on average, 6 minutes longer from their parking places than now, and making public transport faster by fifteen minutes; or

(b) increasing all parking charges by 2s., introducing road pricing in the peak hours so as to charge 1s. per day on average, ensuring that car users have to walk, on average, 3 minutes longer from parking places than now, reducing public transport fares by 9d., and reducing waiting times (for public transport travel) by 3 minutes.

These are quoted solely as examples: other possible combinations of changes can be explored by the same method.

The analysis does not indicate in what general direction Leeds should seek to bring about the required changes in z-values. There are likely to be substantial side effects which need close examination. A more fundamental point is that one class of measures, those which provide disincentives to the use of cars, is virtually costless in public finance terms, and may indeed yield a net revenue. It could be argued, however, that there might be high social costs. However, those measures which involve increasing the attractiveness of public transport require substantial financial investment in new or improved public transport systems. The improvements may not, in strict accounting terms, be economically viable, but they would yield high social returns. To decide how much of the reduction in the relative advantage of private over public transport (the z-value) should be achieved by disincentives to car use and how much by public transport improvements requires an assessment of the "costs" of possible undesirable side effects of disincentives (*e.g.* pressures to decentralise city centre activities) and of the benefits, measured in the widest terms, of an improved public transport system (such as the reductions in travelling time for users of the system, car owners and non-car owners).

Evaluating a Public Transport System. We now suggest how the model might be used to give a tentative estimate of the diversion of car owners which a proposed public transport system might achieve. Suppose we are considering a rapid transit line following a radial route from a residential suburb into a central business district. Ignoring future residential development which might be attracted to such a line if built, we proceed to define a corridor as the catchment area of the line. Within the corridor and covering its whole area, a representative sample of car owners is obtained. On the basis of information given by them, and information about the performance characteristics of the proposed rapid transit system (travel times, frequencies, etc.), z-values can be calculated for each person in the sample. Since information is needed from the sample only about the car journey, and not about another alternative mode, it is likely that it could be obtained from existing transportation study data banks (or from the questionnaires, if the data on store is not sufficiently detailed) provided the sample taken in the corridor was in fact large enough. From each z-value, individual probabilities of choice of car can be calculated; the mean value of these probabilities gives the best estimate of the proportion of car owners who would use their cars, and the proportion who would be diverted to the new line.

This method has the advantage over the use of − say − diversion curves on zonal data that individual characteristics such as walking times or costs are not used in aggregated form for inter-zonal predictions; they are used in disaggregated form up to the point where individual probabilities of choice are calculated, and only these probabilities are aggregated. The method could also show, for instance, how many car owners had *returned* to using their cars after the building of a motorway into a city centre, such as the M4 from Slough and Maidenhead into the West End of London.

Any such improved public transport system will, of course, attract a large number of existing users of other public transport. Even the financial viability will ultimately depend on these; and judgments of the benefits accruing will take account of the reductions in travelling time experienced by *all* users of the system. We cannot attempt to predict people's choices between public transport modes, but we believe that a model of the same general nature as that used here to explain choices between private and public modes of transport will do this.

We should emphasise that the method of prediction described above has not been attempted anywhere, and we have little idea of the operational problems that might be encountered in trying to apply it; for instance, we have not calculated what the minimum sample size would need to be. There may also be important conceptual problems: for instance, a radically new transport system might well have substantial redistributive effects on work trips originating in the corridor, and might invalidate the predictions based on modal choices alone. The secondary effects, arising from changes in congestion and travel times on the parallel road, might also upset the predictions. But we hope the method might at least indicate orders of magnitude of diversion of car owners.

Appendix A: The Model

It is assumed that the decisions to travel, to travel for a specific purpose, and where to travel, have all been made. Two modes are available for travelling, and a model is required to describe the choice made between these two modes. The model still holds if more than two modes are available, because in general a choice will always resolve into a choice between two alternatives. Let us start, however, with h modes.

We assume a number of "dimensions" of travel (1 to k) each of which gives rise to some disutility (such as travel time, walking time, cost, etc.). Suppose that the measure of dimension p (1 to k) for mode i (1 to h) for person j (1 to n_i) is d_{pij}. Further, let the importance of this dimension, or its "contribution to disutility", be λ_{pij}.

Then the disutility of the pth dimension of mode i for person j is $\lambda_{pij}d_{pij}$, and the disutility of travel by that mode, for that person, is

$$D_{ij} = \sum_{p}^{k} \lambda_{pij}d_{pij}.$$

This is the simplest linear form. One might argue that the

contribution of a dimension to disutility is not linear — for instance, we may not mind waiting 3 minutes for a bus, but we may mind more than three times as much if we have to wait 9 minutes. One might argue that the effect of one dimension depends on the *value* of another dimension — *i.e.* that $\lambda_{pij} = f(d_{pij})$ — for instance, the overall travel time may become more important if we have had to wait with aching feet for a train. One might argue that adding up different contributions to disutility does not represent how people feel about a given mode of travel. All these are valid points; but let us try this simple model first. There are good precedents for expressing total disutility as above.

We then postulate that a traveller will choose that mode i for which $D_{ij} < D_{1j}$ $D_{2j}, \ldots, D_{bj}$ (not including D_{ij}), *i.e.* the mode with minimum disutility. If some change in circumstances changed the values of one or more dimensions of his disutility, and this caused an alternative mode to assume a lower value of D than his preferred mode, we should expect him to change his mode.

However, since one can reduce the choice to two modes it may be preferable, instead of comparing absolute disutilities, to define a *relative* disutility of one mode compared to the other. It may be that people tend to perceive characteristics of the modes relatively to one another, rather than separately and absolutely. For instance, absolute journey times of, say, 40 minutes by train and 35 minutes by car may not in themselves be important, if the traveller is willing to sacrifice a time of that order of magnitude to accomplish the journey. But the *relative* measure may be important — the fact that the train takes 5 minutes longer, or 5 minutes longer *in 35 minutes.* If the latter possibility is allowed, one cannot define R_j, the relative disutility for the jth person, as $R_j = D_{1j} - D_{2j}$.

A more general form is needed:

$$R_j = \sum_p^k \lambda_{pj} f_p (d_{p1j}, d_{p2j})$$

where f_i is a more general way of expressing the relativeness between dimensions expressed for each mode. In the original form, the choice of minimum D implied that relativeness was measured by the difference between d's; in the more general form, this may be the ratio of d's, or the logarithm of the ratio, or something else. In the original form, if R_j were negative, $D_{1j} < D_{2j}$, and mode 1 would be chosen; vice versa if R_j were positive.

In the more general form, if R_j were low mode 1 would be chosen, and if R_j were high mode 2 would be chosen. If

$$x_{pj} = f_p(d_{p1j}, d_{p2j}),$$

then

$$R_j = \sum_p^k \lambda_{pj} x_{pj}.$$

Empirical work will examine which way of expressing "relativeness", *i.e.* which form of f_p, comes nearest to explaining behaviour. A more fundamental task will be to develop a method for finding the weighting factors λ, and for predicting what people will do when we know their R_j's. Those dimensions which turn out to be unimportant — *i.e.* to make an insignificant contribution to relative disutility — will yield statistically insignificant values of λ.

In order to find values of λ, one must reduce the kn values of λ_{pj}. One approximation is to assume the weighting factor for each dimension to be the same over the whole population; alternatively, different sub-categories of the population may be given different values of λ but a common λ within each sub-category for each dimension. In expounding the method of analysis, the first approximation is used; thus

$$R_j = \sum_p^k \lambda_p x_{pj}$$

is the general relative disutility function.

If people in choosing between two modes behaved exactly according to the model, and if all relevant dimensions were characterised, there should be a set of weighting coefficients, λ's, such that all users of mode 1 have relative disutilities (of mode 1 with respect to mode 2) below some "threshold" and all users of mode 2 have relative disutilities above this threshold. If there were any sets at all, however, there would in general be *more* than one set of weighting coefficients that separated the R_j's for mode 1 users and mode 2 users. That set which separated the two populations best could be said to be the best explanatory set. Predicting modal split would consist of calculating the relative disutility for a particular person, given information about the relevant dimensions, and examining whether this relative disutility fell above or below the modal split threshold.

This method is useful as a starting point, but no more. Its assumptions and requirements are wide-ranging. It assumes, firstly, that people behave rationally, *i.e.* according to the model; secondly, that the same weighting coefficients apply to everyone; thirdly, that all relevant dimensions are taken into account; fourthly, that there is access to the entire population of users of both modes. Further, nothing has yet been said about the meaning of "separation" or about how to find the optimal set of weighting coefficients. In fact, it is extremely unlikely that in any real case a set of weighting coefficients could be found which would separate the two populations completely; it is very likely that there would always be some misclassification of people — that is, users of mode 1 with a value of R_j above the threshold, and users of mode 2 with a value of R_j below the threshold. The criterion of separation could then be to minimise the number of misclassifications. This is not the only possible criterion, but it is one which is suggested by Beesley's work on Ministry of Transport employees.[26] Another might be to minimise the number of misclassifications, each one weighted by its distance — or the square of its distance — from the threshold.

The Two-Variable Case. Beesley's work was not aimed at explaining modal choice but at finding the rate of trade-off between money and time which would best explain modal choice in terms of these two variables. Although he did not express it as a disutility function in the way described here, his task could be expressed as finding those weighting coefficients which give rise to least misclassification: the ratio of these weighting factors then gives the required trade-off, *i.e.* the value of time. He did not compare users of one mode with users of the other, but compared, within one mode, those people who chose a time saving at extra cost with those who chose a cost saving but incurred extra time. Those in the latter group were then transposed into the same quadrant and the task was to find the line through the origin which best separated the two groups of points. This transposition made the problem of choosing the line exactly the same as if the characteristics had been observed within two groups,

[26]M. E. Beesley, "The Value of Time spent in Travelling: Some New Evidence," *Economica*, Vol. 32 (1965).

one using each mode, the latter group enjoying values of time difference and cost difference as given by the transposed points in Beesley's example. The best threshold line can be found by simple algebra, or almost by trial and error on the graph itself, and the gradient of the line gives the ratio between the weighting coefficients. Suppose the best threshold line is of the form

$$y = -mx$$

where x is the time saving (a negative number), y is the extra cost, and m is a positive number. Points representing people's values of time and cost difference can be taken as $(x_i y_i)$, and their distances from the line are given by

$$d_i = \frac{mx_i + y_i}{1 + m^2} = \frac{m}{1 + m^2} x_i + \frac{1}{1 + m^2} y_i$$

This is identical to the expression of relative disutility, where $m/(1 + m^2)$ and $1/(1 + m^2)$ are the weighting coefficients, $d = 0$ gives the threshold, and d itself is a measure of the excess disutility of one mode over the other.

In Beesley's exercise, it is necessary to assume that this separation line passes through the origin in order to transpose one set of points into the same quadrant as the other. But when we are comparing users of two modes and plotting them in the same quadrant, it would not seem necessary to assume that the threshold line passes through the origin — i.e. that $d = 0$ at the threshold. This would be equivalent to assuming that the marginal value of time is equal to the average value of time — which is not necessarily true. It would seem better to develop a method without this assumption and to see what the results yield. A marginal value of time so obtained might be more reliable, since it is not constrained to be equal to the average value of time; it is, however, required to be constant in this linear formulation.

We need to examine the criterion for choosing the "best" line. In Beesley's exercise the criterion chosen was the simplest — that of minimising the number of misclassified points. If the two populations differ in size, the number of points in one group is weighted to compensate for this, and misclassification is minimised on that basis. One criticism of this method is its extreme sensitivity to the position of points near the threshold; Beesley took pains to point out that the results from his analysis could be taken as little more than a guide.

But a much more fundamental criticism can be made of this criterion. The points used for the analysis are obtained from a sample drawn from a population of commuters. Any results obtained will apply to the population only within certain limits of confidence. Now the confidence of the estimates of value of time will depend on how sensitive these estimates are to possible variations between one sample and another. We have already said that these estimates are very sensitive to sample points near the threshold. An alternative method which would be much less sensitive to sample-to-sample variations involves using the sample in a less direct way, by characterising the population from which it was drawn and then using the resulting population attributes to achieve minimum misclassification. In particular, this could mean that the sample would provide best estimates of the means, variances and covariances of the factors (in this case time and cost differences) for the population, and a more sophisticated model, using a normality assumption, would then be used to derive values of the coefficients for minimum misclassification – by implication for the whole population.

The only conditions under which it could be argued that this latter method would provide poor estimates would be that the distributions of the factors in each population (i.e. for each mode) were grossly different from normal. If this were so, however, then doubt would be cast equally on the validity – as estimates for the whole population – of results obtained from the simple, pseudo-graphical misclassification procedure. There is already in this simple procedure an implicit assumption about the distribution of the factors in the population from which the sample is drawn. One final point is that the procedure has been used only for two variables: it would seem that an increase in the number of variables could make it extremely unwieldly. Clearly, a more streamlined method is needed.

To use the sample to provide best estimates of means, variances and covariances for the populations using each mode, and then to seek minimum misclassification with respect to a k-dimensional region (where there are k explanatory factors) is exactly what linear discriminant analysis does.

The Discriminant Analysis Approach. We have thus derived, from first principles, a discriminant analysis solution: from basic notions of disutility and choice advancing to the simple misclassification criterion used by Beesley, and subsequently to a form using total population characteristics, in a way that is both behaviourally and intuitively valid. The relative disutility function becomes what is known as the discriminator or discriminant function.

It can be shown that the method of solution can be derived from two different standpoints: that of minimising misclassification with respect to some presumed threshold or region boundary, and that of not using the threshold concept at all, but of seeking instead to find conditions in which the separation between the two populations, as measured by the square of the difference between their means, is greatest in relation to the variance within each population. It can be seen intuitively that this will in fact achieve minimum overlapping of relative disutility values. In the second approach, the ratio of "variance between" the populations to variance within each population is maximised by using the weighting coefficients as variables, and consequently optimal values of the weighting coefficients can be found directly.

The first approach is due to Neyman and Pearson,[27] and the second, which will be expounded here, is due to Fisher.[28] In both, necessary conditions are that the distributions of the factors are multivariate normal, and that the two populations are homoscedastic with respect to the factors — $i.e.$ that the covariance matrices of factors are the same for each population. This requirement will be discussed later. For the purpose of developing the model these conditions will be assumed to hold.

Discriminant analysis has been used in many fields — particularly biology and botany, where there are special problems of classification. It was in this context that Fisher developed his approach. The discriminant function, or relative disutility function, takes the form

$$z_{ij} = \lambda_1 x_{1ij} + \lambda_2 x_{2ij} + \ldots + \lambda_k x_{kij}$$

or

$$z_{ij} = \sum_{p}^{k} \lambda_p x_{pij}$$

[27] J. Neyman and E. S. Pearson, "On the Problem of the Most Efficient Tests in Statistical Hypothesis," *Philos. Trans. A.* Vol. 231, 289-337.

[28] R. A Fisher, "The Use of Multiple Measurements in Taxonomic Problems," *Ann. Eugen. Lond.* 7, 179 (1936).

where z_{ij}, x_{pij} and λ_p are the relative disutility, factor value and weighting coefficient respectively for the pth factor ($p = 1$ to k) of the jth person ($j = 1$ to n_i) in the ith mode in the total population ($i = 1, 2$). From this, the square of the distance between the means of the populations is

$$(\bar{z}_1 - \bar{z}_2)^2 = \left[\sum_p^k \lambda_p (\bar{x}_{p1} - \bar{x}_{p2}) \right]^2$$

and the variance within the population is

$$\sum_p^k \sum_q^k \lambda_p \lambda_p C_{pq}$$

assuming homoscedasticity, where C_{pq} is the common covariance matrix. (It can be shown that for discriminant coefficients to be independent of sample size, this must be the common covariance matrix, not the sums of squares and products matrix.) The task is to maximise

$$G = \frac{\left[\sum_p^k \lambda_p (\bar{x}_{p1} - \bar{x}_{p2}) \right]^2}{\sum_p^k \sum_q^k \lambda_p \lambda_q C_{pq}}$$

with respect to λ_p, $p = 1$ to k. Differentiating with respect to λ_p and assigning $\partial G / \partial \lambda_p = 0$, we have

$$\sum_q^k \lambda_q C_{pq} = \frac{\sum_p^k \sum_q^k \lambda_p \lambda_q C_{pq}}{\sum_p^k \lambda_p (\bar{x}_{p1} - \bar{x}_{p2})} (\bar{x}_{p1} - \bar{x}_{p2})$$

Multiplying through by C^{pq}, the inverted matrix of C_{pq}, and summing over $p = 1$ to k gives

$$\lambda_q \propto \sum_p^k C^{pq} (\overline{x}_{p1} - \overline{x}_{p2})$$

Since the disutility function has no absolute value, we can choose any convenient constant. Here we shall say that

$$\lambda_q = \sum_p^k C^{pq} (\overline{x}_{p1} - \overline{x}_{p2}) \tag{1}$$

The discriminant, or disutility, function is now of the form

$$z_{ij} = \sum_q^k \sum_p^k C^{pq} (\overline{x}_{p1} - \overline{x}_{p2}) x_{qij} \tag{2}$$

In our problem we do not know the population means and covariances, so values of means and covariances calculated from the sample are used as maximum likelihood estimates. We then have

$$\lambda_q = \sum_p^k \hat{C}^{bq} (\hat{\overline{x}}_{p1} - \hat{\overline{x}}_{p2})$$

and similarly for z.

An important aspect of the discriminant analysis described here is the validity and significance of its results. Kendall[29] suggests three ways in which one can ask whether a discriminator is "significant".

First, there may be a real difference between the populations but they may be so close together that a discriminator is not very effective. This difference is measured by the errors of misclassification, which, though minimal, may still be large. Or there may be a real difference between the populations but the sample may not be large enough to produce a very reliable discriminator; this is really a

---

[29]M. G. Kendall, *The Advanced Theory of Statistics*, Vol. II (third ed: London: Charles H. Griffin, 1951).

matter of setting confidence limits to the function or to its coefficients. Or it may be that the parent populations are identical and that a discriminant function is illusory.

When we are dealing with choice of mode, there is no doubt that there are two different populations of people — one travelling by one mode, the other by the other mode — so the third case (of an insignificant discriminator) could never apply. If the first case applies, it seems that one interpretation of the populations being "so close together" is that the factors used to characterise the relative disutility of one mode to the other do not include the important ones; another is that the assumptions of consistency and rationality implicit in the model are so tenuous that no set of factors can achieve an effective discriminator. If either interpretation is right, significance can be measured in terms of the probability of the observed discrimination occurring at random; for this the variance ratio (see below) is an appropriate indicator. Since the variance ratio involves measures of both the "distance" between the populations and the numbers in the sample, it can also indicate whether the sample is large enough to provide a reliable discriminator.

If the abilities of different factor sets to explain modal choice are being investigated, and each factor set provides a "significant" discrimination in terms of the variance ratio, then the distance between the populations is a direct measure of how good each factor set is, in terms of discrimination, for a given sample size. A more generalised measure is the multiple correlation coefficient which can compare different sample sizes and different relative proportions in the two populations using different modes. The multiple correlation coefficient is itself something of an absolute measure of discrimination, since it indicates how much of the variation in the sample is explained wholly by the discriminant analysis.

The extent to which individual factors are significant in the discriminant function can be ascertained from a comparison of their coefficients with the standard errors of these coefficients. Standard errors have no direct interpretation in terms of the discriminant function itself, but it is possible to derive these standard errors with reference to the equivalent multiple regression problem.

Kendall[30] indeed describes how the whole task of assigning values to the coefficients in the discriminant function may be tackled by a multiple regression approach. In this, a dummy dependent variate y is introduced, taking values $n_2/(n_1 + n_2)$ and $-n_1/(n_1 + n_2)$ for users of mode 1 and of mode 2 respectively, where n_1 and n_2 are the numbers of users of mode 1 and mode 2. With the two matrices of

---

[30]*Ibid.*

observations $x_{p_1 j}$, $x_{p_2 j}$, put together into one matrix $x^1{}_{pj}$ ($j =$ 1 to $n_1 + n_2$), this new matrix is regressed on the dependent variate vector y_j in the normal way. Kendall shows[31] how the resulting vector of regression coefficients, μ_p, is proportional to the discriminant coefficients, λ_p, thus:

$$\mu_p = \lambda_p \frac{n_1 n_2}{n_1 + n_2} \left(1 - \sum_q^k \mu_q (\overline{x}_{q1} - \overline{x}_{q2}) \right)$$

However, to make the discriminant coefficients independent of sample size, the derivation above inverts the covariance matrix, not the sums of squares and products matrix. Thus the equivalence between regression coefficients and discriminant coefficients *as derived above* is:

$$\mu_p = \lambda_p \frac{n_1 n_2}{(n_1 + n_2)(n_1 + n_2 - 2)} \left(1 - \sum_q^k \mu_q (\overline{x}_{q1} - \overline{x}_{q2}) \right)$$

or

$$\mu_p = \lambda_p \frac{n_1 n_2}{(n_1 + n_2)(n_1 + n_2 - 2)}$$

$$\times \frac{1}{1 + \dfrac{n_1 n_2}{(n_1 + n_2)(n_1 + n_2 - 2)} \sum_q^k \lambda_q (\overline{x}_{q1} - \overline{x}_{q2})}$$

i.e.

$$\mu_p = \lambda_p \frac{K}{1 + Ka}$$

where

$$K = \frac{n_1 n_2}{(n_1 + n_2)(n_1 + n_2 - 2)} ,$$

and

$$a = 2d. = \overline{z}_1 - \overline{z}_2 = \sum_p^k \lambda_p (\overline{x}_{p1} - \overline{x}_{p2}).$$

---

[31] *Ibid.*, p. 345.

For researchers who have ready access to multiple regression computer programs the regression approach will be much more convenient than discriminant analysis, particularly where comprehensive analysis of variance using a stepwise process is available. But if we are to use the regression function as shown below in the expression for the estimation of probabilities (this estimation derives directly from the form of the discriminant function), it will be necessary to convert the regression coefficients into "discriminant coefficients" by a factor derived from the above expression of proportionality, *i.e.*

$$\lambda_p = \mu_p \frac{(n_1 + n_2)(n_1 + n_2 - 2)}{n_1 n_2 \left(1 - \sum_{q}^{k} \mu_q (\overline{x}_{q1} - \overline{x}_q)\right)}$$

Reverting to the analysis of variance for the regression function, it can be shown that the total sum of squares

$$SST = \frac{n_1 n_2}{n_1 + n_2}$$

and the sum of squares due to the regression function

$$SSD = \frac{n_1 n_2}{n_1 + n_2} \sum_{p}^{k} \mu_p (\overline{x}_{p1} - \overline{x}_{p2})$$

$$= \frac{n_1 n_2}{n_1 + n_2} \left(\frac{Ka}{1 + Ka}\right)$$

The correlation coefficient is clearly given by

$$R^2 = \frac{Ka}{1 + Ka}$$

The error (or residual) sum of squares is

$$SSE = \frac{n_1 n_2}{n_1 + n_2} \left(1 - \frac{Ka}{1 + Ka} \right)$$

Residual variance is SSE divided by degrees of freedom, *i.e,*

$$S^2 = \frac{n_1 n_2}{n_1 + n_2} \left(1 - \frac{Ka}{1 + Ka} \right) / (n_1 + n_2 - k - 1)$$

Variance due to the discriminant function is SSD/k, *i.e.*

$$S_1{}^2 = \frac{n_1 n_2}{n_1 + n_2} \left(\frac{Ka}{1 + Ka} \right) / k$$

and the variance ratio is $F = \dfrac{S_1{}^2}{S^2}$

Thus the standard errors of the regression coefficients are

$$s.e. \; (\mu_p) = \sqrt{S^2 \, C'^{pp}}$$

Standard errors of the discriminant coefficients are given by

$$s.e. \; (\lambda_p) = \sqrt{S^2 \, C'^{pp}} \; (1 + Ka)/K$$

It is worth emphasising that C'^{pp} is an element of the inverted matrix (of sums of squares and products) *which would be used in the regression analysis*, not the inverted covariance matrix used in the discriminant analysis. The difference is that the regression matrix is calculated over the whole matrix of observations x'_{pj}, while the discriminant covariance matrix is the result of "pooling" the separate covariance matrices for each population. If a discriminant program is being used, a simple conversion can be used to obviate the need to calculate a regression type matrix from scratch:

$$C'_{pq} = (n_1 + n_2 - 2) C_{pq} + \frac{n_1 n_2}{(n_1 + n_2)} d_p d_q$$

where

$$d_p = \overline{x}_{p1} - \overline{x}_{p2}, \text{ etc.}$$

Most of the above indicators depend on the normality and homoscedasticity assumptions, and it is appropriate to develop ways of testing the sample for this. Homoscedasticity can be said to obtain if corresponding elements of the covariance matrices of the two populations lie within a factor or two of each other, with no more than one in twenty departing from this. An indication of normality can be obtained from the shape of the frequency distributions of each factor in the two populations and the shape of the final z-value distributions. A further measure of normality at the area of overlap is whether or not the best-fitting exponential function for predicting modal choice probabilities is significantly different from the theoretical form based on the normality assumption. Finally, the actual percentage misclassification can be compared with the theoretical misclassification.

It will be noticed in the analysis of data that comparisons are made between the results obtained by different sets of factors, and the criterion often used to choose between them is the correlation coefficient, R. In this context we clearly require to know whether differences between values of R are significant or not. This can be tested by using Fisher's transformation

$$z = (1/2) [(\log_e(1 + R) - \log_e(1 - R)]$$

and the property that z is normally distributed with standard deviation $1/\sqrt{n-3}$. But it is not clear whether this applies in our particular case, and an alternative approach has been adopted. This involved deriving an empirical estimate of the variance of R, using the "jack-knife" technique. For this, discriminant analysis was run ten times for one particular set of factors on only 90 per cent of the data, leaving out a different 10 per cent each time. If R_i is the correlation coefficient for each run, then the variance of R is given by

$$\hat{V}(R) = \frac{n-1}{n} \sum_i^n (R_i - \overline{R})^2 \quad \text{where } \overline{R} = \frac{1}{n} \sum_i^n R_i$$

where n is the number of runs on the above basis, which is 10 here. The results of applying this are discussed in a footnote to the text.

Modal Prediction. The purpose of discriminant analysis in botany and biology is usually to classify; the purpose here would be to classify according to mode, that is, to predict modal choice. Now in the natural sciences discrimination can often be achieved with a very small number of (or even no) misclassifications; a deterministic classification is then entirely satisfactory. The greater the amount of misclassification at the optimum, the less appropriate is a deterministic classification procedure. (It will be remembered that 20 to 25 per cent misclassification is typical here.) It would be unrealistic to expect a model such as this to be very accurate in predicting any one person's modal decision under certain conditions, because, as has been mentioned already, some sweeping assumptions regarding consistency and rationality are implicit in the model. For planning purposes we are not interested in each individual's behaviour on its own, but in the behavior of people in aggregate, whether aggregated by zone or in other ways. Fortunately, in predicting aggregate behaviour, we can assume that the net effect of eccentric, idiosyncratic factors is small, because, being random, they will tend to cancel. But prediction of choice of mode on a binary, deterministic, "above or below threshold" basis *is* in a sense attempting to predict each individual's behaviour, since the threshold is discontinuous. A much more satisfactory method is to assign a probability that one mode is chosen rather than the other, where this probability takes a value which depends on the value of the relative disutility function. Prediction would thus involve calculating the z-value for a commuter and assigning to him a probability of choosing one mode on the basis of this value, rather than assigning him definitely to one mode or the other according to which side of the threshold value his z-value fell.

A theoretical expression for probability of choice can be derived as follows. Suppose we represent graphically the frequency distributions of values of z, relative disutility of travel by mode 1, for users of both modes. The best estimate of the probability of a commuter with a given z-value — say z' — choosing mode 2 is the ratio of the ordinate of the mode 2 distribution at z' to the sum of the ordinates of the mode 2 and mode 1 distributions at z'. If these frequency distributions are represented as $F_1(z)$ and $F_2(z)$, and $p_2(z)$ is the probability of choice of mode 2 at z, we have

$$p_2(z') = \frac{F_2(z')}{F_1(z') + F_2(z')} = \frac{1}{1 + F_1(z')/F_2(z')}$$

Under present assumptions, $F_1(z)$ and $F_2(z)$ are both normal distributions with the same variance. Let $z_1 - z_2 = 2d.$, and let $Z = z + t$, where t is chosen so that $\bar{Z}_1 = -\bar{Z}_2$, *i.e.* the origin is shifted so that $Z = 0$ is midway between the means of the two distributions. Let the variance of each distribution be σ^2. Then we have

$$F_1(z) = \frac{1}{\sqrt{2\pi}\sigma} \, e^{-\frac{1}{2}(Z+d)^2/\sigma^2}$$

and

$$F_2(Z) = \frac{1}{\sqrt{2\pi}\sigma} \, e^{-\frac{1}{2}(Z-d)^2/\sigma^2}$$

Thus

$$p_2(Z) = \frac{1}{1 + e^{-\frac{1}{2}[(Z+d)^2 - (Z-d)^2]/\sigma^2}}$$
$$= \frac{1}{1 + e^{-2dZ/\sigma^2}}$$

Now it can be shown that when the constant term in equation (1) above is set to unity, then G in Fisher's maximisation criterion, used to derive equations (1) and (2), takes the value of the distance between the means, $2d.$, and this distance between the means is equal in value to the variance. That is,

$$2d = \sigma^2$$

The probability expression becomes

$$P_2(z) = \frac{1}{1 + e^{-z}}$$
$$= \frac{1}{1 + e^{-(z+t)}}$$
$$\text{or} \quad = \frac{e^{(z+t)}}{1 + e^{(z+t)}}$$

More generally, if the numbers of people using the two modes are different, there is an *a priori* probability, not equal to one half, that one mode will be chosen more than the other. If n_1 and n_2 are the numbers using mode 1 and mode 2 respectively, it can be seen from a diagrammatic representation that the ordinate of $F_2(z)$ will be inflated relative to $F_1(z)$ by a factor n_2/n_1. That is, $F_2(z)$ can be taken as

$$= n_2/n_1 \; \frac{1}{\sqrt{2\pi}\sigma} \; e^{-\frac{1}{2}(Z-d)/\sigma^2}$$

and $F_1(z)$ as before. Thus

$$p_2(z) = \frac{1}{1 + (n_1/n_2)\, e^{-2\,d\,Z/\sigma^2}}$$

$$p_2(z) = \frac{1}{1 + (n_1/n_2)\, e^{-(z+t)}}$$

or $\quad \dfrac{(n_2/n_1)\, e^{(z+t)}}{1 + (n_2/n_1)\, e^{(z+t)}}$

This relationship is an S-shaped "logistic" curve.

In the use for prediction purposes of results based on analysis of a sample, there are two possible approaches. Firstly, the value of t can be found — it is the distance from the origin of the point midway between the means of the two distributions (the constant term) and probabilities predicted direct from the above expression. Another approach, which uses the sample data more directly, is to gather, from the actual frequency distributions of z yielded by the sample data, values of $F_2(z)/(F_1(z) + F_2(z))$ for equal sub-ranges of z-values covering the area of overlap of the distributions. These values are then used as probability estimates, and together with the corresponding z-values are fitted to a generalised version of the probability function:

$$p_2(z) = F_2(z)/(F_1(z) + F_2(z)) = \frac{ek(z+c)}{1 + e^{k(z+c)}}$$

This can be done by reducing the expression to a linear equation in z and log $(p/1 - p)$ as follows:

$$p = \frac{e^{k(z+c)}}{1 + e^{k(z+c)}}$$

That is

$$\frac{p}{1-p} = e^{k(z+c)}$$

$$\log\left(\frac{p}{1-p}\right) = k(z+c)$$

and a linear regression of $\log(p/(1-p))$ on z can be carried out. Note especially that the closeness of k to 1 and of c to t in such a regression will indicate the closeness of the distributions to normality for the z-range considered, and is one indication of the general validity of the normality assumptions inherent in the analysis.

The following describes the application of this to the problem of "calibrating" a predictor from the car-bus results described in the text.

Now calculations are easier if distributions are "standardised", that is, if for instance the car users' distribution is reduced by n_1/n_2, or in this case by 166/376. The expression to fit is then

$$\log(p/(1-p)) = k(z+c)$$

where p is the (standardised) proportion of car users in the total number of commuters with z-values lying in intervals 0.5 wide. The following values were calculated from the two frequency distributions of z-values for the sample, using Set 3 at 2d. a mile.

Car-bus data

p	Mean z for the interval
0	-2.0
0.157	-1.5
0.160	-1.0
0.220	-0.5
0.465	0
0.435	0.5
0.692	1.0
0.765	1.5
1.000	2.0

Linear regression gave the following result, with correlation coefficient of 0.93:

$$\log (p/(1 - p)) = 1.04 (z - 0.431)$$

That is,

$$p = \frac{e^{1.04(z-0.431)}}{1 + e^{1.04(z-0.431)}}$$

or, in non-standardised form,

$$p_s(z) = \frac{2.26 \, e^{1.04(z-0.431)}}{1 + 2.26 \, e^{1.04(z-0.431)}}$$

since $376/166 = 2.26$.

Now the point halfway between the mean of the car users' z-values and the mean of the bus users' z-values works out at 0.461. Hence the probability expression fitted to the sample is very close to the expression based on a normally variate population, which is

$$p(z) = \frac{2.26 \, e^{z-0.461}}{1 + 2.26 \, e^{z-0.461}}$$

Thus the sample is close to normality for the range of z-values at the overlap for the two frequency distributions; this lends weight to the whole analysis. A further test is to see how well the process of summing the probability of choice of car for each person in the sample, on the basis of the fitted expression above, actually reproduces the overall car-using proportion. The actual car-using proportion is $n_2/(n_1 + n_2) = 376/542 = 69.4$ per cent. Calculating $p_s(z)$ for each person in the sample, summing for the sample, and dividing by 542 yields a car-using proportion of 69.1 per cent, which confirms again that the sample distribution conforms closely to normality.

Appendix B: Homoscedasticity and Multicollinearity

This appendix examines the covariance and correlation matrices of Set 3 at 2d. a car-mile, to test for homoscedasticity and to investigate the possibility of multicollinearity between variables. The following table gives the ratio of covariances between the car-using population and the bus-using population for the four significant factors; for homoscedasticity, all except one or two of these ratios should lie between 0.5 and 2.0. There is a particular problem with the use-of-car-for-work factor: this takes only one out of two values in each case, and in the bus-using population no person uses his car for work occasionally; so values of infinity result.

Overall travel time difference	1.55			
Excess travel time difference	1.47	1.32		
Cost difference	-0.656	-0.091	0.535	
Use of care for work	∞	∞	∞	∞

Excluding the "use of car for work" factor, 4 out of 6 ratios lie within the required range. It is clear, then, that conditions of homoscedasticity are not strictly met. Unfortunately, while the literature maintains that these conditions should be met, there is nothing to indicate how accurate or inaccurate are results obtained under conditions such as those prevailing here.

Examination of the two correlation matrices of seven factors, one for car users, the other for bus users, reveals that out of 42 intercorrelations only 9 are significant at the 1 per cent level, and of these only two are greater than 0.30. These two are the correlations between overall travel time and excess travel time for each population (0.489 and 0.477 respectively). This is to be expected, since one is a component of the other. To test whether there was any association over and above this intrinsic connection, a separate correlation analysis was carried out on excess travel time and net in-vehicle time by each mode for each population. The correlations between excess travel time and overall travel time less excess travel time were as follows:

Car users:	for bus travel	0.075
	for car travel	-0.068
Bus users:	for bus travel	0.150
	for car travel	-0.189 significant as 5 per cent level

These correlations are nowhere near large enough to upset the use of the discriminant function for prediction purposes, provided that changes in excess travel time are also included as changes in overall travel time.

About the Contributors

William J. Baumol was born in 1923 in New York City. He received his Bachelor of Social Science Degree at the College of the City of New York in 1942 and his Ph.D. from London University in 1949. He is a member of the Department of Economics at Princeton University. His main areas of interest are Economic Theory, Welfare Economics, Urban Economics and Regulatory Policy. His principal books are *Economic Dynamics,* 1951, 2nd ed., 1959; *Welfare Economics and the Theory of the State,* 1952; *Economic Processes and Policies,* L. V. Chandler, co-author, 1954; *Business Behavior, Value and Growth,* 1959, 2nd ed., 1967; *Economic Theory and Operations Analysis,* 1961; *The Stock Market and Economic Efficiency,* 1965; *Performing Arts: The Economic Dilemma,* 1966, William G. Bowen, co-author; and *Precursors in Mathematical Economics: An Anthology,* 1968, Stephen M. Goldfeld, co-author. He has also written various articles for professional journals.

Michael E. Beesley was born in 1924. He graduated with B. Com. and Ph.D. from Birmingham University in 1951. After being a Reader in Economics at The London School of Economics, University of London, he became Professor of Economics at the London Graduate School of Business Studies in 1965, becoming Faculty Dean in 1969. Between 1965 and 1968 he was Chief Economic Advisor to the Ministry of Transport, London. His main research interests lie in the area of the economics of government-industry relationships. He is the author of many publications in the field of cost benefit analysis, transport economics and industrial economics.

Anthony J. Blackburn was born in Antwerp, Belgium in 1937. Educated in England and the United States he obtained a Bachelor's Degree in economics at King's College, Cambridge University and a Ph.D. in economics at the Massachusetts Institute of Technology. He is currently Assistant Professor of Economics at Harvard University and a member of the Program on Regional and Urban Economics in the J. F. Kennedy School of Government. His research interests are in the fields of economic theory, urban economics, transportation and econometrics.

Kelvin J. Lancaster was born in 1924 in Australia. He studied mathematics and geology (B.Sc. 1948), and English literature (B.A. 1949, M.A. 1952) at Sydney University, then economics at the London School of Economics (B.Sc. (Econ.) 1953, Ph.D. 1958). He has been on the faculty of the London School of Economics (1955-1961), Johns Hopkins University (1962-1966) and, since 1966, has been at Columbia University where he is currently chairman of the Economics Department. His research interests are mathematical economics and economic theory. His principal publications are *Mathematical Economics*, Macmillan, 1968, *Introduction to Modern Microeconomics*, Rand McNally, 1969 and numerous journal articles.

John P. Mayberry was born in 1929 in New Haven, Connecticut and received his college education at Upper Canada College and the University of Toronto (B.A. 1950) where he pursued an honors course in Mathematics, Physics and Chemistry. He obtained his M.A. and Ph.D. in Mathematics from Princeton University in 1954 and 1955, respectively. He was employed as operations research analyst for the U. S. Air Force for some nine years. He also worked for shorter periods for Princeton University, RCA and Mathematica, Inc. Since October 1959 he has been with Lambda Corporation in Rosslyn, Virginia. He is author or co-author of numerous papers and has made contributions to Mathematical Economics, Stochastic Processes, Statistical Decision Theory, Logistics, the Theory of Games, Topology and Graph Theory.

Leon N. Moses studied economics as an undergraduate at Ohio State University. He obtained his Ph.D. at Harvard University in 1953. At Harvard, he was on the staff of the Harvard Economic Research Project from 1953 to 1956 and Assistant Professor from 1956 to 1959. He is presently Professor of Economics at Northwestern University. He has also served as Director of Research of the Transportation Center at Northwestern. His teaching and research interests are largely in urban and regional economics and transportation. His publications include numerous articles and chapters in books and journals such as the *American Economic Review*, the *Review of Economics and Statistics*, the *Quarterly Journal of Economics* and the *Journal of Political Economy*.

Richard E. Quandt was born in 1930 in Hungary and emigrated to the United States in 1949. He studied economics as an undergraduate at Princeton University (B.A., 1952) and obtained his Ph.D. from Harvard University in 1957. Since 1956 he has been on the faculty of Princeton University, currently serving as the chairman of the Economics Department. His research interests are in econometrics, mathematical economics, corporation finance and transportation. His principal publications are *Microeconomic Theory: A Mathematical Approach* (with J. M. Henderson), McGraw-Hill, 1958, *The New Inflation* (with Willard L. Thorp), McGraw-Hill, 1959, *Strategies and Rational Decisions in Securities Options Markets* (with B. G. Malkiel), M.I.T. Press, 1969, and numerous journal articles.

David A. Quarmby was born in 1941. He studied engineering and economics as an undergraduate at Cambridge University (B.A. 1962), and subsequently obtained a Diploma in management studies at Leeds University (1963). From 1963 to 1966 he was on the faculty of Leeds University, as an assistant lecturer and then lecturer in the Department of Management Studies; during this time he developed his research interests in transport planning and analysis, and in 1967 obtained his Ph.D. (Leeds University) for a dissertation on modal choice. In the autumn of 1966 he joined the Mathematical Advisory Unit of the then newly formed Directorate of Economic Planning at the Ministry of Transport, subsequently becoming Economic Adviser and head of the Research and Development Branch of MAU. His main work at the Ministry of Transport has been in the methodological improvement of travel demand models, particularly for regional and interurban transport planning, and in the development of model-based economic evaluation techniques for the cost/benefit appraisal of transport investments. In mid-1970 he left to become Director of Operational Research at the London Transport Executive. His publications include articles and papers on modal choice, public transport planning, the value of travel time, and highway planning in multi-purpose public projects.

Harold F. Williamson Jr. obtained his Ph.D. in economics from Yale University in 1969. He was a research economist at the Transportation Center, Northwestern University when he co-authored the article reprinted in Chapter 10. Since 1964, he has been on the faculty of the Department of Economics at the University of Illinois. His research interests are in urban and regional economics, location theory and transportation. His principal publications have been on the topic of Chapter 10 and on the location of economic activity within metropolitan areas.

Alan G. Wilson was born in 1939 in Bradford, England. He studied mathematics as an undergraduate at Cambridge University and first worked in the theoretical nuclear physics field at the Rutherford

High Energy Laboratory, Harwell (1961-1964). He entered the urban studies field through a Research Unit in the Institute of Economics and Statistics at Oxford University (1964-1966), and became Mathematical Adviser to the Ministry of Transport (1966-1968), where he was concerned with models of transport systems. He is at present Assistant Director of the Centre for Environmental Studies in London, and from 1st October, 1970, has been appointed Professor of Urban and Regional Geography at the University of Leeds. His first book, *Entropy in Urban and Regional Modelling,* is in press (to be published by Pion Ltd.) and he has written many journal articles. He is editor of *Environment and Planning* and associate editor of *Transportation Research.*

Kan Hua Young was born in 1936 in Taiwan and came to the United States in 1961 after graduating from National Taiwan University (B.A., 1959). He studied economics as a graduate student at Columbia University and obtained his M.A. in 1963 and Ph.D. in 1969. Since 1966 he has been on the staff of Mathematica, Inc., a private research organization located at Princeton, N.J. At present he is also lecturing at the City College of New York. His research interests are in econometrics, theory of consumer behavior, operations research, and transportation. His dissertation is entitled *A Synthesis of Time Series and Cross Section Analyses: Demand for Sugar in the United States.* His research works have been published as several journal articles.

Author Index

Author Index